The Supe's Handbook

The Supe's Handbook

LEADERSHIP LESSONS FROM AMERICA'S HOTSHOT CREWS

Angie Tom

Desert Rat Press, Twin Falls, Idaho

Published 2021

Printed and bound in the United States of America

ISBN-13: 978-1-7356991-0-3 (trade paperback)

ISBN-13: 978-1-7356991-1-0 (e-book)

Cover design: Tanja Prokop, Book Design Templates

Editing: Christina Dubois Publishing Services

Book Design: Andrea Reider, Book Design Templates

Illustrations: Samantha Orient, DrawScience Media Solutions

Cover photo: Mike McMillan, Spotfire Images. (Los Padres superintendent Stan Stewart, Oak Hill fire, Vandenberg AFB/Los Padres NF, October 1994.)

Publisher's Cataloging-in-Publication data

Names: Tom, Angie, author.
Title: The supe's handbook : leadership lessons from America's hotshot crews / Angie Tom.
Description: Includes bibliographical references and index. | Twin Falls, ID: Desert Rat Press, 2021.
Identifiers: LCCN: 2021902731 | ISBN: 978-1-7356991-0-3 | 978-1-7356991-1-0 (ebook)
Subjects: LCSH Wildfire fighters. | Wildfires. | Forest fire fighters. | Forest fires--Prevention and control. | Wildfires--Prevention and control. | Leadership. | BISAC Biography and Autobiography / Fire & Emergency Services | Technology & Engineering / Fire Science | Business & Economics / Leadership
Classification: LCC SD421.32.W47 .T66 2021 | DDC 634.9/618--dc23

In Memoriam

Ben Charley
Paul Gleason
Ken Jordan
Dave Matier
Stan Stewart

It takes some pretty twisted individuals to want to go out there. You spend $300 for a pair of boots to get you there, sweat your damned ass off in horrible friggin' terrain, and then go out and physically torment yourself and put yourself at risk. I mean, that's an odd bunch of ducks out there on the side of those mountains. They all have that in common: they love it, even after what you put 'em through. My God, that's team building at its best. Wouldn't you agree? I mean, that's where it's at.

—J. W. Allendorf

CONTENTS

Foreword

Experts in every profession operate at a higher level than the rest of us; their extensive experience and expertise are what set them apart. We are captivated by the ease with which they operate, the pace they sustain, and their adaptability to rapidly changing conditions; ultimately, it is their performance, and the results, that earn our respect. We observe these experts in action; we analyze their behaviors and marvel at the outcomes of their decisions. We try to emulate what they do, often to no avail. If we could just talk to them. We want what they have, whatever that may be. We want to know what they know; we want to be able to do what they do—the way they do it. We want the benefit of their expertise. We wish we could ask them questions and discuss the finer details of their own journey to expertise.

In *The Supe's Handbook: Leadership Lessons from America's Hotshot Crews*, Angie Tom gives us access to not just a single expert in the field of wildland fire but 35 of them. She shares with us her insightful seven-year journey of interviewing interagency hotshot crew (IHC) superintendents, each a leader of his or her own highly-skilled 20-person hotshot crew. There are several schools of thought when it comes to hotshots, hotshot crews, and specifically hotshot superintendents. Superintendents, whether you hate them, love them, hate to love them or love to hate them, your position is probably warranted. Some past experience(s), personal or otherwise, colors your viewpoint and little can be done to change it. Superintendents possess a high degree of confidence, and they know how to get things done. They have strong opinions and assertive personalities, and they can be blunt. Most superintendents can and will discuss, debate, and/or rigorously defend their positions, which can be off-putting at times. One cannot help but ask: what makes these assholes so damn special? In the case of these hotshot superintendents, it is their effective leadership in an environment few can fathom. Don't get me wrong—not all superintendents are great leaders and, likewise, not all of them are perfect assholes. Similar to most data sets, one can plot leadership effectiveness with a bell curve as well as by the degree of one's "asshole-ness." Most of the interviewees in this book fall on the right half of the leadership curve—one or two standard deviations above the mean—and there are a few outliers.

By design and happenstance, hotshot superintendents are faced with a continuous stream of complex challenges in a highly dynamic environment. The inherent risks within the wildland fire environment provide them with countless opportunities to develop their fire expertise and hone their leadership skills. Much of what superintendents know and do is unspoken outside of their work environment, but that should not limit the applicability or marginalize the impact of what they have to offer you.

As a "plank holder"[1] on an interagency hotshot crew, I can tell you there was not a superintendent's handbook to be had anywhere, but I wish there had been. When I first became a superintendent, I relied upon those who came before me, those who would take my calls and answer my questions—and I had lots of questions. Good fortune, good friends, and fellow superintendents ensured that I would not fail. So, many years later, when I first heard of Angie's project, it was either the stated intent or the working title that made me want to participate. By the time

---

[1] If you are involved in the initial stand-up of a unit, a new base, or are a member of a newly commissioned navy ship, someone who is there at the beginning of things to make them work, then you are a "plank holder."

Angie got around to interviewing me for her project, she had already talked to more than 30 tenured superintendents. I had worked with most of them and respected them all. There was no question or hesitation on my part, as I had already received a few calls from previous interviewees, each endorsing the intent as well as the author. Angie established her initial credibility based on her performance as a member of the Prescott Hotshot Crew and, later on, the Payson Hotshot Crew. Credibility and respect at any level on a hotshot crew are not easily earned and can be short-lived if your commitment wanes.

With no obvious boundaries, Angie's carefully-crafted questions become powerful tools, and her first-hand experience as a hotshot provides you with an insider's perspective. She asked these superintendents the questions any young firefighter would want to ask, given the access. Angie also uncovered several helpful nuggets of wisdom for those who aspire to be a superintendent themselves one day. Moreover, it may even provide a current superintendent with a different solution or perspective to some commonly faced challenges. What quickly becomes apparent is that there is no one way to develop your own fire and/or leadership expertise, nor is there a single path to becoming a superintendent. There are some commonalities in their backgrounds, their motivations, and their values, but there is no checklist or template to follow. A common priority among the best of them is a "no compromise" attitude when it comes to the safety and welfare of their crew, followed closely by a bias for action.

Personality-wise, superintendents can be quite unique. There is, however, an undeniable—perhaps even a demented—sense of amusement with the nastiness of the job. Many hotshots take great pleasure in the harsh environments, the inherent physical demands, and the lack of symmetry in it all. It seems that the endless hours of hard work in ugly terrain amidst chaos connects them with other like-minded team members. The sweat, the stank, and the suck factor are the glue that holds them together.

That is how they earn their crew colors and why they wear them with so much pride.

Experience cannot be taught in the classroom, and leadership cannot be learned without leading. More than a how-to book, this is a collection of how-I-did-its from 35 IHC superintendents. It is up to you to extract the lessons you want and/ or need from the multitude of wisdom-filled responses. There is much to be learned from these highly observant critical thinkers. Superintendents are risk managers, decision-makers, and problem solvers. Superintendents and the hotshot crews they lead are force multipliers: they make more possible, and they can make everyone around them more effective. The leadership lessons within are derived more from the application of leadership (the art) than from the classroom (the science). Given the universal nature of leadership, much of what these leaders have to say can be learned and applied to your own leadership opportunities or challenges, whatever they may be.

Lastly, the culture of our interagency hotshot crews has produced countless highly effective leaders over the years. Contained within *The Supe's Handbook: Leadership Lessons from America's Hotshot Crews* are several of the stories and lessons these superintendents learned along their own leadership journeys. Enjoy.

—Anthony "Crobar" Escobar
Santa Barbara, California
June 26, 2020

Preface

"Supt" is the correct abbreviation for the title "superintendent" in all its uses: head of a school district, administrator in the Protestant Church, the person with the giant keyring in an apartment building, and the lucky person responsible for keeping 19 other rowdy, pyromaniac knuckleheads alive, fed, paid, and headed in the correct direction for six months. I chose to use "supe" because it reads more like an actual word. As a bookworm, a word nerd, and a fire person, my eyes stub their figurative toes on "supt" when it's used as a word rather than an abbreviation.

I got the idea for this book during the 2000 fire season, my second with the Prescott Hotshots. One of my duties that year was playing chauffeur for my boss, Curtis Heaton, driving the supe truck. We were passing through Payson, Arizona, home of the Payson Hotshots. Their supe, Fred Schoeffler, was known and respected for his sharp intellect and willingness to speak his mind. The small button pinned to the radio harness he wore on fires said it all; over a white background, a red slash crossed out a stylized drawing of a squatting, defecating bull—the universal "No BS" sign.

I asked Curt, "How long has Fred been supe here?"

"A long time—20 years or so."

"How many supes are there who have been around as long as he has?"

"Not many, and fewer all the time."

"I bet those guys have learned a lot that other people don't know. Someone should ask them."

It didn't occur to me that I could be the one doing the asking until after the 2001 season. Certain that I was done with fire, I set about applying to medical school, but the idea stuck with me. I had always been preoccupied with questions like, "What does it mean to have a good crew?" "How do supes know who to hire?" "How does someone become a good boss, a good fireman?" "Why do they do this for so long?" Those questions cross-pollinated in my brain with stories I was hearing in the news about the knowledge and experience gap corporate America would face as the baby boomer generation retired. I also picked up the idea somewhere that organizations must reinvent the wheel, as it were, if that knowledge isn't passed on. Instead of advancing, they stagnate or fall back a step while they relearn valuable lessons as if no one had learned them before. Perhaps this was bad for firefighter safety. I did some research: hadn't anyone else talked to longtime supes to find out what specialized knowledge they might be taking with them when they left? Nope.[2] I did find an excellent piece of Forest Service history called *Memorable Forest Fires: Stories by US Forest Service Retirees* (1995), which had a similar premise, but there was only one hotshot superintendent in it. I decided to go for it.

I wrote to Fred Schoeffler, requesting an interview, and I did the first recording in winter 2001–02. I made a list of everyone he said I should interview. Prescott supe Curtis Heaton suggested I contact Jim Cook, former supe of Arrowhead and Boise, who had become the Forest Service's wildland fire leadership guru as national training projects coordinator. I interviewed Jim and some other Region 5 (R5) supes when they came to the 2002

---

[2] Since then, the Wildland Fire Leadership Development Program, The Smokey Generation, and the Wildland Fire Lessons Learned Center have captured and published memories and lessons learned from hotshots and other wildland firefighters in print and on video.

Region 3 Hotshot Workshop, and everything snowballed from there. I met more supes and got more referrals and references. Eventually, the list of who to call reflected a consensus of who was respected for their firefighting ability, their skill at training subordinates, and their reputation for turning out hard-working, proficient crews year after year.

I discovered I wasn't quite done with fire after all. While sitting in a university lecture hall preparing to take the medical school entrance exam, I said to myself, "Nah, I'm going back to the woods." My scores were decent enough to apply, so the time and expense of prepping for it weren't a complete waste. I put in five more fire seasons, which allowed me to keep doing interviews and typing transcripts full-time in the off-seasons. After 35 interviews in 6 years and 14 seasons of fire with the Forest Service, I decided to stop. I told myself I'd still finish the book, but somehow there never seemed to be enough time when I had to work year-round. For a while it didn't seem quite so urgent: I had moved to a part of Michigan far from any federal land or wildland fire activity, and I'd lost touch with everyone I'd known in fire. The supes' voices were always with me, though, their words popping into my head at relevant times or showing up in my stories of the good old days in fire.

They say if you love it, fire gets in your blood. After realizing I needed to live "out West," I moved from Michigan to Colorado, and Fort Collins happened to be both fire and hotshot country. I started working on the book in earnest. One July I could see and smell smoke and hear the helicopters running buckets to an extended-attack fire in the foothills every afternoon, and I knew I wanted back in. I took a job at the local Forest Service dispatch office the next summer, and the summer after that I went to work for the Bureau of Land Management (BLM) and Twin Falls Helitack. I finished the book and started looking for a publisher.

When I first imagined asking senior supes if I could interview and record them, I expected resistance, even hostility:

"Why the hell should I talk to you?" That shows you how little I knew then about supes and hotshots, even after seven seasons of being a crewmember. Before this project, longtime supes were larger-than-life to me, caricatures drawn by people who'd probably never worked with or for them. They were recognized, pointed out, and discussed with respect and curiosity. I was surprised and relieved when instead of being a bunch of grouchy old farts (although most of them would probably chuckle and say that's exactly what they are), the supes turned out to be some of the most gracious people I've ever met. They were generous, friendly, and helpful. They took my project seriously, perhaps because they saw that I was serious about what I was doing. Many thanks to all of them for everything they did for me and for what they've always done and continue to do for "the kids."

This book took 14 years to complete, including a stretch of about 4 years where I left it nearly untouched. That's a long time, but I don't regret it because I believe the book is better for it. There are young people who arrive on hotshot crews as fully fledged adults and professionals, but they're the exception. I happened to be one of the many dumbass kids who did some growing up there, and this project helped me even more.

I asked all the supes nearly the same questions from a prepared list, though other questions sometimes presented themselves as we talked. I was most interested in everyone's thoughts on building and training a crew, lessons learned, fire behavior, changes they'd seen over their careers, and career planning. I picked my favorite responses to each question and grouped them together for readers to compare and contrast. Stories told by individual supes are scattered throughout. Section introductions and other input from me are minimal. The supes' answers have sometimes been sparingly edited by me or my editor, only to improve readability. In some spots I inserted a sentence or thought from another part of the interview because it fit so well. Explanations of terms/abbreviations/acronyms familiar to hotshots and other fire folks are provided to give readers with little to no experience with wildland fire a little help.

Some of you will wonder why I didn't include your supe, or maybe even you yourself. There were a few supes who didn't return my emails, calls, or letters; and there were one or two who flat-out refused, even after prodding from friends who'd already done interviews. Others simply weren't mentioned often enough when I asked, "Who else should I talk to?" There were even a couple I know I should've talked to and didn't. It was great fun, but I finally had to stop doing interviews and put together a book, or I would never get it done.

There are many strong opinions in this book, and I don't expect readers to like or agree with them all. I used the answers that translated best to the printed page for comparison with and contrast to others. I tried to include enough variety to allow readers to pick and choose the ideas they most identify with to help them progress as leaders and firefighters.

Introduction

I offer the following widely dispersed text as a briefing for readers unfamiliar with what hotshots actually do. I got my copy from Tony Sciacca in 1998 when he was supe at Prescott and I was visiting as a prospective applicant. It was taped to the office door, and I asked him if I could make a copy of it. He started out on Flagstaff, so he may have one of the original letters as well. I think of it as one of the foundations of hotshot culture, like "Two more chains!" and the 4-4-40.[3] It's still accurate, even with all the changes time and technology bring. Gary Olson, former supe of Happy Jack and Santa Fe and recipient of one of the originals, says on his website, OurFireGods.com:

> *The original letter was sent to all returning Hotshots, and all of those who applied to be Hotshots, for the USFS, Coconino National Forest, Region 3, in 1976, and only that year. It was written by Bill Buck, Fire Control Officer, Coconino National Forest, although Bill's ever-present assistant, Steve Servis, probably contributed to it. Even though wildland firefighting history has recorded the author as "Unknown."*

---

[3] "Two more chains!" is the traditional answer to the question, "How much farther?" regardless of context. In other words, don't ask: you probably don't want to know, and it'll probably change anyway. Horseshoe Meadow supe Ben Charley gets credit for starting it. *Two More Chains*, newsletter of the Wildland Fire Lessons Learned Center (Spring 2015), 11. The 4-4-40 is one of the many "challenges" wildland firefighters goad each other into, usually when they're really bored: drink 4 quarts of water (usually from the one-quart government-issue canteens) in 4 minutes, and hold it down for 40 seconds. Rarely achieved, always entertaining—except for onlookers susceptible to sympathetic vomiting.

So You Want To Be A Hotshot?

Perhaps you should really know what a hotshot crew does. This statement is prepared for your study and serious consideration to purposely discourage those who might be erroneously informed or those better equipped both mentally and physically to apply for less demanding but equally important work with the Forest Service. We do have many jobs that pay the same and are equally challenging, equally rewarding.

The very term "hotshot" means many things to many people. To those of us who recruit, train, and work hotshots, the job title is anything but glamorous. From experience we know that firefighting is 90 percent physical for the hotshot crew. The nature of the work is demanding. Only those of high strength, agility, coordination, and stamina can cope with the sustained work required of the average hotshot.

As a hotshot, you will be required to not only produce physically, but to live together, eat together, and sleep together in close, crowded conditions. Complete compatibility is in itself a difficult challenge.

You must take orders and carry those orders out at all times, day after day. The emotional strain is extreme, and the competitive pressure of your peer group is always present. For a crew is only as good as its weakest member.

When not on fire duty, you will be required to engage in daily structured physical fitness training that consists of a two- to three-mile run, coordination exercises, push-ups, sit-ups, chin-ups, rope climbs, squat thrusts, abdominal stretching, and the obstacle courses.

The rest of your day will be like every other day: hard labor using hand tools (ax, shovel, saw) and usually piling brush, digging holes, picking up garbage, cleaning toilets, sharpening tools, and similar tasks. You will be expected to be ready at all times to answer fire calls on the district, forest, region, or out of region. This requires you to be on a 24-hour alert.

On the fireline, the hotshot crews are singled out for the hazardous, difficult assignments. It is normal for hotshot crews to be on the first shift 32 hours before relief is available. Succeeding shifts of 14–18 hours are necessary. You will normally be "spiked" out away from the main fire camp, thirsty, hungry, and sleeping on rocky ground, too often without even paper sleeping bags. You'll hardly have the luxury of washing your hands, much less the facilities to bathe. You'll be filthy, exhausted, underfed, and hurting. There will be no privacy, no sanitation, no shelter, no laundry, no doctors; however, first aid is available.

The hotshot crew is so named because of the need for tough, knowledgeable, hard individuals who can be sent ahead of the main contingent of ordinary labor crews and independently drive holding lines around critical segments of the fire, hold their lines, and survive. You will be required to pack heavy loads up and down extremely mountainous terrain (hose packs of 70 pounds); fell large trees with either power saws or crosscut saws, buck trees into shorter lengths, haul blocks of logs, deadfalls, and brush out of the fire path; dig three- to ten-foot-wide firelines to mineral soil; build retaining walls; haul hose; pack heavy portable pumps and tanks; and burn out your line before the fire gets there; and then start extinguishing spot fires over your lines. That's not the end of it. The dirty work of mop-up begins: digging and scraping all hotspots out and extinguishing the heat source. Other features of the job are living in and breathing smoke for days, contending with poison oak, poison ivy, poison sumac, cactus, thorns, ticks, gnats, flies, snakes, scorpions, spiders, rolling rocks, and falling debris. It's dirty, hot, dusty, and freezing cold.

Obviously, we're looking for superior individuals to fill our hotshot crews. If you can live and excel with the job I've described, then we want you. We care not about your sex, color, race, or religion; but if for any reason you cannot live up to these standards, then I encourage you to do yourself and the rest of the crew a favor and apply for other than hotshot work.[4]

---

[4] Gary Olson, "Hotshots," Wildland Firefighters, accessed September 30, 2020, http://ourfiregods.com/WhatsaHotshot.html.

PART ONE

MEET THE SUPES

It doesn't take any particular pedigree to become a supe. Some in this book grew up in Southern California, one of the hearts of hotshot country, and others came from "back East." Some had always wanted to be firemen, and others didn't choose it as a career until they'd been at it a while.

Richard Aguilar (El Cariso, 1974; Wolf Creek, 1975–1997)
Richard Aguilar began working for the US Forest Service in New Mexico in 1957 when he was recruited for a fire while on his lunch hour at another job. He became a full-time employee on the Gila National Forest in 1962 as the helitack foreman and packer. He moved to the Klamath National Forest in 1968 to become an engine foreman. In 1974 he became superintendent of the El Cariso Hotshots. In 1975 he accepted the job as leader of the Wolf Creek Job Corps fire crew, a joint project of the US Department of Labor and the Forest Service. The crew received hotshot status in 1985, and he remained there until his retirement in 1997. He currently teaches fire classes in Spanish for private fire contracting companies and for the Forest Service in Puerto Rico.

J. W. Allendorf (Wallowa–Whitman, 1980; Arrowhead 3, 1981)

John "J. W." Allendorf began chasing fires with a shovel across his bicycle handlebars in Santa Barbara County, California, while he was still in elementary school. He began his Forest Service career after serving in the army, including time in Vietnam. His first job was on an engine at the Chuchupate Ranger Station on the Mount Pinos District of the Los Padres National Forest (LP). He joined the Los Prietos Hotshots the next season and worked there until he left for an appointment as a Los Padres engine driver. He spent a season with the Redding Hotshots and then returned to the LP as the helishot crew foreman. He became supe of the Wallowa-Whitman Hotshot Crew in 1980. In 1981 he was the supe of Arrowhead 3, one of the Park Service's first hotshot crews, working out of Yellowstone National Park. After some time away from fire, he moved to the Mendocino National Forest for an engine foreman job, eventually becoming a station manager and prescribed fire manager. He followed an interest in law enforcement by attending the Forest Service's law enforcement academy while on the Mendocino. He worked fire and law enforcement simultaneously until he left for the Six Rivers National Forest and a supervisory captain's position in law enforcement. He moved to Region 1 to serve as a patrol captain, later promoting to patrol commander, and retired from the Forest Service in 2006.

Dennis Baldridge (Laguna, 1990–2009)

Dennis Baldridge followed high school buddies to the El Cariso Hotshots in 1971 to begin his fire career. He stayed three seasons and then went to the Ramona helitack crew on the Cleveland National Forest. In 1975 he took a mid-season appointment on the Palomar Hotshots, a new crew. He finished the season with Palomar and then went back to engines. He stayed with engines, except for a brief stint as foreman of the Laguna Hotshots, until the Palomar district established a new crew in 1987: "a Type 2 crew with all minorities and women with no experience, with the goal of outplacing them to hotshot crews." He ran that crew until it lost its funding in 1990. He then lateralled over to the Laguna supe job and remained there until 2007, when he was promoted to Region 5 Southern California training officer. He retired from that position in 2009. After working on projects as a contractor with the R5 regional training officer and the California Conservation Corps, he went to work for San Diego Gas and Electric, first as a contracted fire marshal in 2011 and then a full-time fire coordinator in 2014. He is a founding member of the US Hotshots Association.

Bob Bennett (Horseshoe Meadow, 1989–2006)
Bob Bennett's chance meeting with founding Horseshoe Meadow supe Ben Charley may have determined his career direction. The two hit it off on a fire on the Klamath National Forest, where Bennett had begun in 1971 with engines, prevention, and timber. He moved to a Southern California BD [brush disposal] crew to see more fire and then came back north as one of Horseshoe Meadow's original squad leaders when Charley started the crew in 1974. He took an appointment on the Palomar Hotshots on the Cleveland National Forest in 1975 but returned to the Sequoia National Forest the next year. He ran a BD crew on the Sequoia for three seasons and then went back to Horseshoe Meadow in 1979 as a foreman. He became Horseshoe Meadow's second supe in 1989 and remained there until he retired in October 2006. At this writing, he works as an AD [administratively determined] dispatcher during fire season. He is a founding member of the US Hotshots Association.

Ron Bollier (Silver City, 1993–1995; Carson, 1996–1997; Fulton, 1998–2013)
Ron Bollier began his career in 1981 on an engine on the Angeles National Forest and joined the Dalton Hotshots in 1982. After

four years on Dalton, he went to the Prescott Hotshots for the 1986 season and then returned to Region 5 for an appointment on an engine on the Los Padres National Forest. He spent 1988 to 1993 on the Los Padres Hotshots and then took his first supe job running the Silver City Hotshots in New Mexico in 1993. He moved to the Carson Hotshots supe job for 1996 and 1997. He became the Fulton supe in 1998 and served there until 2014, when he accepted a division chief position on the Humboldt-Toiyabe National Forest. He became deputy forest fire chief of the Boise National Forest in 2016. In 2017 he retired from the Forest Service and went to work for the Nevada Division of Forestry as state fire management officer (FMO), his current position.

Charlie Caldwell (Redding, 1967–1986)

Serving his crewmates after being picked up and thrown behind the town bar was one of 18-year-old Charlie Caldwell's early duties on the 40-man Shasta Hotshot Crew in 1954. Caldwell started out as lead brush hook, and he was crew foreman by the time he was 20. The crew was discontinued after the 1956 season, and he became the engine foreman on the Shasta Lake Ranger District for the Shasta-Trinity National Forest. He detailed to the Redding Smokejumpers for the 1965 fire season and maintained his jump qualifications until 1974. In 1966 he was assigned as a fire guard along Interstate 5 for three months while it was being built through the Shasta-Trinity National Forest. He spent the rest of that season as a squad leader with an FAA [Federal Aviation Administration] parachute rigger's license for the Redding Smokejumpers. In 1967 he became the superintendent of the newly formed Redding Hotshots, a training crew designed to provide foresters with fire experience. He retired from the crew and the Forest Service in 1986. After 11 years with the Shasta County Sheriff's Office, 2 years driving a log truck, and 8 years as a journeyman electrician with Contra Costa Electric, he retired from full-time work in 2005. He took some time for hunting and his family and then returned to work in 2008 on the air support unit for the Redding Air Attack Base.

Barry Callenberger (Palomar, 1979–1982; Eldorado, 1982–1988)

Barry Callenberger started with the Forest Service in 1972 on the Dripping Springs Ranger District on the Cleveland National Forest after four years in the navy. He was the Palomar Hotshot Crew's foreman from 1976 to 1977. The crew was cut for the 1978 season during the "great hotshot massacre," but when it was brought back the next year, he became the supe. The crew regained hotshot status in 1980, and he remained there until 1981, when Palomar was cut again. He became Eldorado's supe in 1982 and left in 1988 for fuels and prescribed fire jobs at the district and regional levels. Following an early retirement, he switched to the private sector, working for Northtree Fire International, after which he became—and continues to be—an independent fuels management consultant.

Ben Charley (Horseshoe Meadow, 1974–1989)

Ben Charley had already served 20 years in the Marines and retired as a gunnery sergeant when he began a second career with the Forest Service in 1966. He started out in recreation on the Hume Lake Ranger District on the Sequoia National Forest but moved to fire prevention and later became an engine foreman. He was assigned to the Horseshoe Meadow Handcrew as its first crew boss when it was established in 1974. The crew earned its hotshot status in 1980, and he stayed on as supe until his retirement in 1989 at age 61, making him possibly the oldest working superintendent on record. After retiring from the Forest Service, he drove fire crew vehicles for the Special Operations Company and the California Department of Forestry and Fire Protection

(CDF) until 2002. He also served as the elected tribal chairman for the Dunlap Band of Mono Indians during his retirement. He died in 2015.

Jim Cook (Arrowhead, 1981–1995; Boise, 1996–1998)

Jim Cook began fighting fire in 1975 on California Polytechnic University's Blue Card crew after hearing about firefighting from his roommate, a Plumas Hotshots crewmember. After a season with an Ochoco National Forest helitack crew, he joined the Sawtooth IR [interregional] crew and moved up to assistant superintendent by 1979. He joined the Fire Operations program in Boise in 1980 for additional experience. When the National Park Service established the Department of the Interior [DOI]'s first hotshot crews in 1981, he became Arrowhead's founding superintendent. He stayed with Arrowhead until 1996, when he returned to the Forest Service to run the Boise Hotshots. Leaving Boise in 1999, he become the Forest Service's training projects coordinator at the National Interagency Fire Center (NIFC), retiring in 2012.

Steve Dickenson (La Grande, 1990; Redmond, 1994)

Steve Dickenson was only 16 years old when he became a helitack crewmember on the Ochoco National Forest in 1972. He worked his way up to foreman by 1976 but took time out to work on the Negrito Hotshots from 1973 to 1975. He rappelled out of La Grande, Oregon, for the 1977 season and jumped out of the base there from 1978 to 1982. After a few seasons away from fire, he became the foreman of the Union Hotshots. Remaining at Union until 1991, he then went to Redmond, Oregon, as an aircraft dispatcher. In 1995 he became the base operations supervisor for the Redmond Smokejumpers. He went to NIFC as an intelligence coordinator in 1999 and served as base manager for the North Cascades Smokejumper Base from 2001 to 2003.

Anthony Escobar (Kern Valley, 1983–2001)

Anthony Escobar began his career in 1973 on the Los Prietos Hot-shots on the Los Padres (LP) National Forest. He also worked as a seasonal crewmember on LP engines and the helicopter. In 1979 he received his career-conditional appointment and worked on the Arroyo Grande Flight Crew through 1982. He detailed to the BLM [Bureau of Land Management] as the founding superintendent of the Kern Valley Hotshots in 1983 and served there until 2001, when he became the Central California District's deputy FMO [fire management officer]. Returning to the LP in 2007 as the Forest Service FMO, he retired from that position in 2013. He has served as a board member of the US Hotshots Association.

Dan Fiorito (Union, 1996–2006)

Dan Fiorito began his career in the middle of the busy 1975 fire season on the Del Rosa IR crew. Working the 1977 Hog fire on an engine sparked his interest in the Pacific Northwest and big timber fires, and he moved on to BD crews on the Six Rivers and Rogue River forests. While on the Rogue, he filled in with the Prospect Hotshots, and he went to the crew full-time in 1982 when they were transferred to Klamath Falls, Oregon, and became the Winema Hotshots. He left the crew to gain experience on engines from 1985 to 1986. He was detailed as the Winema foreman in 1987. After being promoted to an AFMO [assistant fire management officer] position on the Winema in 1988, he decided to return to the hotshot program in 1996 as the Union supe. Though he retired in place in 2007, he has remained active in fire, first as a safety officer and with the Type 3 teams on the Umatilla and Wallowa-Whitman National Forests and currently with the La Grande Fire Cache.

Paul Gleason (Zigzag, 1979–1990)

Paul Gleason got his first fire job in 1964 on the Angeles National Forest. He worked on the Dalton Hotshots until 1970, except for a year's service in the army. He took time off for college and returned to fire in 1974 on the Okanogan National Forest as assistant foreman for a Regional Reinforcement Crew. After becoming assistant superintendent of the Zigzag Interagency Hotshots in 1977, he promoted to superintendent in 1979, remaining there until 1992. Before retiring from the Forest Service in 2001, he served as a district FMO and forest fire ecologist on the Arapaho-Roosevelt National Forest and deputy FMO of the Park Service's Rocky Mountain Region. He then served as an adjunct professor for Colorado State University's wildland fire science program until his death in 2003.

Lance Honda (Redmond, 1992–1997; Prineville, 1997–2009)

Lance Honda started out on the Olympic National Forest, working on a BD crew to put himself through college. He earned degrees in English literature and physical education while working nearly ten seasons on engines, helitack, and burning/suppression crews. He moved to the Rogue River Hotshots in 1978 to continue both his education and fighting fire. After earning a master's degree in outdoor education and a teaching certificate, he taught school in winter and worked on the Rogue River crew in summer. After "burning out on being a teacher," he became a full-time hotshot, moving up to squad leader and foreman while the crew became the Winema Hotshots. He accepted the supe job at Redmond in 1992 and the one in Prineville in 1997. He retired in place at Prineville in 2009. At this writing, he still goes out on fires, teaches fire courses, volunteers, and substitute teaches.

Ken Jordan (Sierra, 1998–2014)

Ken Jordan's first fire job was with the CDF in 1974. After jobs at the Orange City and Miller stations, he joined the El Cariso Hotshots as a sawyer in 1976. He received a career conditional appointment at El Cariso in 1979. From 1980 to 1984, he worked on an engine on the Cleveland National Forest, starting as a crewmember and working his way up to acting captain. He returned to the El Cariso Hotshots as a squad boss in 1985. In 1986 he served as the foreman on the Palomar Type 2 training crew on the Cleveland National Forest. He was hired onto the Sierra Hotshots as a captain in 1987 and remained at that position through 1991. After spending the 1992 season as the superintendent of the Bald Mountain Helishot Crew on the Stanislaus National Forest, he returned to the captain's job at Sierra the next year. He advanced to the supe job at Sierra in 1998 and retired from there in 2014. In retirement he taught fire classes and went to fires and, in the off-season, took groups from his church on international aid missions and wrote short stories. He died in 2016.

Steve Karkanen (Lolo, 1990–2011)

Fire and ice have been the cornerstones of Steve Karkanen's work life since 1979, when he joined the BD/fire crew on the Ninemile Ranger District on the Lolo National Forest. The next season, he joined the initial attack crew on the Lolo's Seeley Lake Ranger District. Over the next ten seasons on the district, he spent summers as an engine foreman and fire operations supervisor and winters as an EMT [emergency medical technician] and professional ski patroller. He became supe of the Lolo Hotshots in 1990 and retired in place in 2011. He served as director of the West Central Montana Avalanche Center until retiring from that position in 2016.

Greg Keller (Eldorado, 1985–1996; Modoc, 2000–2007)

Greg Keller wanted to be a National Park Service ranger in 1974, but he settled for the Forest Service's offer of an engine job on the Descanso Ranger District of the Cleveland National Forest. He was fascinated by his first glimpse of the El Cariso Hotshots at fire school, and two seasons later he found his "life calling" in the hotshot world on the Laguna Hotshots. He left for the Stanislaus

Hotshots in 1975 and then moved to the Eldorado Hotshots as a foreman. He became supe in 1985. After the 1995 season, he took a "sabbatical from fire" to be the deputy North Zone fire staff officer on the Boise National Forest. Seven years later, he returned to the hotshots as the founding supe of the Modoc Hotshot Crew. Upon retiring from the Forest Service as a battalion chief, he went to work for the Southern Idaho Timber Protective Association and retired for "the second and final time" in 2016.

Kurt LaRue (Diamond Mountain, 1993–2001)

Kurt LaRue began his career in 1976, dividing his time between Tanker 328 on the Sequoia National Forest's Hume Lake Ranger District and filling in on the Horseshoe Meadow Hotshots. He stayed busy in the winters running YACC (Young Adult Conservation Corps) and CETA (Comprehensive Employment and Training Act) BD crews and started with Horseshoe full-time in spring 1979. Later that season, he was moved to the Fulton Hotshots as assistant superintendent. He went to the Stanislaus Hotshots in 1983 as a sawyer and worked his way up to assistant superintendent. After the 1992 season, he left for the supe job at Diamond Mountain. He ran the crew until July 2001, when he became a staff officer in the BLM's operations group at its NIFC office in Boise. He retired from the BLM in 2010 and took a job with the Texas Forest Service, supervising dozers and firefighters to "finish his career working on the line with kids again." He retired from the Texas Forest Service in 2014 and currently works as a private contractor. He has served as vice president of the US Hotshots Association.

Craig Lechleiter (Redding, 1986–2002)

Family connections helped couch-surfing young Craig Lechleiter land his first Forest Service job on a trail crew on the Big Bear Ranger District in Southern California in 1969. He moved to an engine and worked a season there before being drafted into the army. When his tour was over, he returned to the engine and became the assistant foreman after spending some time in fire prevention. He "got the hotshot bug" while detailing with the Redding Hotshots for the 1975 fire season and spent the next two seasons as a foreman for the Ojai Hotshots on the Los Padres National Forest. In 1978 he became the Redding Hotshot Crew's lead foreman and was promoted to superintendent in 1986 when Charlie Caldwell retired. He remained the Redding supe until his retirement from the Forest Service in 2002. He began running crews for the CDF on the Lassen-Modoc Unit the same year and retired from CDF/Cal Fire twice—once in 2006 and again in 2009, after reinstatement in 2007.[5] From 2011 to 2016, he served as the Schonchin Butte Fire Lookout in Lava Beds National Monument, and in 2017 he began a new lookout position at Timber Mountain on the Modoc National Forest.

Shawna Legarza (San Juan, 2002–2007)

Making money for college and having fun were the only things Shawna Legarza expected from her job on a Nevada BLM engine crew in 1989. Fire turned out to be a good fit, and she moved to the Black Mountain Hotshots, staying there while she worked her way through her bachelor's and master's degrees. In 1997 she went up to Alaska to run the North Star Fire Crew for two seasons and also try an AFMO [assistant fire management officer] job. In 2002 she became the founding superintendent of the San Juan Hotshots and remained there until 2008. After working as a station manager, dispatch center manager, district FMO, and forest FMO, she became deputy director and then director of Region 5 Fire and Aviation. She was appointed national director of Fire and Aviation Management for the US Forest Service in 2016. She earned a doctorate in psychology in 2013.

---

[5] In 2007, the California Department of Forestry and Fire Protection (CDF) was renamed Cal Fire.

Mark Linane (Los Prietos/Los Padres, 1973–2001)

Mark Linane grew up in a Forest Service firefighting family and filled out the first and only application of his career in May 1963 for a job at the Rincon Station on the Los Padres National Forest. He became an engine captain during his second season and served as helitack foreman during his third. He bounced between the Rincon and San Marcos Stations as an engine captain from 1967 to 1970. After getting "burnt out on engines," he took a stint as a dozer operator and then served as the Redding Hotshots' assistant foreman for the 1971 season. In 1972 he took on a fuelbreak project as a Mountain Drive engine captain, "out on the farthest end with a couple dozers and 12 of the biggest . . . misfits you've ever seen in the world." Mark's group outworked the one coming from the other end, run by the other candidate for the Los Prietos hotshot superintendent job, and Mark took the crew in 1973. He retired from the Forest Service in 2001 but remains in the fire service, working for the Ventura County Fire Department as a training specialist and on varied projects for the Forest Service and its contractors. He is a founding member of the US Hotshots Association.

Ted Mathiesen (Arroyo Grande Flight Crew, 1990–2007)

Ted Mathiesen started working for the Forest Service in June 1970, on the Eagle Lake Ranger District of the Lassen National Forest. After a season in recreation, he went to the Bogard engine on the same district. He got his permanent appointment in 1974 on an engine on the Plumas National Forest and then switched over to running a BD crew. He transferred to the Los Padres National Forest in 1977 and become the Arroyo Grande helishot crew foreman in 1980. He became the Pozo engine foreman on the LP after the crew lost funding and became superintendent of the Arroyo Grande Flight Crew in 1990. He retired from that position in January 2007.

Dave Matier (Midnight Sun, 1992–1997, 1999–2007, 2009–2010)

Dave Matier's first fire job was with the Smokey Bear Hotshots from 1978 to 1983. After trying self-employment for a few years, he returned to fire in 1987, in Alaska. He became the Midnight Sun supe in 1992. He took a break from running the Suns in 1998 to become the project inspector and program manager for the Alaska Fire Service hotshot crews, but he returned the next year and remained there until 2007. He began his third term as supe of Midnight Sun in 2009 and retired in place in 2010. He died in 2015.

Paul Musser (Flagstaff, 1990–2004)

While still in high school, Paul Musser began his fire career with Cal Fire at Oroville's Butte County headquarters in 1971. After time on the Mendocino and Eldorado National Forests as an engine crewman, driver, and captain, he joined the Eldorado Hotshots as a captain in 1983. He took over the Flagstaff Hotshots in 1990 and stayed there until his retirement, just before the 2005 season.

Greg Overacker (Stanislaus, 1979–2006)

Greg Overacker started out as a crewmember on a Model 40 engine on the Stanislaus National Forest in 1967. After time in prevention and on the BD crew, he detailed to the Stanislaus Hotshots as a squad leader. He moved to the Fulton crew in 1976 as an assistant and then became supe of the Stanislaus Hotshots in 1979, where he served until his retirement in March 2006. He is a founding member of the US Hotshots Association.

Ron Regan (Del Rosa, 1977–1997)

Ron Regan spent his entire career on the San Bernardino National Forest, starting in 1961 on a Mill Creek engine. The next season he went to the Converse Hotshots and worked two and a half seasons there. After being drafted in 1964 and serving in Vietnam, he was back on the San Bernardino in 1966, serving as an engineer and then foreman on a Converse engine. He moved over to the Oak Glen Station in 1969 and worked there until he was hired as a foreman on the Del Rosa IR crew. He was promoted to superintendent in 1977 and served there until his retirement in 1997.

Brit Rosso (Arrowhead, 1996–2006)

Brit Rosso began his career with two years on a BD crew on the Eldorado National Forest in 1984. He soon became interested in hotshot crews and went to the Arrowhead Hotshots in 1986 as lead saw. He became Arrowhead's third supe in November 1996 after working his way up through the saw boss, squad boss, and foreman positions. He promoted to Sequoia-Kings Canyon National Park FMO in 2007 and became director of the Wildland Fire Lessons Learned Center in Tucson, Arizona, in 2010. He retired in 2019.

Bill Sandborg (Fulton, 1970–1983)

Bill Sandborg began working for the Forest Service in 1959. After 12 years on engines as a crewman, operator, and captain, he became the superintendent of the Fulton Hotshots. He served there for 12 years and then 11 years as a battalion chief before retiring. He currently ranches and grows oranges in California.

Fred Schoeffler (Payson, 1981–2007)

Fred Schoeffler's Navajo language skills got him his first Forest Service job as an engine crewmember on the Williams Ranger District of the Kaibab National Forest in 1972. He divided the next season between running a thinning/fire crew at the Williams Ranger District and a spot on the Oak Grove Hotshot Crew on the Angeles National Forest. After spending the 1974 season on the Payson Hotshots on the Tonto National Forest, he moved over to the Payson helitack crew as a squad boss. He returned to the Kaibab National Forest in November 1975 for jobs on the Chalender Ranger District as a TSI [timber stand improvement] crew foreman and assistant foreman on the helitack crew. He went back to the Tonto in 1978 as a station manager and engine foreman on the Pleasant Valley Ranger District and moved over to the Payson Ranger District in 1981 to become the Payson supe. He retired in place in 2007. He still goes to fires as a safety officer and researches fire weather and fatality fires. He has also served as a board member of the US Hotshots Association.

Stan Stewart (Los Padres, 2000–2009)
Stan Stewart became the Los Padres superintendent in 2000, after serving 23 seasons as a captain for Mark Linane. He began his career in 1971 on a helicopter in Idaho and moved to the Los Padres National Forest at the end of 1973 for an engine job. He joined the hotshot crew in 1974 and became a captain in 1977. He retired in place at LP in 2009 and served as founding president of the US Hotshots Association. He died in 2017.

Art Torrez (Vista Grande, 1994–2004)
Art Torrez's career began in 1974 as a crewmember for Vista Grande's inaugural season. He spent 29 of his 30 hotshot seasons with the crew, leaving only for an appointment on the Laguna Hotshots in 1977. He returned to Vista Grande the next year as a squad boss and promoted to captain in 1981. He became supe in 1994 upon his mentor Kirby Moore's retirement and served there until 2004, when he accepted the job as Southern California training officer. He became the Southern California Geographic Coordination Center manager in 2008 and promoted to assistant director of operations of Fire and Aviation for Southern California. After his retirement in 2012, he went to work for the California Governor's Office of Emergency Services as the Region VI assistant chief.

Greg Vergari (Union, 1980–1987)

Greg Vergari started fighting fire at age 14 on Call When Needed [CWN] crews for what was then the Pennsylvania State Forestry Department. He continued working on CWN crews through college in New York State and then started his US Forest Service career in 1974 on a suppression crew on the Lincoln National Forest. He moved to a helitack crew on the Wallowa-Whitman National Forest in the middle of the season and then worked on an engine in Ruidoso, New Mexico, for part of the 1975 season. He became a smokejumper in 1975 and continued jumping until he went to the Wallowa-Whitman Hotshot Crew as foreman in 1979. He was hired as the Union Hotshot supe in 1980 and continued there until 1987. was After serving as the AFMO for the Wallowa-Whitman's La Grande Ranger District from 1989 to 1994, he was the FMO for the Council Ranger District on the Payette National Forest from 1995 to 2000. He became Region 4's regional operational safety officer in 2000 and the Payette's deputy fire staff officer in 2003. In May 2004 he took a detail as fire staff officer of the Humboldt-Toiyabe National Forest and became the permanent staff officer in October 2004. He retired from the Forest Service in July 2008.

Rusty Witwer (Mendocino, 1978; Hobart/Tahoe, 1979–1995)

The fed-up father and godfather of "juvenile delinquent" Rusty Witwer conscripted him into the CDF on the Nevada-Yuba Ranger District in 1967. In 1970 he became an engine driver for the CDF's Orange County District. Filling out a Forest Service application while waiting for a friend at the Tahoe National Forest's Truckee Ranger District brought him to the Hobart Handcrew in 1971 as a seasonal GS-4 [in the federal government's general salary schedule] foreman. The crew earned hotshot status in 1972, and he left in 1974 for a TTO [tank truck operator] job on the Truckee District. He spent the 1975 season with the Redding Hotshots and then went back to the Hobart Hotshots as a GS-6 foreman with a 13/13 appointment[6]. He became the superintendent of the Mendocino Hotshots in 1978, but the crew was cut in August of that season. He went to the Hobart Hotshots as supe in 1979 and remained there through 1995. From 1995 to 1999 he was an AFMO on the Truckee District, and from 1999 to 2004 he was the Pacific Island coordinator for the Forest Service and FEMA's [Federal Emergency Management Agency's] international cooperative fire programs. He became Region 5's fire training officer in 2004 and retired from that position in 2007.

Craig Workman (Black Mountain, 1988–2005)
Craig Workman began his career on the Modoc National Forest in 1971 by walking into the district office in Tulelake, California, and telling the FMO he was looking for work. He started the next day, and by 1976 he was the station manager at the Dry Lake Guard Station. He "started getting the bug to be a hotshot" from a detail to the Redding Hotshots for the 1975 season. He joined the Hobart Hotshots in 1979 and stayed there until 1984. In 1985 he became an AFMO on the Truckee Ranger District and in 1998 was appointed founding superintendent of the Black Mountain Hotshots. He retired in place in 2005.

---

[6] There are three types of employment levels for federal wildland fire jobs: temporary, career seasonal, and permanent. Temporary employees work seasonally and receive limited benefits only while employed; they are terminated and rehired from year to year. Temporary appointments are limited to 1,039 hours of base time, roughly six months. Career seasonals (officially titled "Permanent Career Conditional") may or may not work year-round, depending on funding. They receive benefits but are likely to be furloughed for part of every year. Career seasonal appointments are often called "13/13s," referring to their guarantee of employment for 13 biweekly pay periods with the possibility of working up to 13 more. There are also 18/8 career seasonal positions. The terms "WAE" (when actually employed) or "intermittent employment" refer to an older form of career seasonal appointment. Permanent employees work year-round, and their positions are often referred to as "26/0s," referencing their guaranteed 26 pay periods of employment per year.

Bob Wright (Sacramento, 1990–2002)

Volunteer work for a high school horticulture class introduced Bob Wright to fire and the California Division of Forestry in 1969. In 1971 he split time between the CDF's experimental heli-jumping program and his CDF station in Napa. In 1973 he moved to the Umpqua National Forest as a helitack foreman. From 1973 to 1978 he worked on the Umpqua in helitack, BD, and as a dozer operator. From 1978 to 1989 he ran the Diamond Lake Ranger District's 20-person BD/suppression crew. He became Sacramento's supe in 1990 after the AFMO job he held in 1989 in Cottage Grove, Oregon, proved a little slow for his liking. He retired in 2002, but he keeps busy hunting, fishing, traveling with his wife Carol, working on his house, and instructing the New Mexico hotshot crews. He has also served as a board member for the US Hotshots Association.

J. W. Allendorf Sees Hotshots for the First Time

I didn't even know what hotshot crews were, but we went to a fire down off of Highway 33, out of Ventucopa, and it was a real steep hill. Just a roadside start, right up the hill, through the chamise, just hauling ass when we got there. Ventura County had come in, and the road cut was so steep that the ladder companies laid their ladders up there. We carried the hose packs up the ladders and started laying hose from there. I wasn't laying hose: I was supposed to be cutting a little pioneer line for the hose lay with a brush hook, so that's what I was doing. About two hours into it, these two buses pulled in. It was getting dark, and I had no clue who the hell these guys were, but they unloaded, and I was watching them. Of course, having been in the military, it was like, "Wow, this looks like some kind of military deal going on here." These guys got off the bus, all lined up, got the tools out. Pretty soon the headlamps were going on, chainsaws were starting. It was Texas Canyon and Los Prietos. I asked Archie Abeyta, "Who the hell are these guys?" and he goes, "Those are the LP 'shots and Texas Canyon 'shots." I'm going, "'Shots? What the hell are those?" and he goes, "Watch these guys." By then the fire had outrun us, and we were just laying hose. It was really pretty leisurely as far as I was concerned, just squirting a little water and putting the hose lay in. The fire was over the top of the hill, still burning toward the top, and the hotshot crews each took one flank and got cranked up. I was going, "Holy shit. Whoa." I mean, I was impressed. I was going, "Damn!" Because, I mean, the brush was flying, saws were roaring, headlamps, shouting, all this stuff, and I'm going, "That's what I want to do." It was funny because, actually, LP beat Texas Canyon to the top by a pretty good margin, so I was going, "That's the crew I want to get with."

Dan Fiorito's First Fire

I remember my first day with the Forest Service. I showed up in July 1975 in the middle of fire season and was assigned as a firefighter on the Del Rosa IR hotshot crew. The foreman took me into the office and had me jump up and down on a wooden box—the step test—and said, "You're in shape. You'll do all right." Then we played volleyball for a while for PT [physical training]. Then this buzzer goes off, the fire whistle, and it was, "Oh, we've got a fire, get your stuff." I asked, "What stuff? No one told me to bring any stuff." I just had what I was wearing: a t-shirt, my boots, and Levi's. They said, "You know, like underwear and socks and stuff."

I called my girlfriend up and told her to go to my folks' house—I was just 18—and get my clothes and bring them to the station because we were heading to Ontario to fly out. We waited around as long as we could, then loaded up on the crew bus and headed down the hill. We were driving down the road and I saw Meg, who is now my wife of 23 years, coming in her orange VW Bug. I said, "Wait, stop, there is my stuff." They stopped the bus, and I grabbed my stuff and got a quick good-bye kiss.

We got to Ontario and loaded up on the Convair, a twin-engine prop plane. This was my first airplane flight. We flew to Redding. We got on a school bus and drove through the Shasta-Trinity National Forest, past Shasta Lake and Whiskeytown Lake, to the Whiskeytown airport. We got the word that we were going to the fire the next day, and we got some food and bedded down for the night at the Whiskeytown airport. We got up the next morning and drove to a drop point in a National Guard deuce-and-a-half [two-and-a-half-ton truck]. Since we flew, we had no fire tools. At the drop point, there were three piles of tools: Pulaskis, shovels, and McLeods. The foreman told me, "Grab a McLeod," so I walked over and stared at the three piles of tools. I knew what a shovel was but not what a Pulaski or a McLeod was. I was standing there thinking, "Hey, that axe thingy looks like a cool tool," and I picked up a Pulaski. About that time, the foreman started yelling at me, "You dumb shit, that's a Pulaski! Here, this is a McLeod!" He handed me this rake-looking thing with a long stick attached to it. I was thinking, "Why didn't he just tell me to pick up a freaking rake?" but you didn't want to say anything because it was all just so intimidating. That was the extent of my fire training prior to hitting the fireline for the first time.

We hiked up the ridge and started digging line downhill on this big timber fire. El Cariso was digging in front

MEET THE SUPES • 21

of us about a quarter mile down the ridge. There was no Nomex at that time. All we had was our jeans, boots, cotton fire shirts, metal hard hats, and military web gear with four water bottles, a file, and a fire shelter. I didn't have a Filson cruiser vest yet, so I stuffed my lunch down in my shirt. All of a sudden, the fire started rolling up the ridge through the crowns of the timber, and I heard someone yelling, "Get back up the hill to the black!" So there I was, running up this steep ridgeline to get up to the safety zone. I looked back and saw one guy pushing another guy on his butt with a McLeod, hollering, "Go, go, go, get your ass up the hill!" I was thinking, "Oh great, my first day on the job and I'm gonna die."

We made it up to the black, and here comes El Cariso just ahead of the fire. The fire blew over the ridge, and we sat there watching it for a while. Then someone said, "Eat your lunch." It was about 105 degrees that day, and I was kind of freaked out, nauseous, and not real hungry, so I ate an orange and gave the rest of my lunch away to some of the other guys. Things calmed down and we went back at it, tying our line in down to a road in the drainage below. By the time we got the line in it was getting dark, and I was getting pretty hungry. A couple of guys walked up the road with green knapsacks and started handing out C-rations to the crew. Like I said, I was getting real hungry; I grabbed a box of C-rats and started opening a can of spaghetti or what- ever it was, and the foreman came up and started yelling, right in my face, "Did I tell you that you could eat?!" I was sitting there just shaking like a little kid. "No," I said. Then the guy just turned around and told the rest of the crew, "Go ahead and eat." Just like that. They just screwed with you, all the time, trying to tweak your brain. Those guys were hard- core all the way. But it was good, and I learned a lot about fire that first year.

Never Forget Where You Came From
(because someone else definitely has a story about it)

Ben Charley, founding superintendent of Horseshoe Meadow, recalls his first meeting with Bob Bennett, his longtime foreman and successor as supe. Bennett is now widely known simply as "Horseshoe Bob," and those who know them both liken their relationship more to father and son than anything else.

I met Bob on a fire up on the Klamath. We started talking; I didn't know him from Adam, and he didn't know me either. He says, "Where do you work?" and I said, "Off the Hume Lake [District]." He says, "Can I get a job down there?" I was running the engine then. I said, "Come on down. I'll hire you," never thinking he'd do that. Come April, I drove into the station, and there he was. So I hired him. Been with me ever since. (Laughs.) I've got a lotta fun about Bob. I could tell you stories about Bob. I could talk all day about Bob and tell you a different story every time.

PART TWO

SO YOU WANT TO BE A SUPE

What It Takes, Ways to Get There, What You Can Expect

Whether you want to grow up to be like them or just wonder what makes them tick, the supes explain how and why they've made this all-encompassing job their calling as well as their lifestyle and talk about what they think it demands in return.

Why are you well-suited to fire?

Kurt LaRue (Diamond Mountain, 1993–2001)
Well, by this time in our lives, at the age where we are doing some of these interviews, who's to say whether we were all well-suited to fire in the beginning, or was it fire that warped the personality to match it. I think after this amount of time, they've probably had a tremendous impact on each other.

I enjoyed the challenge. I think that was the big part when I was younger. I enjoyed the challenge, and it gave me the freedom to do what I wanted a lot of the year. I don't know that I would've been very successful somewhere if I had gotten into a go-to-the-store, go-to-an-office, go-to-the-garage, drive-the-truck, or any other job I would've ended up with where you do the same thing day after day after day. On the surface, hotshotting is the same day after day after day, but you know from doing it that it's not. Every day has its own bizarre little peculiarities. You know, the old joke among hotshots is: if you don't like where you are, just wait a day or two. You don't know where you're going to be next. That appealed to me. It was a thing of continuous change.

Brit Rosso (Arrowhead, 1996–2006)

I love it. Because I truly love it, it just boils down to that. I get up in the morning, and I love the job more every day, even with all the continuing administrative restrictions and constraints. It's a love of the job, the level of satisfaction that I get out of it, the camaraderie, the mutual respect I have from others of the same caliber who also hold themselves and their crew program to the same level. I think that's the key: it's the love of the job. I don't know how to put it in any other words. It's not going to read well in a book, but it is what it is.

Dave Matier (Midnight Sun, 1992–1997, 1999–2007, 2009–2010)

I have no clue what suits me personally for fire—something to do with my upbringing in the military. I'm a creature of habit; I have routines—not in the fire world, you can't be routine on fires—but the structure thing. Like I said, I did 18 years in the military without being in it, and this is just an extension of that, I think.

Dennis Baldridge (Laguna, 1990–2009)

I think adaptability, the ability to change with what's going on. . . . I can do a lot of things at once. I like the challenge of a lot going on—especially on the scene of a fire, where there's a lot happening. I like that, so it suits me when there's a bunch going on. If nothing's happening, then I'm bored. I like the travel. (Laughs.) The whole thing. I just fell into it, and I couldn't think of doing any other job.

Mark Linane (Los Prietos/Los Padres, 1973–2001)
Hard-headed. Stayed fairly physically alive, even though I've had umpteen thousand knee operations. Fought through them, always came back. Got a strong work ethic, and with the hot-shots, that's what you do: work. Didn't have a problem making decisions. I can make a decision.

Loved working with the kids; I think it kept you young that whole time. Working with old people, you get old. Physically, you get old anyway, but you can get mentally old, and working with the kids keeps you young. That's probably a good thing. And then there's that huge thing of developing people. For me, it was 27 generations of kids. I still see a lot of them, and they all come back, and it's a pretty tight family. That was a lot of it—developing and training kids, watching the successes, watching the failures. There were a lot more successes than there were failures by a huge percentage.

Leaders and good supes: made or born?

Kurt LaRue (Diamond Mountain, 1993–2001)
I've got kids at home, so I remember watching little kids. Some little kids are just naturally always leaders. Some little kids are just followers. So I think there is a born component to it. I don't think anybody will be very effective if they don't study, learn some, and pay attention to things. Like with anything else to do with human nature, you've got each end of the bell curve. There are those people who just naturally are leaders and don't seem to have to work at it much, and there are other people who couldn't lead sailors to a whorehouse. I mean, they can piss off empty rooms. They are never gonna be a boss. (Laughs.) And then there's the great mass

of us in the middle who have to work at it, watch other leaders we respect, learn some skills, and read about it.

Brit Rosso (Arrowhead, 1996–2006)
The question is always asked, are leaders born or made? I would say both . . . because there are folks who are almost born leaders, but there are many traits that make a good leader. Then they decide, or someone takes them under their wing . . . in order to develop them into a more effective leader—so it's both. There are some who are born with leadership traits, and then they're nurtured and developed, and they grow. There're some who don't come with any of those traits but really want to strive to be a better leader, and they work on self-development, and someone might help them.

Fred Schoeffler (Payson, 1981–2007)
I think most are naturally leaders. You can make good supervisors, but the person has to want to be one. There's a lot of responsibility and extra effort involved. Some of the best supervisors were the ones who were smartasses or minor troublemakers. Giving them progressive responsibilities, especially on fires, often allowed them to blossom and shine. Being a leader is a sacrifice; however, I've found it to be very rewarding.

Craig Lechleiter (Redding, 1986–2002)
Made. Definitely made. They're made before you ever see them. Their families start the process. . . . Religious beliefs, society in general, I think, program them. At least the ones who came here . . . were basically all the same kind of people. . . . They all wanted the same thing. That's why they bonded so fast when they got here. In a week they felt as though they had known each other for six months already. They had so much in common, and their values were all the same, their goals were all the same; it was really easy to have fun.

Leaders are definitely made; we were just a phase of their development when they got here. Born? There's nobody born a leader. It's all who you're exposed to. You became a successful quarterback on a football team or a superintendent. Somebody drove you in that structure, shoved you along, and instilled the leadership qualities. That's my take, anyway. They gave you the self-esteem or confidence to be what you are.

Dennis Baldridge (Laguna, 1990–2009)

I think part of it's what you're born with. There are some traits, I guess, that you grow up with. Part of it has to do with the environment you're brought up in; and then you can be made by getting the right folks putting you in the right direction and teaching you things, and being able to learn from your mistakes. We learn better from making a mistake than being told how to do it right. It's just the way we are. So, I think given some basic skills, a supervisor can be made. A good leader can be taught, but not everybody can learn.

Also, in the early days . . . you were promoted to management or supervision because if you could pound nails the fastest or cut line the best or last the longest, then obviously you were going to be a supervisor. It wasn't looking at any skills necessary; it was just you were technically able to do your job . . . , and it didn't take into consideration being able to work with people, being able to do paperwork, the administrative end of it. We're really not taught that stuff. It's thrown on us when we get the next promotion. But that makes it hard, because if you can't do it, then it looks bad if you have to get demoted because you didn't do a good job. I think that's changed quite a bit.

Charlie Caldwell (Redding, 1967–1986)

Ain't no way a person can be born a good crew boss, so I scratched that off my list as soon as I looked at it. I wrote in my notes, "Hard work, dedication, and acceptance by peers." You've got to show somebody something, or you're never going to be a crew boss. You don't do it on your own. You've got to be motivated. You've got to pay attention to everything that's going on around you. You've got to learn this stuff, and you've got to let your boss know ... that you know this stuff. You've got to perform, and you kind of work your way into a crew boss position.

The arts of listening, reading, and speaking are some of the keys to being a damn good crew boss. A lot of people don't know how to listen. That's probably one of the toughest things in instructor training: getting people to listen. As I'm talking, I'm talking probably 50 to 100 words a minute, and your mind is thinking 2,000 words per minute. So for me to project to you, if I want you to learn, I have to keep your interest level there.

Craig Workman (Black Mountain, 1988–2005)

I think every supe that I know, or leader that I know, probably started as a child or a kid and maybe was a leader in sports, or maybe worked on a farm or a ranch or took a lead role fairly young. That's the sense I have: you started very young to build. I haven't seen very many people who didn't already have a glimmer, at 20 years old, who didn't already show something that really developed. But I may be wrong.

Lance Honda (Redmond, 1992–1997; Prineville, 1997–2009)

I don't believe people come out of the womb as leaders. I don't even believe we're predisposed from the womb, that it's in a person's DNA. I think that leadership comes from how we were raised as a person, in our families, in our experiences and the choices that we make, and how our personalities are formed. . . . That's where I believe leaders come from. Can leaders be developed? Yes. There are qualities that can be developed in people who aren't predisposed to that through their upbringing. They can, if they pay attention and work on that, just like shooting a basketball, or just like your lung capacity can be developed.

Leadership skills and qualities can be developed if you pay attention.

Art Torrez (Vista Grande, 1994–2004)
I would say that they are made. I spent 18 years from the crewperson to the captain level; and then my mentor, Kirby Moore—I was in his hip pocket for the last two years because he realized that his time was coming to leave the service. You can never learn enough when you've got that type of sponsorship or even that type of relation with the person who's teaching you how to fight fire or how to take care of your people and so forth.

What makes someone a leader?

J. W. Allendorf (Wallowa–Whitman, 1980; Arrowhead 3, 1981)
One thing that people think—and I believe it too—makes you a leader in some respects [is] . . . if I see things in the Forest Service . . . I speak up and call bullshit on things, and I appreciate people who I work with doing the same. . . . I personally feel that that's how you develop a program and make it better: by making your thoughts known. People who do that, I always respected them, although bureaucrats—and God knows this outfit's full of those bastards—they don't much care for it. They want just a no-waves operation. You don't get change and you don't get good quality with no waves. You gotta go out and rattle the fuckin' bushes, I think. (Laughs.)

Can you make a leader out of someone who's not a natural?

Dan Fiorito (Union, 1996–2006)
Back in the old days, the superintendents I knew were the biggest storytellers and very charismatic. It seemed like that kind of

person made it up there to those jobs, for whatever reason, but I don't think that you have to be that. I think you have to have some basic skills as far as reading people—people skills. At the beginning of the season, you have five months to get to know your new crewmembers as well as you can. You start giving them things to do, different tasks, and learn how they respond to different situations and stresses. Over a couple of seasons, I think you are going to identify the folks who have leadership skills. Then you can start sending them to classes like "Fireline Leadership" to get the background, and then bring them up through the ranks. Some people will be ready in three years, some it will take ten years, and some may never be ready, and that needs to be okay.

I don't think we can take everybody and make them leaders. We can take many people and make them leaders by observing what their strengths are and working on their weaknesses. We have eight permanent positions on the crew now. That is three more than we used to have. I would like to see some GS-4s as permanents so we have a career ladder in place for those potential leaders. But our budgets and other issues—like finding ways to send temporary employees to advanced training—are some of the challenges we face in building a professional wildland firefighting organization.

I have some great guys who are just studs, want to work hard, and have a lot of fun in the woods, but they think they're immortal or something. They are young and they have never been hurt or seen anyone get hurt. They don't have the attitude that everything's got to be safe all the time. It doesn't matter what you're doing: whether you're shooting a flare gun, filling drip torches, falling trees, or whatever. It's the little things I notice people do that makes me think of them as being leaders, the ones who are going to do the safe thing all the time. Nobody can do it all the time, but they are conscious of it, where some guys are like, "Aw, that was great!"—they have a close call, a near miss, and they think it was real fun because they got their adrenaline going. Well, it is great and fun, until they get hurt; then the fun stops. I guess that is my main thing: I look for people who are aware of what is going on around them and have a really high level of wanting to be safe and keep their crew safe.

Richard Aguilar (El Cariso, 1974; Wolf Creek, 1975–1997)

If a person wants to become that leader, to get a job like that, you can make them. First, you have to build his confidence, that he can do it. And once he knows that he can do it, he'll work along with you and you can push him, and he can become that person, the leader. But he has to build his confidence that he can do it. It's just like a job that you want really bad, but you're not very good at it, but if you set your mind to it, you're gonna do it. You're gonna work on it, and you'll do it.

Barry Callenberger (Palomar, 1979–1982; Eldorado, 1982–1988)

I don't necessarily agree with the "you're born to be a leader" kind of stuff. Maybe, but I don't think you are. You have to be born with a little bit of incentive to want to be in charge or be the leader. . . . It's not necessarily a priority, because I think if you're open-minded and you're willing to look at other styles of other people and how they do things, and learn the good things from that, you're going to become a good leader. And if you're not, it doesn't matter if somebody had waved a wand over you when you were little.

You don't have to be the big junkyard dog. I never looked at myself as that. When I became a superintendent, I never felt like I was a stereotypical superintendent. But things were changing, too. A lot of things were changing. So what was stereotypical then isn't today, although there are some people who like to think [so]. (Laughs.)

Rusty Witwer (Mendocino, 1978; Hobart/Tahoe, 1979–1995)
I'm convinced there are very few people in the world who are raised to be known as a bad worker. So why do we have bad workers? I used to hammer this into all my captains: the wolf teaches all her cubs to hunt, and we have to do the same thing.

One of the things about being a supervisor is the fact that— especially in crew dynamics—you have 20 people and they're all bonding together. But inside of that group dynamic there are cliques, and there are people who clique together for numerous reasons. Mainly they clique together to be the "mod squad" or the "cool" guys versus the "uncool" guys, and a little bit of that is—I think—okay. But as supervisors, you need to spend more time with the people who are not in the clique when there's a break. As long as they're trying, you're working with them to try to improve them. Those are the folks the overhead needs to spend time with.

It's so easy for new overhead to hang in with the clique because they're part of the clique, and the reason why they're overhead is because they were part of the clique. They need to de-clique and spend more time with the people who are new to the crew or maybe having a little more difficulty hanging. What that does is send a message that it is 20 people, and it isn't 8 people who build this line and make this happen and look out for each other. It really helps to build the team thing. I think this has changed a lot from my day.

Now, I see here at the apprenticeship academy signs of what I think good leaders are: running with the folks at the back, helping them to reach their potential development. Because you're not the fastest runner or can't do the most pullups doesn't mean you're not the best worker on the crew. It's taking that kind of scenario and, like the wolf with the cubs, making sure that the mama wolf is with all ten cubs and just not the six at the front of the line. That's a biggie, and over the years I had people who were not part of the clique, were what I called the "shitbird"—everybody needs someone to pick on—that actually became career people in the Forest Service and became good supervisors. That is much more of a winner than taking the number-one top dog . . . and some of those never became good supervisors. There's a difference between how fast and how strong you are, how long you can keep your eyes open, versus becoming a good supervisor. What I used to hammer into my folks I'm seeing more [of] now here at the apprentice academy: that it's a team effort, and everybody needs to hit their potential. Some people just need more time with a supervisor than others.

How did you develop your leadership skills?

Bob Bennett (Horseshoe Meadow, 1989–2006)

School of hard knocks. I don't know. I've made so many mistakes. I was lucky in my career that of all the supervisors I had, I think I had only one really crappy supervisor. I always had good FMOs and good supervisors who helped me. They let me make mistakes, and if they saw me going down the wrong path, they would talk to me. When I was a captain, I was pretty vocal and outspoken, and I'm probably lucky I ever became a supe because I was that way. I was a hard charger, and I didn't care who I made mad. I'd speak my mind, and I wasn't very diplomatic. That had to be beat into me. It was a hard lesson to learn because I thought I was always right, but I had good people to help me through that. Now, I'm not the most diplomatic person in the world; I am more diplomatic than I used to be. And I listen better now, where in the past it was always a little more my view. Now I take in a little more. I think age has mellowed me. . . . Hanging out with the guys in that room [at the R5 Hotshot Workshop] has made me better. Sharing your experiences or saying, "Hey, am I screwing up here? Am I doing it right, or do you have a suggestion?" It's listening more, communicating more. . . . It comes with age and then having good supervisors, too, who trust you and know that you're going to be all right somewhere down the line. But it was mostly hard knocks—I mean, big hard knocks at times.

Jim Cook (Arrowhead, 1981–1995; Boise, 1996–1998)

My dad was a football coach, and I guess I kind of had mini-leadership skill training since I was born, I don't know (laughing). I lived in three states and seven towns before I graduated high school, and I think the skills I got from that were adapting to new situations and dealing with different kinds of people all the time. I used team sports as my doorway, my way in, so that was probably a part of it. Played one year of college football, and then I was too slow to be a wide receiver and too small to be a tight end, so I was a ski bum for a year and kind of worked around, building log houses, and did a lot of different things before I got into fire—worked on a ferry boat, did a lot of different things. I saw a lot of different work environments and how people responded to different types of leadership, different types of supervision. I was probably an average to maybe good athlete, but I always managed to have a knack for getting people to be enthusiastic about whatever it was we were engaged in, so maybe that was part of it.

That was a good question, because I never really thought about it. But once I got into the fire business, I just kind of fell into it, and it never really occurred to me to think about career. I think a lot of it was because it was such a team endeavor. It was natural, and I enjoyed it, whether as a crew member, a subordinate leader, on up. It was just something that I liked.

Stan Stewart (Los Padres, 2000–2009)

Well, I was lucky. I had a good teacher for that. I won't say it came easy, but I got to watch, and I was around long enough I got to watch guys who knew what they were doing. That's pretty much how I developed: watching others. Watching what worked well, watching when you made a mistake: [and saying,] "Oh well," and trying not to repeat it. . . . All the years I was being a captain, I had a lot of time to watch other people do stuff. Probably didn't need that many years, but whatever.

There're a variety of leadership styles out there, and I'm not sure that some of the ones who were around when I first started would work anymore. You'd probably be in trouble all the time. But there are a bunch of different ways to make stuff work. I think mine was just from watching and being in the right place at the right time to learn a lot.

Greg Keller (Eldorado, 1985–1996; Modoc, 2000–2007)

I would say that I got my leadership skills from my father. He was a taskmaster. He was a hard and dedicated worker, and he never accepted anything but the best from me. I said, "Come on, Dad, that's good enough," and he goes, "Get in there and do it right." It didn't matter if I was mowing the lawn, washing dishes, making my bed, vacuuming: it had to be done properly and correct. It didn't matter if it was a very physical job or simply picking up a newspaper and folding it and putting it away in a box. There was a reason behind doing it, there was a method to do it right, and he only accepted a right job.

Steve Karkanen (Lolo, 1990–2011)

Through the school of hard knocks. Getting out was the key thing, and seeing a lot. Getting out and seeing how other people operated, being on crews where I liked some aspects, disliked others; that was pretty important.

I've talked to a person. . . . He's a GS-11, not even in fire. He thinks he can go out and be an IC [incident commander] on a fire, based on being on a hotshot crew as a detailer for part of a season. We sat him down, and we said, "You have to know how to run chainsaws, you have to know how to deal with tools, you have to know about water handling, you have to know about the vehicles, you've gotta know about dealing with people. You can't just go out and be an IC." You can't just go out and be a leader. I mean, there are people out there who think they can do that, and that's really scary. And, to a certain extent, [with] our agencies' task book system and the way we're dealing with some of our apprentices, we're forcing people into positions where they're going to be responsible for people—people's lives—and they don't have that basis of understanding that you need to have to be able to lead people. This person thought they could be a leader without having that basic level of understanding of what really goes on out there.

Richard Aguilar (El Cariso, 1974; Wolf Creek, 1975–1997)

I think I had to become sort of a young bully myself, because immediately, when I went to school, I didn't know one word in English. And when I arrived at school the first day, I was not allowed to talk. I spent two years sitting in a corner because I couldn't speak the language. I had to start learning things by myself. And then, because I was small, I had to learn to fight. I had to learn. I became that way. Pretty soon, people [said], "Hey, you're okay!" And that's why I developed these things my way. (Laughs.) You want to be part of my crew? This is the way we do things here.

Dennis Baldridge (Laguna, 1990–2009)

Some was growing up and learning from my parents, and then some was in the Forest Service. . . . I couldn't quit because that's how I was brought up: you start a job, you finish it no matter what. And then I just took mental notes and said, "I'm never doing that when I'm in charge. I think I learned kind of the opposite of the way a lot of people did: I learned what not to do. I saw the bad stuff. I learned some better skills from dealing with the bad people, and I started looking at people who I thought were doing a good job supervising and picking out traits that I liked. It took a while, because you try on different styles, and you find what worked for this person doesn't necessarily work for you.

Ron Bollier (Silver City, 1993–1995; Carson, 1996–1997; Fulton, 1998–2013)

(Laughs.) It came from a lot of trial and error. Came from learning the hard way. Came from making mistakes. . . . A mistake, you can learn from it. You'll have another chance at it. You'll be able to be put in that position and hopefully make a good decision. You learn from trial and error.

I worked for some good supervisors . . . I worked for some superintendents who were excellent, and I had some not-so-excellent. I had some who I knew I didn't want to be like. I just learned everything I could from the good ones in the time that I had to spend with them. You try and take all that, and you try and use it yourself and do your own thing.

You want your own program; you want to be your own self. Don't be somebody you've worked for. That doesn't get it. Be your own person. Whether people like you or not, they're gonna tell you.

Mark Linane (Los Prietos/Los Padres, 1973–2001)

Some I got from upbringing. Probably was my grandfather. Grandfather had a super-strong work ethic. He worked a ranch. He worked seven days a week, except for church—a half-day on Sunday—till he was 97. . . . Had a couple great football coaches who taught me how far you can push people, how there has to be some pain so there can be some gain.

I told you about Alfonso [Archuleta] . . . : he would say, "Mark, sometimes when I get excited, you'll have a hard time understanding me. If I do that, you call me on it and make sure you know what's going on." I think that kind of gave me a clue, because he was a great fireman: if you've got a weakness, let people know what your weakness is so they're aware of your shortcomings and they can work around 'em. Not being afraid of telling people what your weaknesses are.

Got some stuff from some old-time firing bosses who took you under their wing. Had some bosses who weren't afraid to give you the responsibility, the authority, and the expectation that whether you really knew the job or not, you were going to do your damnedest to do it and get it done.

Probably a lot of trial and error stuff: "Oh shit, that didn't work." Looking back, probably was tougher on some people than I should've been. As I got older, would've spent some more time trying to develop them as opposed to shitcannin' 'em. There were probably some salvageable souls that I thought were dogmeat at the time. Maturity probably brought some of those changes from the time when you thought you were invincible and you ran up and down hills like a deer, and as time brought on some wisdom, you knew you were getting slower. And some pretty great role models: Lyn Biddison. Like I said, I started with some responsibility with a season and a half, and I was an engine captain. I listened; I tried to role model after guys who had a lot of respect, to listen to them when they made initial attacks, took command on a division or as a line boss back in those days. I'd pick out the ones who I thought really had their shit together and try and make myself more like them.

Craig Workman (Black Mountain, 1988–2005)
I probably got it started when I was a kid growing up on a farm. I'd work in the fields running field hands, putting out irrigation pipe, weeding fields, and picking potatoes, all these different types of chores. I'd run 20, 30 people out in the fields doing that, and that was probably at 13, 14 years old.

Ben Charley (Horseshoe Meadow, 1974–1989)
We all had to work. There were three of us, three brothers, and he worked us hard, which is all right. When I left here, I was 15. Didn't know a damn thing. Marine Corps got me and, whoa, I tell you, they worked me over. But I learned. And then I guess

wartime made you grow up pretty fast, too. I got initiated before I was 20 years old: I knew what I wanted.

What does it mean to be a supe? What does it take?

Bob Bennett (Horseshoe Meadow, 1989–2006)

The superintendent's job—and I didn't realize it until I became one—is probably the most powerful job in the Forest Service, in firefighting. Because once you get that title, it's a position that can be abused. I was a captain, and the guy was a division supervisor, and I was trying to get a tactic across to him, and he wouldn't listen to me. I had to go to my superintendent and say, "Hey Ben, we gotta do this and this," and he goes, "Okay," and he goes over and talks to this guy. . . . About two weeks later Ben retired and I was the supe, and the same guy, when I suggested it, didn't blink twice. It was just the position, going from a captain to supe with the same guy over a two-week period. . . . It's a powerful position that can be misused, or it can be used to an advantage, too. . . . You can abuse that power at times if you don't watch yourself. It is the greatest job in the world.

Ron Regan (Del Rosa, 1977–1997)

That's a good question, because I always wanted to—with every fire situation—analyze it: why this happened, and how come this didn't happen, and why it burned downhill, how come it's spotting all over the place. You just go back to fire weather and how it dictates what the fire's going to do. And you've got to have that kind of built-in savvy to know when things aren't right. My crew and I even got kicked off a fire in the '90s because I wouldn't allow them to get into an unsafe situation. I tried to instill in my foremen to scout and assess the fire weather before making any decision that would put crewmembers' lives in jeopardy. I never put anybody in a fire shelter when I was a superintendent, and we never got in a position where we were going to have that happen. I feel blessed that that never happened to me, and I feel sad for the folks who have been through that.

Fred Schoeffler (Payson, 1981–2007)
Every hotshot superintendent obviously has a slightly different leadership and management style, but as a leader, you have to lead and take command when it's required. That means no playing, such as burning out and the like, when you're in charge. . . . If you want to play, then delegate your command to another for that time. When you have delegated someone else to be in charge of an operation and they're doing just fine, leave them alone and monitor the situation and make suggestions if need be, but let them do their assigned job. Otherwise, when you're in charge, then be in charge.

What do good supes have in common?

Greg Keller (Eldorado, 1985–1996; Modoc, 2000–2007)
We are so different. The things we have in common are an ability to lead, an ability to work in tough situations. I think we have abilities to make a good pie out of a mess of junk and make it taste good sometimes. The individual characters and characteristics are so vastly different that if you looked [from] one superintendent to another, you'd say they are almost 180 degrees different. The one thing they have in common is they are superintendents; they have become successful in their own right, and so what that shows is there's no one way to be successful in this business. I don't think you can make a cookbook recipe and say, "Here's a superintendent," because we are all so vastly different, but we do have some things in common. It's got to be the heart; the drive; the initiative; the pride we take in the organization, and ourselves, and our programs; and the ability to lead, the ability to recognize. Understanding the interrelations between

fire, fuels, and topography and being able to put that together. Knowing when and where to put a line, and knowing where and when to fire. Knowing when to pull the trigger and how fast to go, and having the balls to do it sometimes. And not being afraid to stand up in front of high-level managers and take on situations that other people would shy away from. I think, by and large, the superintendents can be counted on when the chips are down to do what is possible and what is safely possible where other people might find it easier to walk away from it.

Jim Cook (Arrowhead, 1981–1995; Boise, 1996–1998)

They love the ABCs: anarchy, bedlam, and chaos. They love to step in and just run with it when that's going on. That's the best, because that's when they can utilize the background they have and be the most effective. And I think most of them call their crew members "kids." Their kids.

Stan Stewart (Los Padres, 2000–2009)

I think they all strive to put out the best product they can have. All the ones I consider good supes, they're always out to be the best that they can be, a lot like the army says. They've all got a lot of pride in their jobs. They're the same guys who are training their crews and teaching 'em and mentoring and doing all that other stuff that makes a good crew. A lot of that is just the pride and the love-of-the-job stuff. You have to have that, or I don't think you're going to be effective in any of these jobs. You have to love the job, or have a hell of a lot of like for it to produce something good, because it takes energy to do it. Most of the supes are pretty high-energy, going a hundred miles an hour.

Brit Rosso (Arrowhead, 1996–2006)

You cannot be a good superintendent if you do not have respect from your crew. Respect from your peers. A good superintendent has both: respect from the crew and respect from their peers—their fellow superintendents. I think that's a very important trait of a good superintendent. And, of course, self-respect.

A sense of tradition and duty, that we are not only doing the right thing, that it's our duty to hold these hotshot traditions and standards to a certain level. Also, there's a mutual respect amongst each other that goes without saying. . . . A big part of it is just the respect from others and from your crew, and having a strong work ethic, and having a program that performs.

Paul Musser (Flagstaff, 1990–2004)

Desire. You have to really want it to be any good at it. People who are just moving through it or it's just kind of a thing to do, I don't think put much effort into the job. They do all right in certain aspects of it, but I think you have to have the desire and the love for the job to be really good at it.

Barry Callenberger (Palomar, 1979–1982; Eldorado, 1982–1988)

I do not know a superintendent who is selfish and doesn't have his crew in mind no matter what he does. You aren't a superintendent very long if you don't put the crew number one. It doesn't mean that you're their best buddy, but you have their interests as paramount. If you don't have that, don't even be a superintendent.

Another thing I don't think people understand about superintendents: you may be a friend of somebody that's an engine captain, but when it comes down to the crew, that's it. You're their number one; they become number one, when you're at work and sometimes after work, and if you don't, it doesn't work. . . . If it's a good relationship and it's not one built on "drinking buddy" and stuff like that, then it's going to be a good crew. If it's not, it's not going to be a good crew, and it won't function well.

I've seen a lot of times when crews drink a lot together and the superintendent drinks with them. It builds a relationship, but

I don't think it's as good a one as if you'd have a few drinks with them [and then] let them party on their own. But you do keep their interests number one. It's impossible not to, and people don't understand that. That's what gets superintendents in trouble with their bosses: they stand up to them and that gets them into trouble. If they were a good supervisor, they would understand that, but I've seen supervisors who were [once] superintendents who forget about that.

It's totally different, I think, from any of the other crews how that superintendent has to make that crew number one. It's important, and that's where it gets tough. Sometimes it becomes number one, and your wife is number two, and that doesn't work. But as long as you're at work, they're number one, and you respect them and they respect you, and you take care of them and keep 'em from getting abused by your boss.

I always said that the best job in the Forest Service is the foreman on a hotshot crew. It's the best job. They have the respect of the crew, they work with the crew, they have a good time with the crew. They've got the superintendent who gets beat to death all the time over what the crew did some night downtown. [Foremen are] the go-between, but they don't take the heat. You take the heat as a superintendent. That's your job. The best job I ever had in the Forest Service was the foreman on a hotshot crew. Superintendent was okay—that's the second best. (Laughs.) After that it's downhill. There are no better jobs.

J. W. Allendorf (Wallowa–Whitman, 1980; Arrowhead 3, 1981)

They believe in themselves and their crew. [The] crew is an extension of [the supe], and believes in their ability to get around any goddamn fire you take 'em to, one way or the other. I mean, they're determined, tenacious sons o' bitches. They all seem to love life and a damn good challenge on a regular—preferably a frequent—basis, and they're addicted to adrenaline.

Greg Vergari (Union, 1980–1987)

Humility, self-confidence with the realization they are responsible for the lives of 19 other people, not just themselves. You can tell that type of supe. Always working on being an effective leader. Always giving the unit they are working for more, so that when they leave, the place or person you worked for knows they had a hotshot crew working for them.

Dennis Baldridge (Laguna, 1990–2009)

I would say a passion for their job and their crews. I know where I'm at, and I know the ones who I hang out with, and what I see in them is that we all are professional wildland firefighters. We all want to fight wildland fire, and we want our crews to do a good job at it. We want them to perform well; we want them to look good. They make us look good; we don't make them look good. Without getting that desire into the folks who are working for us, we have nothing. I see that in the superintendents I admire. They're good trainers, they're good supervisors, they're good coaches. They know how to fight fire, and they know how to work with their people. It's just fun to work with one of them.

Charlie Caldwell (Redding, 1967–1986)

Hell, I've got that question marked out there. I thought all supes were good. (Laughs.) I really think the ability to put together a team for the type of work that they do. Maintain a safe and effective firefighting team. They have to have a personnel orientation in their mind; they have to deal with all the personnel problems, and if they don't, they're not going to make it as a supe. The personnel problems are probably one of the bigger things that you have to deal with; and in the past, hotshot superintendents have not gotten the recognition for being "middle managers"—that's what I call 'em. You've got all these new titles and positions now. Basically, the superintendent has to be a good personnel manager. He really has to be, because of the exposure and everything hotshot crews are involved in—everybody's got a problem.

Bob Wright (Sacramento, 1990–2002)

They've all got good hearts, even though they could be assholes. They all are really basically good people with good hearts, and they all respect each other. They're just good guys. I would've stayed in there till I was 90; just didn't work out. I miss 'em. I really miss 'em.

There's a different aspect in life now: we do other things, harassing each other on the phone. We've already got plans: "When we retire, we're gonna do this." In fact, when we went and saw Ben Charlie and [Bob] Bennett last Christmas, we called a bunch of old supes on the phone when we were there. Ben and I were talking, and he says, "You know, all the old guys don't forget other old guys. They all keep in touch. They all remember." He was right. You always keep in touch. No matter what they're doing. Because there's a bond there. It's probably like a soldier going to war . . . because you're going through the same thing, and nobody can take that away from you. You've always got that bond. I think that's it, basically. Some of 'em drink better beer than others. (Laughs.)

Craig Workman (Black Mountain, 1988–2005)

I think all of us love these kids, in all different ways, and that's what keeps us going: the love for these people we work with.

Mark Linane (Los Prietos/Los Padres, 1973–2001)

Good supes have integrity, are honest with their people, have got good people skills. Any leadership role we have in the modern day, I think people skills are more important than maybe even technical skills. Work gets done through people, and you've got to have good people skills. . . . Respect for their people, good people skills, good initiative, good confidence—they've gotta be self-confident. Technically proficient, tactically proficient. Safe, but not super-safe. They're not pulling the safety card because it's too hot, it's too cold, it's too steep. It's a shitty job, and you'd better realize that the sun doesn't get any less hot, the mountains don't get any less steep. Suck it up: you've gotta do it.

They've got to persevere and have good perseverance. Physically fit. It's tougher to do if you get older—injuries and what have you. He wants to learn, so he dabs his foot into other things, tries to better himself, not just be the supe but takes assignments to become a division boss, operations chief, and works his way up to being an incident commander, even if only a Type 3 or Type 2, so he can step up and take charge when he has to. Is a good trainer, believes in teaching people: a good teacher. Those are the ones who are probably the most successful.

Art Torrez (Vista Grande, 1994–2004)
(Laughs.) The willingness to work, the willingness to make sacrifice to help someone else. . . . Probably the most important is the willingness to communicate with somebody when they see something right or wrong.

Why did you stay a supe for so long?

Dave Matier (Midnight Sun, 1992–1997, 1999–2007, 2009–2010)
This is what I want to do. Everybody asks me that, and I totally enjoy the work. The travel, the places I get to see, the people I meet. I like being in shape. I like the challenge: it's different all the time. No matter how small or big the fire is, it's always different. I thrive on that. To me, the more chaotic it is, the more of a challenge it is to me. That's what I get out of it, and I have fun. I have good kids who work for me, and I like sharing with them my experiences and my knowledge and exposing them to all the things that I see, and not being a full-time employee. I don't know how these guys do it: I like to be busy, and as it is, I

spend enough time in the office. It's not all about that, especially up there in Alaska. Everybody was made to do something, and this is it for me.

Ted Mathiesen (Arroyo Grande Flight Crew, 1990–2007)

Big one is having the winter off away from the direct supervision other than the captains. That's one: you get a break. You gear up, you hit this plateau, you're going along, and all of a sudden fire season's over. It's hard to gear up, and I'm always in denial when it's over. But after annual leave and, say, the first of the year, then it's a good thing. . . . All the memories from last year come back. Then you start thinking about what we're going to do different this year.

The captains are here all winter, and we're close, and we talk. Right now we're recruiting. . . . We're kind of in and out, regroup, and here it is the middle of March. It's happening pretty soon. We're all looking at the hills and going, "Yeah, this is what it's gonna be." It's pretty easy—for me, anyway.

Kurt LaRue (Diamond Mountain, 1993–2001)

[Working half-years] was huge over the years. It's a physical and mental challenge to pay attention, stay sharp even in trying situations. There's a camaraderie and stuff that goes with it I enjoyed. It funded a very comfortable lifestyle.

To me, a perfect season would've been: bring the crew on, go out, stay out until the season was over, come home, turn the gear in, and go get laid off, come back and see what size the checks were, and laugh my way through the winter. That would've been a perfect season. It fit my personality. It was the height of the Consent Decree[7]; the agency wasn't too thrilled to have me around, and I was looking to leave. It paid for the lifestyle I liked,

---

[7] The Consent Decree (No. C-73-1110-SC) is a 1979 agreement to settle a class action suit brought against the US Secretary of Agriculture by women employees of the Forest Service alleging that the Forest Service had discriminated against women in hiring and promotions. A similar suit was subsequently filed and settled on behalf of Hispanic Region 5 Forest Service employees.

and through a lot of the early years I was fairly convinced I was going to do something else in a few years anyway: "I'm gonna build houses and bend nails full-time for a living." I had a large section in there—I guess you could say I was in denial. (Laughs)

Richard Aguilar (El Cariso, 1974; Wolf Creek, 1975–1997)
That's the job that I knew how to do best. I didn't know anything else. I made my decision that I was going to be a firefighter from the first, in 1957, and I didn't go to school. I was the same as these Job Corps kids—a dropout—and that's what I knew. I knew that I couldn't change to another job. I turned down three FMO jobs while I was at Wolf Creek because I knew I was doing good here. One of the things that I was afraid would happen: that it would not go on, that something I built here that it took me so many years and I had to fight to get done—we would lose it.

Greg Vergari (Union, 1980–1987)
I only stayed eight seasons. I had to get out because I felt like I was going to haul off and hit some division supervisor or operations section chief because of the stupid things I thought they were doing on fires. Best move I made was to get off the crew. People who stay in hotshots, jumpers, etc., can get jaded—not all, but quite a few. I loved my years being a hotshot: it was the best firefighting I ever did.

Jim Cook (Arrowhead, 1981–1995; Boise, 1996–1998)
Number one, it's the best job in the fire service. It wasn't because of all the fires and the adrenaline, because realistically, you might pull 100 shifts a year, and 15 of those might be adrenaline pumps. The rest were just shit work: digging ditches in the woods, I say. The long term motivation, attraction, is building teams.

Ron Bollier (Silver City, 1993–1995; Carson, 1996–1997; Fulton, 1998–2013)

Why have I stayed a supe so long? I enjoy it. I enjoy having the program at Fulton. I enjoy teaching the kids. I enjoy teaching them and mentoring them and bringing them along. Five, maybe six years ago, I couldn't tell you this. I wouldn't know what to answer. Now, with what we're doing at Fulton, I enjoy being able to give them things that they can take forward and use wherever they go. There're not very many of us left who do that.

It's really enjoyable to see kids who work for you go above and beyond and become better than I will ever become, whether they stay in the agency or not. I have kids who worked for me, now they're Kern County firemen, they're LA County firemen; they're doctors, lawyers, going to college. They're staying in the agency and running their own crews. Why would I want to give that up? It's the best of both worlds: you're managing something, you're still free—free as in you're not tied down to a district. You're not tied down to an everyday job; you're not tied down to the political end. To a point you are, but you're not. It's a little safe haven.

Ron Regan (Del Rosa, 1977–1997)

I enjoyed the camaraderie with the different superintendents in Region 5 and Region 2, and you learn to respect each other's call on certain situations. You know you can expect the highest quality of work out of those guys, and it's a you-guys-versus-the-fire situation. You're going to be out there sometimes without any air support or any water support, and it's up to you to make the right call when you don't have logistical or tactical support. That's what stimulates me to do that type of work.

Mark Linane (Los Prietos/Los Padres, 1973–2001)

I had the best job in the Forest Service. It was working with the crew. You're really independent, and you really don't have a boss.

You've got an administrative boss, but when you're on the road, you're the man for calling the big shots that affect your little world. Got to see a lot of country. Didn't get stuck being a hotshot at least most of my career. Still a hotline adrenaline junkie. Have always loved initial attack since the first day I started in '63. I'd still rather go to an initial attack than any big fire.

Art Torrez (Vista Grande, 1994–2004)

I would say that it's the camaraderie. I've been really fortunate to, first, make really good friends. Each of the superintendents within our region, I'm close to. I respect them, and I would hope they feel the same way. As far as the crew stuff, you know, it was very competitive when I was growing up, and I think the competitiveness is still there, to a certain extent. It's just like playing the big game, the championship game. You're in there for the rush, and you come out a winner. (Laughs.)

Bob Bennett (Horseshoe Meadow, 1989–2006)

I think a lot of it is the people you surround yourself with. If you surround yourself with good people, that's going to bring out your good qualities too, in the tight fraternity that we have. A lot of it is just respecting each other. We joke around, and we're pretty brutal with each other at times, but we are honest with each other. We keep each other in check at times.

Charlie Caldwell Looks Out for His El Cariso Pals

When we went to Wyoming, I went to the plans section— [Del Rosa supe] Ken Tortez and I did this—and said, "The El Cariso crew, they're right on the border there, of Mexico, and they have to have an onion in their lunch every day." Ron Campbell comes to Ken and me in the evening and says, "Are you getting an onion in your lunch?" "An onion?

What do you mean, onion in your lunch?" "Everybody on my crew's got an onion in their lunch." (Laughs.) So, yeah, we used to mess with each other like that. It was kinda fun.

What is your career planning advice?

Ted Mathiesen (Arroyo Grande Flight Crew, 1990–2007)
Wildland fire use, I think, is huge. . . . If I was starting my career now, I would jump into that because not only is it a real beneficial thing for the forest, but it's a lot of fun. I think we should be doing that and encouraging that as a national program. . . . I think that's the future, the real future.

You can tell . . . the ones who are Forest Service/BLM types or the ones who want to be municipal. I don't discourage either one, but it takes kind of a special person to do the wildland end. I guess the advice would be just continue to educate yourself. . . . Don't bounce from station to station to station every year. Get established, and then be honest and evaluate what your career goals are. . . . It's pretty easy to map out a path to get there. But you do need to set goals; don't just be enamored: "This is what I'm going to do. I'm gonna be a Pulaski forever."

Kurt LaRue (Diamond Mountain, 1993–2001)
Don't do what I did! I am not the model of what your career should be. I got into 'shots and stayed in the 'shots all the way until I got my current job [with BLM Fire Ops]. You can get away with doing that, but you would be far better off getting a more varied work history. I got very lucky getting into the job where I'm at. Certainly, if you're going to map out a career, work year-round, put in the retirement money, and all that traditional stuff, then you need to branch out a lot more than I did. Do different things and learn more about the entire agency, not just the 'shots.

Steve Karkanen (Lolo, 1990–2011)

I really encourage the younger folks to go back or to stay in school and get some kind of a degree. I don't care whether it's in political science, in forestry, or in one of the biological sciences. . . . It's going to be required that they have X number of credits anyway . . . so now's the time to get it done and get that out of the way . . . before it's mandated and old guys like me have to go back to school. (Laughs.)

Brit Rosso (Arrowhead, 1996–2006)

I would recommend to those coming up in fire management to get a diversified background before they set that final goal where they want to end up. A little bit of rotor time, some engine time, some hand crew time, and then decide, "What did I enjoy the most? Where can I be the most effective? What did I have the most fun doing?" and then go from there. Try all three. That would be my recommendation.

It's worked well for me, personally, staying on the same crew, especially when my goal was to become a superintendent, because I've spent all that time on the crew. I understand all the crew history, and the crew's been around for 25 years.

Paul Musser (Flagstaff, 1990–2004)

I would recommend moving forest-to-forest and at least moving from one region to another region. When I was in Region 5, it was always, "The hicks of the Southwest"—Region 3 and stuff like that: "They're so far behind in everything." It was a tremendous difference coming down here out of Region 5. I think that gap has closed a lot because the hotshot organization works a lot closer together than they did 15 years ago. We're also a lot more mobile than we were 15 years ago, so I think that has helped. Then you get to Region 3 and it's, "All those people in Region 5," so you know, it just goes back and forth. I think it's good to be able to see different regions.

[Why did you want to move to the hotshot crew when you were already an engine captain?]

Couldn't get enough fire experience on the engines. Not enough large fire experience. Also, being on the Mendocino and the Eldorado, neither one of those has high numbers of fires. It's a lot of urban interface and stuff. Because of the number of critical locations, they won't allow the engine captains to go off-forest very much during fire season, so they couldn't keep current.

I knew I needed to fight fire and lots of it to be any good at what I do. You can't fight two or three large fires . . . in a year and hope to think that you're any good at it because you don't see enough changing situations. You don't deal with enough. Even with our incident management teams: they fight a few fires from start to finish, but they don't get a lot of experience on going stuff.

Barry Callenberger (Palomar, 1979–1982; Eldorado, 1982–1988)

(Laughs.) That's a tough one. I've always felt that anybody who wants to spend time in the Forest Service particularly needs to experience hand crews, whether it's as a crewman or as a foreman, and whether it's hotshots or another crew, it's important to do that because they mean so much to the agency and they're important pieces of it. And if you can do it as a hotshot, that's even better, but it doesn't have to be. Then you can go wherever you want to go. If you want to go to helicopters, you want to go to engines, finish your career, or move your career in another direction, that's great, but at least a year to two years on hand crews is really important.

J. W. Allendorf (Wallowa–Whitman, 1980; Arrowhead 3, 1981)

Well, I would tell 'em to do what they want to do, do what they believe in and where their heart is. Go there. That's the most important thing. It isn't about GS level or anything else; it's about what makes you happy, what you feel good about. When you drive home from work every night, do you feel like you've contributed—not just to the overall organization but primarily to the people you supervise and you're responsible for? What have you given them every day? And if you get satisfaction from what you're doing, forget the GS level and keep on doing it.

My advice to people is go where your heart is and stay with it. If things change for you, then follow your new interest. That's what I did, and I don't have any regrets about it. Although I have to tell you: I enjoy my job in law enforcement, but I miss the shit out of fire every day. I have it written in my will that when I die, my wife is going to put my LP Hotshots hard hat on my head before she slams the lid. That's for real, and she's gonna do it.

Greg Vergari (Union, 1980–1987)
Do what you love; don't do it just for the money. Once you start to chase fire because the money is too good to quit and you need to maintain your lifestyle, you're dangerous to yourself and others. There is life after hotshots: smoke jumping, helitack, etc. The fire organization needs good overhead in its management ranks.

If they're not getting opportunities where they are, they need to move. You need to move around. You make your own choices, and it's tough. I wish I could go back now, and I wish I could have moved more through my career. . . . If you're not happy and you're not getting it where you are, move until you do find somebody who you can work for, you enjoy, and you learn from. I see a lot of people just staying in one place, trying to make it fit, and maybe it's not right. It's a big world. You've got choices, and there are a lot of options. If you don't have too much baggage, head on out until you find what you like.

The 401 series was initiated to try to help those wanting to be professionals in the fire arena get into a professional series without going back and getting a degree. Fire management in both

DOI and DOA [Department of Agriculture] thought this was a good idea. Prior to this, as a technician you could only get to a GS-12, and there were very few 12s—only a few assistant fire staff positions. Now, with the right coursework and experience, you can get to be a 401 and go to the top. This seems easier in the DOI than the Forest Service, and you can validate this statement by looking at the vast numbers of BLM, NPS, FWS [Fish and Wildlife Service], and BIA [Bureau of Indian Affairs] folks in the 401 series and how much faster they got into the 401 series than the Forest Service employees. I am one of the very few who has made it to 401 in the Forest Service. Hopefully, that will change.

Craig Lechleiter (Redding, 1986–2002)

You're not going to get rich working this job. If you want to make the money, you need to work for a state, county, or city fire department. I promoted that to the younger generation. You're not going to make any money working for Uncle Sam. You're going to stress out your spouse. She or he is going to have to work. Your standard of living is going to have to be reduced quite a bit. You're both going to have to start figuring out, "What do I love in life?" because you're not going to have the money to do it all. You're not going to have the clothes, the cars, the mortgage, vacations working for the Forest Service. (Laughs.) It is going to take both of you to pull it off. I could go on and on, but I learned through my career that you better be straight up front with everybody right away. You and your family will make many sacrifices through the years. Very few are successful holding onto their dreams along the journey.

Dave Matier (Midnight Sun, 1992–1997, 1999–2007, 2009–2010)

Be patient. . . . You get the full gambit. It's not as much initial attack. That's kind of where the thrill is, and hotshots end up being on fires longer. That's definitely the way a lot of people think, but hotshot [work] is a good way to get that baseline experience for whatever you want to do somewhere down the line in fire.

Dennis Baldridge (Laguna, 1990–2009)

I think at least early in their career they should try each of them, because before you can say you don't want to be something you should give it a shot. I've had a few kids I've told that [who say], "Nah, I don't want to get off the hotshot crew," and they find out that being on an engine or on helitack gives them a little more time at home and fits their needs a little bit better. And I've had the ones who have gone over to the other side for just a short time and decided it's not for them. They come back, and their idea is to be a lifelong hotshot.

Charlie Caldwell (Redding, 1967–1986)

Try some different jobs. Find something that you like to do. Most people think they kind of have to stay where they're at and so on. Look around; see what's available to you. That's basically what happened in Redding. These guys come to Redding, and all of a sudden the doors open for them because they can think the way they want to think and do what they want to do.

Find things that you want to do, and set goals for yourself. . . . You've gotta push yourself because the Forest Service doesn't care. You know, people are [as] expendable as a collapsible canteen. They really are. When there's a money crunch, what's the first thing that goes? People. . . . People are expendable items—there's never been any question in my mind about that—so you've got to make your own way. It's, like, [people will say], "Wow, the Forest Service did right by you!" No, you did right by yourself. . . . I lived through the Forest Service in the early days, when as an employee or as a person, you had no rights at all. Now, I'm saying the door is wide open. . . . People can do whatever they want to do, set their goals, and go for it.

Rusty Witwer (Mendocino, 1978; Hobart/Tahoe, 1979–1995)
If you like doing it, stick with it, but just realize that you are not
going to be able to snap your fingers and jump back into the pond
that's been going by you for the last 20 years with the environ-
mental assessments and burn plans changing and whatnot. In
the off-season, keep yourself involved in those other disciplines:
burning, burn plan preparation, burning quals. The new 401
series has hit it right on the head: it's going to have a Red Card
qualification, but also a prescribed fire qualification, and if you
don't keep up on that end of the scenario, then when you decide
to go, no one else might decide with you.

A good program to get into, even if it's the toughest thing
you'll ever do, is TFM [Technical Fire Management]. I went
through it. Hardest thing I ever went through. Much harder than
any fire, any fire season that I went through, but the tools that I
was given there I actually have utilized in the planning process,
and to some success.

Don't be afraid of those things out there, and keep your
options open. You're not going to get moved just because you
have fought a lot of fire with a shovel. If this is something you
want to do and expand, hotshot experience is a must, and then
it's time to move on. No matter if you're a crewman, foreman,
or a superintendent, the most important part of the equation is
that you did it in one of those forms, and you witnessed the fire
behavior around the nation, and you build on that as you go up
the chain of command.

I know that there's a lot of movement now to build hotshot
crewmen into hotshot superintendents, helicopter crewmen into
helicopter managers. I personally don't believe in that. I don't
think that it's building the knowledge of wildland fire management, and part of that is shifting modules to get a breadth
of experience. Thirty years ago, if you didn't have two to three
fields, you weren't promotable. It just seems like now people are
designing grade lining so they can bring their people all the way

through the program, and I just don't get that. No one's going to tell me that working on a hotshot crew is so scientific that you have to have been born one to become the superintendent. In fact, one of the best superintendents I ever worked for came off an engine crew, and it was his first year ever on a hotshot crew. So that's not a magic answer, and I think cross-pollination is good to do. The more mobile you are to get that when you're younger, the better off you are. You need to see it, and sometimes you're going to find out there's something more than working the end of a tool that keeps firefighting fresh and interesting.

I think probably the big thing is just what I was alluding to . . . : while you are mobile, become mobile. Take a chance at some different positions when you're young, and try to get a breadth of experience. You might be staying for a summer in a place that might not be the dearest place that you want to work, but opportunities that are out there now to move around are awesome. It's a summer; it's a season, especially if you're not permanent. You can always go to Baja or Lake Tahoe in the winter and go to where you want to go, but take advantage of the fire seasons to get around. I think too often people get hung up with a supervisor they like and they feel comfortable with, and they're not willing to test the waters with different groups. I've always told people that it's your job. You work with your supervisor, but your supervisor doesn't dictate your life.

Stan Stewart (Los Padres, 2000–2009)
The handwriting's on the wall now that they'd better get off their butts and get into the 401 world or they're not going to get anywhere. That's the advice we're giving our kids right now: go take some classes and get that out of the way.

It's up to them where they want to go, but every kid ought to spend a couple years on a hotshot crew. They'll never have a better job than a supe job. After they get above that, I don't know if you're going to get anything better. The FMO jobs are all pretty much just babysitters anymore. If you're going to be dealing with problems, you might as well be dealing with your own problems instead of everybody else's as well.

Ron Regan (Del Rosa, 1977–1997)

You've got to have the desire to do it. Probably you'll make your mind up within four or five years: where you want to be, what you want to be in five years. Do you want to be a foreman in five years? Do you want to be superintendent of a hotshot crew in ten years? If that's your goal, then you need to go out and get it. It's not going to happen for everybody. There are a lot of folks here, and one superintendent position. It's a tough shot. I was very fortunate to be the superintendent of Del Rosa. It was a good job for me. I guess I was born to be a hotshot.

Craig Workman (Black Mountain, 1988–2005)

The individual needs to get a wide variety of experience. But I think they also need to temper that with getting good quality experience and getting very good at what they're doing before they go on to the next job. I keep getting the feeling that we have a lot of people who are moving too quickly and not really getting good at one thing before moving on to the next.

Mark Linane (Los Prietos/Los Padres, 1973–2001)

One of the recommendations that I make to the kids at the fire department I work at now is that if you want to have a good background of wildland fire behavior, get on a hotshot crew for two or three seasons. Go back to school, the academy, get your Firefighter 1, get your EMT, and if you can afford it, get your paramedic ticket. Then go to work for a municipal department. You'll always have that good foundational wildland experience on a hotshot crew. You'll understand fire. You'll understand tactics. Direct, indirect, all the stuff—the basics. Then when you get in that agency that pays so much more, you'll have a good background. You'll have a good, basic foundation that'll always be with you, and you can do whatever it is you want to do.

When the [Wildland Fire Apprenticeship Program] academy first came about, we said an academy first should've been assignments on hotshot crews, like they do now after they've been to the academy. Every assignment should've been on a hotshot crew for at least a minimum of a year—one season. Minimum of one season, two preferably. Three is even better. After that they need to step out and start taking some responsibility as a firefighter.

Anything about your career you would've done differently?

J. W. Allendorf (Wallowa–Whitman, 1980; Arrowhead 3, 1981)

No, I don't think so. I've always believed that if you're going to do something, you have to . . . believe in what you're doing. I always believed in what I was doing with the Forest Service, even during bad times when sometimes I got a little disgruntled. I never wanted to pass that on, and I always said I would quit before I became a disgruntled supervisor and passed that on. . . . Basically, I got out of fire when I was getting to that point. I went into law enforcement because I was getting to the point where I wasn't keeping my mouth shut about shortcomings I saw in training and preparation of new firefighters.

Craig Lechleiter (Redding, 1986–2002)

Be a better dad. Be a better husband, brother, son. You lose the connection with those people, being a hotshot overhead. The deeper you get in the hotshot organization, the higher you go, the more disconnected you get from your family, because you inherit another family. . . . They become priority, their development.

You've got these false façades: It'll be all right. My wife's handling that other thing. I trust her judgement. You disconnect, and you live in this Alice-In-Wonderland. You think it'll be fine, until it doesn't go fine. It's something you have to do over a long span to understand whether you're effective in every area.

Dennis Baldridge (Laguna, 1990–2009)
I never would've left the hotshots to begin with. (Laughs.) I moved because I got married. I didn't know I was changing for the experience. The experience was really good. I do regret some of the fires I've missed, some of the big fires. Till I got back in the hotshots, I didn't realize the camaraderie I was missing. It was so much different working on an engine and on helitack. Your little crew had their group, but there was no big group that you identified with. . . . Right now with the hotshots, almost any superintendent in the country could go anywhere there's another crew and find a place to stay for the night. It's just that way. For an engine captain to try and find that, it's not going to happen.

I had some opportunities. I tried the battalion chief job, and it wasn't me, but if the opportunity had happened earlier in my career, maybe I wouldn't be back on the hotshots. . . . I missed out on some years in the hotshots where I wish I'd stayed, just for the learning, the stuff that went on back then. I think I would've done it a little differently.

Bob Wright (Sacramento, 1990–2002)
I would've probably studied a little more on some stuff, as far as being a better supervisor than I was. I thought I wasn't that great of a supervisor. . . . There's a lot of stuff I could've done better, I would've done differently. I was probably an asshole. In the old days . . . your better workers became your foremen. That doesn't necessarily mean that they were better supervisors, but those were the ones they promoted—the good workers, the hard workers. . . . No questions. Low-maintenance. That's how I got into being a supervisor, pretty much. I think I could've been a little better of a supervisor, but then, it's water under the bridge

now. (Laughs.) I still get calls from guys who worked for me, so I guess I did okay.

Rusty Witwer (Mendocino, 1978; Hobart/Tahoe, 1979–1995)
I really enjoy the fact that I've stepped on pieces of ground that nobody else has ever walked on, and those memories will stay with me. So, no regrets at all. I wouldn't do anything different. Just lucky that when I wanted to get out, I was able to get out.

Lance Honda Doesn't Have a Career

I guess I'm atypical: I don't say that I have a career. And there's a distinction between my work and my job. I love my work, which is fighting fire and working with people and teaching. My job is working for the government. People who have careers have ambitions and a career path. I don't have any ambitions beyond working outside on a crew. However, my vision and what I want to leave, my legacy, has changed and evolved over the years. Biggest challenges? (Pause.) Being a better teacher, a better example. Being consistent in saying what I want and what I give. Coming from a more positive place. I end up going crossways with overhead a lot, but I don't have any regrets in that. I regret it if it's affected my crew, but I don't know if that's a challenge for me or not. I assume that it is since I end up not getting what I want sometimes; but if it's a matter of principle, I don't budge very easily, and I don't say I'm sorry very easily if I think I'm right.

Mark Linane's Path to the LP Supe Job

I got a job with the Forest Service in May 1963 on an engine crew. They had a Hispanic engine captain by the name of Alfonso J. Archuleta who had a tough time with English but was a hell of a fireman. He came from New Mexico. That was my first season, and we were going down the coast at night, responding to fires. The two guys in the front of the cab were warm and toasty, and I was freezing my ass off with a blanket wrapped around me in the back of the truck. I looked through that cab and I said to myself, "I ain't going to sit back here very long." My next year, I put a lot of attention into learning how to operate that truck because I figured if I knew how to operate that truck, I'd be able to drive it faster. The next year, the driver of the fire truck had wife problems, and I was suddenly promoted to an engine driver, after one season.

In 1964 I took a shot at driving at San Marcos Station. Then they lost a foreman down at Rincon Station, so with a grand total of one and a half seasons' experience, they wanted me to be the engine captain back at Rincon, where I'd been before.

One of the memorable things of that event was the Coyote fire, which burned about umpteen-thousand houses and 70,000 acres or so in Santa Barbara front country. One of the engines at San Marcos had gotten rolled over. My engine, we'd made initial attack, come back in, and gone to bed. We'd pulled a 48-hour shift. An engine captain whose truck had broken down stole my truck from me and took it to the top of Camino Cielo for a backfiring operation and burnt my fire truck up. So here I was with two crews because I had another crew that was without, since their engine had been rolled over. I went over to the fire truck that had been rolled over and I said, "Is that thing really hurt, or just a little bent metal?" The old mechanic said, "Nah, I'll get it running, Mark. Let me just check the oil." He got it running, and we changed the oil . . . and got the air cleaner working. I had ten people riding on top of my fire truck for the next two weeks; me with a grand total of a year and a half experience, with my nine-person engine crew.

The next year the helitack foreman went away, and I was the helitack foreman for a while. Then the official job opened up at Rincon, and I was the engine captain. I was an engine captain for '67, '68, '69, '70 between the Mountain Drive Station on the coast of Santa Barbara and the Rincon Station. I was burnt out on engines, so I took a summer off to go to Redding, and I was the assistant foreman up there in 1971.

In 1972 I went back to Mountain Drive Station as an engine captain, and that winter we had a huge fuelbreak project. The old FMO sent me out on the farthest end with a couple of bulldozers and 12 of the biggest . . . misfits you've ever seen in the world, and he had the other guy who wanted the hotshot job at the other end with the best kids and a couple bulldozers. And so me and the misfits—mostly the misfits—and a couple of good dozer operators, we ended up accomplishing, like, 70 percent of the project, and they did, like, 30 percent. That was the old FMO's way of figuring out who was going to be the next hotshot superintendent, so he promoted me to hotshot superintendent. I only filled out one application in my entire career, back in 1963, I guess. Times and the system were different then. So then I got the crew.

What are your firefighting and supervision styles?

Jim Cook (Arrowhead, 1981–1995; Boise, 1996–1998)

I would say that my firefighting style is kind of old-school: anchor and flank balanced with work smarter. One of the improvements that we've made: while we may not think our crews are physically as capable as we used to be in a line production sense, I think that at least from our overhead structure we can do a lot more things. Crews are a lot more capable to show up and, say, bust off one foreman to run with a dozer, bust off two kids to set up a pump chance, bust off a guy to deal with water drops or manage a helispot. That didn't happen before. When I first started, it was 20 guys pounding line. That was all you were expected to do. That's what you did, and that was okay. Integrating with other resources is something I think some crews do better than they used to. Some crews still have their nose a little too far up in the air about who they are, but a lot of crews are really coming around, learning to integrate with other resources and get the job done. Supervisory style: set firm expectations, surround myself with good folks, give them responsibility, and expect them to deliver.

Brit Rosso (Arrowhead, 1996–2006)

I would say . . . my firefighting style would be old-school. I'm very much a believer in anchor and flank and staying as direct as possible whenever we can safely engage. And whenever we can safely engage, it's getting after the thing and not sitting there and watching it and talking for four days about what we're going to do: "Is this going to make any sense?"

If I had to put a title on my leadership style, I would say it would be leading by example. I don't mean grabbing the chainsaw from the sawyer and cutting bushes. I mean working hard, being there with the guys, putting in the time and the effort and the enthusiasm that it takes to get the job done right. It's about doing the right thing, even when nobody's around.

J. W. Allendorf (Wallowa–Whitman, 1980; Arrowhead 3, 1981)

I think my firefighting style is . . . just real basic: anchor, flank, take advantage of weather and topo, and stick with the basics. Bottom line is, the actual job—and I think that's why we're held in disdain by so many of the professional dipshits—the actual job itself is nothing more than backbreaking labor. It's the proper application of that labor in the right place at the right time— that's what it's about. Too many of those geniuses have never been able to figure it out, but those of us who have done it, we've got an understanding.

Even if I was the boss, I've always tried to treat everybody as an equal and not put myself above them. Not to say that when it's time to make a decision and get things moving that I won't be direct in explaining what I want and what I expect—but outside of that, I put my pants on like everybody else and I'm no different.

Greg Vergari (Union, 1980–1987)

I'm looking at all the individuals and, you know, who needs some more training, who needs some hands-on, who you haven't spent some time with to get into their head. All the people who fight fire really get into their tactical decisions, how good they are. I mean, I dearly love tactics, but for the bigger picture on that crew you're grooming: you're raising the future firefighters who are going to be management. It's a big job, so I think it's just a knack that you learn being a supe: where do you need to put your energies? I used to make sure that I was riding in back of the vans with the crew every once in a while . . . and bullshitting to find out what's going on in everybody's head, how we're doing.

When I was running the crew, I was very aggressive but prided myself on being smart about things. I liked to work smarter. I tend to be an in-your-face supervisor. If a problem arises, I try to get after it now. I had to teach myself this practice and still find it difficult to do, but I know the benefits of being up-front. This is so important on a hotshot crew, especially where small-unit leadership is the essence of it.

Dennis Baldridge (Laguna, 1990–2009)
(Laughs.) Oh, I don't know. My firefighting style is cautiously aggressive. I don't like sitting around, so I'm antsy when the fire's going, and I want to get the crew engaged doing something, but I don't want them doing something just to be doing something. A lot of times they're sitting while I'm bouncing around trying to find a place to work. That's the way I grew up: we have to be doing something. We need to be making some progress on this fire. If we're not, then we need to be learning from what we're seeing: everybody up, pay attention to what's going on, let's talk about what's happening. That's the firefighting style.

[As a supervisor], I think I was a lot mellower when I was younger because I was more into giving people a chance and really wanting to do stuff. The politics of the job anymore have made it a little bit tougher to do that, so now I try to let my captains run the crew. I give them the guidance, but I have a hard time stepping out of that role [of] being the one in charge. So the best is if I can give them to the captains and then leave, because if I'm seeing them then I'm butting in on their job. I want to let them do what they want to do, let them have their job, but it's hard for me to do that. I'm probably a little intrusive in my style: if I'm there, I want to be running it.

Ron Bollier (Silver City, 1993–1995; Carson, 1996–1997; Fulton, 1998–2013)
I think I'm a very competent, very knowledgeable, very skillful fireman. What kind of supervisor am I? I would say hard but very fair. I would expect the crew that works for me to be hard,

to work hard, be fair to each other, take care of each other. I wouldn't expect them to do anything that I wouldn't do. I would like to think that I'm a good supervisor to give them everything that they need to succeed in their jobs, whether now or in the future, and that we can mentor them, and I can bring them that way.

You can be the superintendent and have very, very dedicated captains who take a lot of the role, and all you can do is . . . share what you know and teach what you know as a supervisor. . . . Know your job, know every aspect of it. Supervising's different than leadership, and that's a hard one. And what kind of supervisor am I? Hopefully, one who listens a lot, because you learn more from listening than you do anything else.

Ted Mathiesen (Arroyo Grande Flight Crew, 1990–2007)

My style of management is kind of delegation, and I think I surrounded myself with folks who all have a little different piece of the puzzle. . . . I'm just the superintendent. The guys who really make it run are the captains.

I've tried to be approachable. I understand I've got the responsibility. I'm responsible to lead these guys. I'm paid to lead 'em, so that's what I'm going to do. I read a lot. I think I have a pretty good rapport with people. I'm a little older and a little wiser.

Lance Honda (Redmond, 1992–1997; Prineville, 1997–2009)

[How do you make being an introvert work?]
Passion. As I've studied leadership—in actual, conscious study of it and reflecting back—I've never not led in some way or form. I was willing to be led, given the strength of the leader or lack thereof, but I didn't realize that most leaders are extroverts. Since I'm interested in people and learning about people, I've taken several personality tests. One of my personality types is based on something called the enneagram, and as introverted as I am, that's what my personality has developed into: leading. It's

not that I have to direct or that I have to be in charge. It's just important that I go in a good direction, that whatever group I'm in is going in a positive, good direction. If I see a need or I have a want to change the direction of where we're going, then I'll step up, step in.

My preference is to keep as low a profile as possible, and my crew reflects that. One of the things that I talk about is understated excellence. That's a reflection of my personality: I don't have to have attention. I prefer not to have attention for whatever I do, but it better be done well. It's just satisfaction to me that it's done well.

A Very Personal Point of View from Craig Lechleiter

Trying different styles and techniques was essential. The "my-way-or-the-highway" approach seemed to fit. That worked for me, as long as I had a strong supervisor like Charlie [Caldwell] backing me up. I had some bad nicknames: Cranky Lanky, Lank the Crank. I wasn't well-liked when I was a captain on this crew. There was a lot of pressure to perform. I had this Charlie Caldwell figure that was one of the most respected people in fire, and not just because he was a hotshot superintendent. I had these trainees working for me who were the best of the best, and a lot of them had as much fire experience as I did when I first got here to Redding in 1978. A few of them had higher Red Card quals than I did, though there was no depth in their quals.

I was my own worst enemy. When I came into this program, my self-esteem was not all that high in being able to live up to what was expected of me. I didn't believe in myself. If it wasn't for Caldwell and my wife, I don't know what I would've done. The pressure was intense to perform at the regional level. It got to me: I finally broke down, physically

> broke down, over it. I mean, rock bottom at home one day, and that's when I really realized who I was. I had to start all over again. Fortunately, Charlie was there for me. He never gave up on me. I cloned myself after him, and it gave me the confidence to succeed in many ways.

What sacrifices are necessary to have a good crew? How have you balanced work and family?

Stan Stewart (Los Padres, 2000–2009)

Well, there's a time sacrifice, obviously. I just got married two years ago, so I was single for 48 years almost, and that makes life easier. It really does. I sometimes wonder how some guys balance kids and the job, wife, and all that stuff. It's hard to do. You have to put time into the job, and pretty soon you start to focus on that job. You've got to do it—to do it well—but it's got to be a happy medium, and the "I used to" stuff starts to show up.

I have an eight-month-old baby at home now, another thing I did at old age. Now between that and the 150-pound dog and the wife, and X amount of time, you're trying to figure out what to do with all that, because there's only so much time. I don't know how guys with a lot of kids all those years did. I know something suffered. Probably the family end, I'm sure, and that's too bad.

I wish we could get all the kids to do that deal [Kevin Gilmartin's presentation].[8] Put that on at the JAC [Joint Apprentice Committee] academy, or do something with it. Would be another good training tool for them. Because there are a lot more married kids on the crews these days, with kids and everything.

---

[8] Kevin M. Gilmartin, a behavioral scientist specializing in law enforcement-related issues, spoke at the 2003 R3 and 2004 R5 Hotshot Workshops about the effects of law enforcement and firefighting careers on emotional and physical health.

Greg Keller (Eldorado, 1985–1996; Modoc, 2000–2007)

I think there are a lot of sacrifices. Number one, your personal life suffers. I don't know if you were here the other day when we had Dr. Gilmartin talking, and he talked about being "up." When we're at work we're up, and we go home and we're on the way downside. I looked around and I could see all the old superintendents going, "Oh, yeah." They were nodding their heads. I looked at my own life and said, "Oh, boy." He had me to a T. Fortunately, I've learned—not by studying, by any stretch of the imagination—through a failed marriage and a tough relationship and what have you.

Steve Karkanen (Lolo, 1990–2011)

Basically, you give up a lot of time, and from May until November, I don't have much of a life other than fire. I think most of the supes will tell you that. The divorce rate among the superintendents is super high. We were talking about this at one point at one of our meetings, and in the California group it was, like, 300 percent. It's because they've been married three or four times, some of these guys, and I got to thinking about that. It's, like, "God, that's really true." I've been married and divorced. My wife worked fire from time to time; she still does.

It's hard on a person's personal life. I have the utmost respect for people who have families—especially if they have kids—if they're married and have kids and are either supes or squad leaders or captains on a crew. I don't know how they do it. It's really hard to maintain that family life. For the folks on my crew who have families, I really watch 'em closely because they really have a hard time. . . . I try to get them back home as much as I can and get them back to their families. If they have family things going on, I have the ability to let them go: to go to weddings, to go to family reunions, or whatever. They need to be able to do that. If you were on a crew back then, 20 years ago, that was it. You didn't get to go anywhere. That was your family for the summer.

I think that's still the case, and most people look at it that way, but we're a lot more flexible than we used to be. We need to be.

Barry Callenberger (Palomar, 1979–1982; Eldorado, 1982–1988)

That really depends. I don't think you really have to sacrifice anything. In some respects, you have to stand up for stuff that gets you into trouble, especially with people who are supposed to be your boss, or on the fireline. But you have to stick up for your crew—that's something that is really important. Sometimes you can stick up for them and not be a jerk about it, and you can get your point across. I always thought that that's what I did best: stick up for 'em and not be a jerk about it.

You definitely make sacrifices when it comes to family. It's a big sacrifice because you are essentially gone: from the time the crew comes on, you're in another world. Sometimes it's hard to take your hat off when you leave the hotshot base and put on another hat when you come home. That is the toughest thing that you have to do. You can be an asshole to your crew, and sometimes you have to be. Then you come home, and you have to be really careful because your family is not your crew.

I would always fall back on, "You married me because I was a hotshot, and I'm still a hotshot." But it was tough. It was tough on her, it was tough on the kids, and it took a pretty special person at home to deal with that because they had to rely on themselves.

You weren't there at the most critical times. You always think that you're the big, brave fireman, and you'll be home when the fire comes home. No. You're never home when the fire comes home. You're somewhere else. And she had to evacuate the house a couple of times.

I saw a lot of my fellow superintendents go through divorce after divorce. It's really a hard transition: to leave the crew at night, to get home on time and to get there for dinner—if you ever did. Have a couple of drinks with the crew and then come home about half in the bag: it's part of getting that cohesion together.

One year I made an extreme sacrifice. I took a summer vacation, and of course it was one of the biggest fire years. I missed about three weeks of fires, away from the crew, but had I not done that, I'm sure it would've ended the family right then.

It's really tough. I don't think people understand that. I don't think a superintendent understands it when he walks into the job. I don't think the people realize what those people on the crew, both the superintendent and the foremen, have to go through if they have a family. . . . It's not just the being gone stuff; it's the whole trying to leave your hat at work, come home and change, because you can't turn that switch on and off. That's the toughest thing, and that was another reason for me to walk away. There's a time and a place: you've got to make a decision if it's important enough to keep the family together.

Ken Jordan (Sierra, 1998–2014)

I don't go for the family sacrifice anymore, because I am divorced and am a single parent of three very successful daughters. My captain's going through it, and I know a lot of people who have kept their families intact better than others who were there with their families every night. So, where I used to think I had to sacrifice my family life, I don't anymore—as long as you've got the tools to keep it together. I don't feel I sacrifice enough in the hotshot world. I need to get out during the wintertime and get more involved nationally.

You have to kind of sacrifice your pride nowadays. Pride used to be huge as a superintendent. You can't do it anymore. You have to have pride in the crew, and that's real important—an important tool to retain people—but as far as pride in yourself as a superintendent, you have to totally sacrifice that. I'm here because I have to be here, because this is my job, and I'm going do the best I can, and I'm no more special than you are. I'm really not. . . . You don't ask for any special privileges: you don't do anything, wear anything, different than the rest of the gang. It's a huge sacrifice as far as your pride, some of the stuff that you have to do to be a superintendent.

It's not about you anymore at that point. It's not about you at all: it's about 20 guys you have to bring home, and if you start making it about you, then they aren't coming home. Something's going to go wrong. Something's going to happen. The communications will suffer; people will not listen to you as much. If you develop a working relationship instead of, "I'm the superintendent, and that makes me special-er than you," that seems to work better, and that's a big sacrifice. It was for me, because I used to think I was stinkin' better than everybody. Then I found out, "You really suck at a lot of stuff," and once I came to that realization, I could build on that. When I found I couldn't do it all myself and I really sucked at a lot of stuff, then I depended on the rest of the guys with their talents, their gifts, to make things better.

Ron Bollier (Silver City, 1993–1995; Carson, 1996–1997; Fulton, 1998–2013)

I hope if you're married that you have an understanding wife and family because that bell goes off quite frequently. It's hard to say, but your outside friendships, outside the agency, don't ever lose 'em, because you get so wound up in the job itself . . . you focus so hard on the job . . . just wanting to have a good crew—building a good crew, being part of a good crew. You sacrifice a lot of stuff—your family, your friends on the outside. Your family's the most important. Hopefully, you have a good wife, a good family, and they support you, because you are going to be gone away from home a lot. And if you're not married and you're single, then you're good to go. (Laughs.)

Ron Regan (Del Rosa, 1977–1997)

Well, your family life takes it a little bit in the back because sometimes you tend to put your job and the crew ahead of your family, and being gone for long periods of time makes life difficult for your spouse and children. I don't know if this is exactly what you want as an answer, but your social life takes a little bit of a back seat, and so does your wife. I was fortunate enough to have a very good wife—who's still with me—to stay by me through the good and the bad.

Bob Wright (Sacramento, 1990–2002)

When I worked for CDF, most of those guys were divorced. That was in the late '60s, early '70s. I was just lucky to have an understanding wife, and we've been married almost 30 years now. You sacrifice your kids and then you try to make time with them, because you're never here. In the beginning, it wasn't so bad because the winters weren't as busy sometimes [after] you got your slash done and your burning done, and then sometimes you'd have spring break, or at Christmas you could go do stuff. We'd try to do trips like that. The kids grow up pretty quick, and you miss a lot of stuff. You miss birthdays, you miss parties, school stuff.

Then your marriage, too, because you're gone all the time. They're lonely, especially some of these new wives who have never been around. In fact, we've got one over here. They're renting a little cabin; it's about as big as this room that we're in right now. She's there all by herself when he's gone. You know what she's going through, because when we first got married we lived in a 13-foot trailer, camped out. Lucky that Carol was working for the Forest Service in recreation, so it wasn't so bad. Yeah, a lot of sacrifices, far as family goes.

I couldn't have done it without my wife—no way—because she stuck with me; and she was a good supe's wife, because the wives or the girlfriends, when they had problems, they could call her up, and she could direct them to places, help them out, or just be a friend to talk to them. She was a big instrument of my career.

Then, like I said, being a good supe, [it's] 24-7. You're doing plans, training plans in the winter; you're thinking of better ways you can work the crew, different ways you can train the crew. The more work you put into it—quality work—the better off the crew will be. But the main thing is you've got to care about those guys and girls. You've gotta show 'em that you care, and don't just talk—show—if they want counseling or just everyday stuff. They used to say never be a friend with your employees, but that's bullshit. You can still be a friend, and if they're a good employee, they'll respect you. If you tell 'em to do something, they'll do it for you. I always was friends with all the good FMOs and rangers I had.

Art Torrez (Vista Grande, 1994–2004)
Definitely, there's all the travel, so you're away from home for long periods of time. There's a lot of time that's put into your training program, your instructing. You never stop learning. I'm a firm believer of that. Some of the other sacrifices that probably come into play are that you can find yourself in more of a father role with all the personal problems [of] the crewpersons you have through the course of a summer. You're playing the role of superintendent and a father figure to some of these folks who are working for you.

Ted Mathiesen (Arroyo Grande Flight Crew, 1990–2007)
[On making his sons try wildland fire for at least one season.]
They didn't have any choice. They didn't have any direction, as far as, "This is what I want to do when I grow up." [I told them,] "Okay, here's what you're going to do. Here's what you're doing this first year. You'll make some money; you'll travel and have a good time. You're going to go work for a guy who used to work for me, and you'll understand a few things about maybe why I

wasn't around all summer." That was the focus with both of the boys.

They got bit by the bug, and then I said, "That's it. You're free to do whatever you want to do. You're an adult now." They've stuck with it, that's what they like, and they've both achieved and will continue to achieve great success, both for the Forest Service and the BLM. I couldn't be prouder of them. . . . I can remember a few years ago on the San Bernardino, Father's Day, the young one and I had dinner together in fire camp. . . . I landed on a helispot one time to pick up some jumpers and the other boy was there, unbeknownst to me. That was kind of a cool thing, the surprise. That brings me some pride and some satisfaction that they've done well.

The one bit of advice I gave them was, "Don't ever use your old man's name. Don't ever say, 'Well my dad this, that.' Just keep your mouth shut, your eyes and ears open. That's the best advice I can give to you." They did, they enjoyed it, and they're still there.[9]

Kurt LaRue (Diamond Mountain, 1993–2001)
[How have you managed to stay married for so long?]
Got laid off for those six months, remember. This will be my 27th anniversary coming up in April. Need to remember that and go buy something. (Laughs) I think it has more to say for my wife than me. I'm no more easygoing and charming or sweet than any of the guys who have led to the 217 percent divorce rate, so it must have more to do with her than me. "Lucky" would be about the only way to put that.

My wife's name is Michel, and over time and all of my travels, she built a life for herself and the kids. I think one of the

---

[9] Mathiesen's older son Josh is manager of the Redding smokejumper base; his younger son Leif has been superintendent of the Kern Valley Hotshots and is now in fire management; his daughter didn't get involved with fire.

things that helped with that is that I was doing this a year or two before I got married. This is pretty much what she was used to seeing when it came about. Michel and the kids traveled about in the summers, and she never let her life and the kids' lives get wrapped around whether I was home or out. It doesn't hurt to kick those big checks home every two weeks to grease things back on the family front while you're gone. But I was laid off for the whole winter. More than one of the springs she looked really relieved when I got our first assignment.

Steve Dickenson (La Grande, 1990; Redmond, 1994)

I remember going to a bachelor party once: guy was all excited, he was gonna get married; it was gonna be his first [marriage]. This old guy on the crew goes, "Of the 52 people who jump here, 48 of us have been married. Out of us 48, 92 percent have been divorced. Out of those 92 percent who were divorced, 12 of 'em got [re]married. Out of those 12 who got [re]married, 9 of them got divorced." This guy—it was his party—just kept slumping down.

I'm working on my second marriage. I will tell you, too, that we don't understand the impact of leaving people behind, and you can't be whole if you don't have your support system behind you. So, another big piece of advice for superintendents: take care of your family. The job is not everything. . . . So many people have been divorced in this business, and where are those people who we started relationships with? We're married to the service. Try not to be married to the service. You don't have to be married to the service to do a good job. When the fire's right, and your trust is right, stay at home and let your assistant take the crew out. . . . Stay home and take care of yourself.

Craig Workman (Black Mountain, 1988–2005)

It's a commitment, and it's been a great sacrifice for my wife. In the summertime, the crew is the focus, and she knows that, but it doesn't make it any easier to swallow. But I don't personally know how I could do the job that I ask the kids to do if I didn't commit as much as I do. I would think every other superintendent has the same vision that I do about that.

What is it like being a founding supe?

Shawna Legarza (San Juan, 2002–2007)
I think that it'll be hard for me to leave. Because it's all my morals and values and inspirations and stuff welded into what I want the crew to be, and taking my thoughts and stuff down to my overhead and to the crewmembers. I have a really close bind to that because I started it. I think when I decide I need to leave or should leave, that it'll be hard to go because my roots are here. If you're taking over another crew, then you have to deal with how they ran that crew before you were there and the different philosophies and attitudes of the crew. If those don't mend to what you want, then I think there will be some issues with that.

Wolf Creek Becomes Richard Aguilar's Dream Job

When they were giving me a tour of the center and I saw the young kids there, I got turned off immediately. I said, "These people are not hotshot material. I cannot make a hotshot out of these guys: [they're] unexperienced." Just before I left the center, a bus full of new recruits came in, and when they got off that bus they looked scared, like they were looking for the escape route. (Laughs.) It brought back memories of when I got off a bus at Fort Leonard Wood, Missouri.

On our way back to Roseburg . . . I kept thinking about it: "My goodness, I was the same age when I got into the military. All of us arrived from that bus, and in six weeks we were ready to kill anybody." I kept thinking, "Well, there's a time where you can change people around." I got wondering how the military changes people so quickly, and then I started realizing that the same people who join Job Corps are the same type of people who go into the military. I figured if the military can fight wars with these young kids, I can fight forest fires.

I had a dream that night that I was running it like the military. I said, "Well, it's not run by the Forest Service. I'll be the only person who knows what I'm doing. Nobody will interfere." Next morning, I told my wife, "We're going to Wolf Creek. I want to accept the job."

How have you changed?

Kurt LaRue (Diamond Mountain, 1993–2001)

I work year-round now. (Laughs) I don't think that I let little things worry me as much. You get older, you get less possessive about other people having ideas and going with their ideas. As a young supervisor, there's an insecurity that comes from, well, just being young. I think as you get older you're more inclined to go with other people's ideas when they have good ideas, to give credit to those who came up with them. I think that kicks in, but it kicks in with age more than anything else.

Ted Mathiesen (Arroyo Grande Flight Crew, 1990–2007)

As a supervisor and a person, I've definitely become mellow, and I attribute that to age. Early in the career, it was all about the job. Made a lot of decisions that were detrimental to the family based on the job, and that's all it was: it was just the J-O-B. . . . Now I realize there's life after six o'clock. I would hope that I could pass on, so it doesn't take all those mistakes for these kids to understand, that it's just a job. I mean, it's a great job, but it's just a job. It's not life. The people who think it's life, they need to get a life.

I see these kids occasionally come to work a little bit on the dark side because of extracurricular activities. I go, "Man, I used to come to work feeling like that." I'm really glad I don't anymore. We encourage that they don't do that, and I think that's a lot less prevalent. I've got a lot of guys who don't drink.

I guess I kind of feel my vulnerability, and I'm at the end of my career, so I know it's all going to end here. It's been great. I want to go out on a good note. I don't want to be bitter. I've seen so many guys go out bitter at the agency, and I look at that—a lot of 'em—and I go, "You know what? You could've done something about that to where you didn't go out bitter. Maybe you could've personally done something so you didn't have those feelings," . . . and it's all how you handle your career.

Stan Stewart (Los Padres, 2000–2009)

Got older. (Laughs.) Mellowed out, as far as trying to be a little more openminded to stuff that I sometimes wasn't. Trying to make sure you're not being selfish: taking care of them first, which sometimes is hard to do. There's always that "me" stuff in there, taking care of yourself.

It's kind of a fine line: you hit your first captain's job, and then all of a sudden you're not everybody's best buddy anymore. When you get to be the supe, you really have to distance yourself even more. You can't be everybody's best buddy and their boss at the same time. . . . You need to take time to know them, for sure. You just can't be everybody's best buddy, and I'm kind of learning that as I go along.

J. W. Allendorf (Wallowa–Whitman, 1980; Arrowhead 3, 1981)

I think I've gotten much more cynical about management in the Forest Service, and distrustful. That's a hell of a thing to say: here

I started as a GS-2, and I'm a friggin' 13 now, and that just absolutely is beyond my comprehension. . . . I think back on how many times I had forest supervisors threatening to give me 30-day suspensions for shooting my mouth off and various other things, and here I am now. Actually, whether I like it or not, I'm management, but I try to temper that with also being real and going out and working with people who actually do the job because now I'm so far removed from it.

I've become more cynical and less trustful of management, but at the same time, I have to say that I dearly love the Forest Service. I pee [Forest Service] green . . . , but I do that not because of Forest Service management but because of the wonderful people I've worked with. I never would've even met those characters. They're what keeps me going, what makes me happy.

Ken Jordan (Sierra, 1998–2014)

As a firefighter, it's much more beneficial to try to be—or at least take the appearance of being—politically correct for the good of the firefighters in the organization. Instead of getting mad, frustrated, upset, pissed off, just find ways to manipulate and adapt because you still have to do it. I've tried to find ways of being better at that and seeing the importance of media, where I didn't before, seeing the importance of leading up to management and trying to keep them involved, and seeing the importance of family and community backing your crew. Before, we were isolationists. If you have the community and the management backing you, then your program will be more successful, and people will be safer.

I used to treat people like crap. I used to just hammer on 'em. I used to grab 'em by the hair and make 'em do pushups, and yell in their face, cuss at 'em using the foulest language in the world. I don't even know how I got away with most of that stuff. That was another battle that I had to fight. I had to change, adapt to something else. The "something else" worked even better, and it was easier.

Greg Vergari (Union, 1980–1987)

I am a lot mellower and not as fast to be aggressive. I don't jump as fast to get something done because I have seen too many false starts. I am aggressive when I need to be and find it easy to disengage when I'm losing or think it is unsafe.

Craig Lechleiter (Redding, 1986–2002)

I think overall I've been influenced by my peers more than anyone. I respect their input more than anything. I feel proud that I became more of the conscience of my California peers, and I take a lot of pride in that. That really is my style. I was more the compassionate, touchy-feely superintendent in the long run. I guess all of us trend that direction sooner or later. It must be getting older and/or wiser that helps us make the transition in life.

Craig Workman (Black Mountain, 1988–2005)

My weakness when I first got with the Forest Service was being [un]comfortable around groups. I'm not a real fluent speaker, and I don't talk a lot. I can tend to be by myself, deep in thought, and forget about others. When I went to Redding, Charlie Caldwell saw in me a person who couldn't stand in front of two people and look them in the eye and tell them something. Immediately, he decided that I was going to teach climbing class because he knew that I was a climber. That's probably one of the hardest things I've ever done, but it's probably one of the best things I ever had to do in my career.[10]

Greg Overacker (Stanislaus, 1979–2006)

Yes, I have changed. Tremendously. I used to run it with a whip and a gun. And could. My personality and everything else lends itself to it, just because I am as big as I am. I am also a normal person in here. There is only a standard 5-foot-8, 155-pound person

---

[10] See Charlie Caldwell's response when told about Workman's story in the "What are your best practices for training?" section on p. 121.

in here. It's a disadvantage to be as big as I am—not just because of physical shape—just the size I am, how noisy I can be if I want to be. I can be intimidating. Yet, it's not a good tool. Is it a tool? Yeah. Does it work? Yeah, it does work. Is it preferred? No.

You want to work things out with people and have them feel comfortable around you. Disarm them. They always think, "Well, here comes that shithead Rax. He's so aggressive." The stories about me precede me to the point where it's almost to my advantage to walk up and go, "Well, hello." They go, "My, he speaks!" I say, "What's the matter? I wasn't gonna hit ya. I came over to talk to you." At the end of the day, they're pleasantly surprised that you can talk and you're a nice person, and you can get the job done. Hopefully, they'll tell somebody else. (Laughs.)

Mark Linane (Los Prietos/Los Padres, 1973–2001)
Well, in two ways: I expected more out of people and expected less out of people. From a two-edged sword side, I probably pushed my people pretty hard early in my career, and the boys could probably tell you there were several times that I over-pushed them. I was too mission focused—more mission focused than people focused. Later on, I probably put a better balance to that. . . . Later on, as maturity set about, I was able to understand the human frailties better. We're all just humans, and we have this huge propensity to screw up in one form or another.

PART THREE

ONCE YOU'RE THERE

Building a Crew, Taking Them Through the Season

All those years of preparation for becoming a supe still leave room for some surprises and growth. Perhaps the following insights will shorten and flatten your learning curve a little.

What it was like as a new supe?

Greg Vergari (Union, 1980–1987)

The first three years as a supe were hard. The learning curve was steep, and I didn't feel like I was doing that well. Truth be known, I probably wasn't. When all the chips were down and I felt like I was standing there naked, I defaulted to basic task accomplishment: doing the things I knew how [to do]. I taught the folks around me how to do the same. After about three years, I learned and started to get more confident. I feel for new supes.

Does your crew have a traditional personality?

Kurt LaRue (Diamond Mountain, 1993–2001)
You would have to ask other crews what it is. For the most part, I've noticed the old cliché is true that they pick up the personality of their overhead. That seems to be what it runs toward. I guess it would be said that my crew is rather grumpy and surly most of the time, not real social—I don't know. (Laughing hard.) You'd have to ask other crews to get that answer.

Steve Karkanen (Lolo, 1990–2011)
That's a question better asked of somebody outside the program, but I like to think that we're flexible, that we're friendly. We don't have a standoffish attitude like a lot of the crews do. That just irritates me to no end: when we're working with a crew that doesn't allow their folks to talk with anybody. . . . I just never quite understood what that was all about. There are still lots of crews out there that are like that. It's bizarre. I mean, we're all out there doing the same job, whether we're on a hotshot crew, on an engine, on helitack, or on a Type 2 crew. We're all the same, and I don't want my people thinking they're better than anybody else. That'll piss me off. And there's always going to be this distinction between the hotshots, the smokejumpers, the folks on a district on IA [initial attack]. There's always going to be a little bit of competition that's there—this rivalry—but there is really no place for it, I don't think. Maybe a little bit in some sense of there being pride, a certain amount of pride—I think that's really important—that, and that we come across as being professional.

Richard Aguilar (El Cariso, 1974; Wolf Creek, 1975–1997)
We used to be the first ones for breakfast. All the time. People didn't understand a lot of why we were the first ones up to eat breakfast. I would go up and ask them, "What time are you going to start serving?" If they said 4:30, we were there at 4:30. The

reason was that I found out guys could get more rest than waiting in line where they would be standing for an hour, moving up slowly until they got their breakfast. We would go in and get our breakfast, and then I had time to go to the briefing. Right after breakfast, when the crew was ready, I would tell the division supe, "My crew's ready anytime," but I knew that it was going to be two, three hours before the rest of the people would be ready—the other crews. I would tell them, "You can go back to bed and sleep for another two, three hours; we'll wake you up. Or go to the rigs and start them, warm up, and go to sleep." They would get more rest.

But when coming back from the line, we tried to be the last ones to eat. If the line was pretty long, it would be wasting time putting them in line. One squad would go find the sleeping area, get things ready. The other squad would go and retool the trucks, the equipment, get the water, and have everything ready for the next morning. Then, next morning, when they were the first ones to eat, they didn't have to wait in line. They'd go right in and eat breakfast, and everything was ready the day before. That was our system.

Barry Callenberger (Palomar, 1979–1982; Eldorado, 1982–1988)

I really believe that the crew always took on the personality of the superintendent. . . . People run into me today and still comment to me on the fact that when the crew got into fire camp, I always hated the sawyers having greasy, oily fire shirts. They thought it was cool, and I go, "No, it's not cool." One, it's dangerous because it's flammable; and two, it looks like crap, so I usually made them get rid of their crummy fire shirts. I ripped one off the back of one of my sawyers one day when I was in finance, and there were a couple of women in there that every time I see 'em, they always tell me about it (laughs): "Oh, that was so good of you when you did that. We're just so glad. All these hotshots come in here, and they stink and everything. I'm glad you did what you did—tore that shirt off. Thanks."

J. W. Allendorf (Wallowa–Whitman, 1980; Arrowhead 3, 1981)

I think for the most part they were known as hard workers and people who liked to have fun. I think pretty much the whole crew—or crews—always had a good sense of humor, and they used that to keep themselves going. Humor was a big part of it.

Your crew's going to be a mirror image of the way you project yourself. It's true, because if you're sloppy, your crew's going to be sloppy. If you're unorganized, they'll be unorganized. Everything, right down the line.

Fred Schoeffler (Payson, 1981–2007)

We have always been aggressive and very fit. Good runners and hikers and hard workers: we have fun working hard. We also have fun in general. One of our traditional mottos is, "Superior skill and daring." Having and using common sense. I looked for progressive and proactive thinkers and doers.

Ken Jordan (Sierra, 1998–2014)

We're real strict and disciplined, but on the other hand, people are very strict and disciplined with each other. The crew [members keep] each other accountable, and it seems to work. Part of the "C" in LCES [lookouts, communications, escape routes, safety zones] is that they have to get along. It's what I tell them, because when they start not getting along, it takes the "C" out of communications.

Everybody gets irritated with each other. I tell 'em, "You work it out before the sun goes down, or you come and talk to me, and I'll work it out for you. You won't like what I do, man," so they do, and then they decided they liked that: they liked getting along. It was sickening. (Laughs.) They hang out after work and stuff.

Greg Vergari (Union, 1980–1987)

We always helped on the fire with what had to be done, whether it was mopping up or whatever, we got it done. It wasn't, like, "Get me off of here. I'm not going to be mopping this up because I'm [on] a hotshot crew." They'd say, "Put the hose lay in," and it got done the right way—cut the trees down, snag the patch. The line was in; it was done right. I don't think we were fancy, but we worked with what we had, and it felt good.

Charlie Caldwell (Redding, 1967–1986)

I highlighted "can-do attitude" because I always had that attitude and tried to instill it into everyone: even if you're not happy, goddammit, act like you're happy to be here, you enjoyed the work, and you'll be happy to come back. Don't ever leave a fire camp knowing you're dissatisfied or they're dissatisfied. Even if, in your own mind, you don't feel that way. I think that is a real important thing to do. Attitudes—without thinking about it—cause efficiency to go way down.

Ron Regan (Del Rosa, 1977–1997)

Each crew kind of goes with the personality of their superintendent. One thing I didn't stand for when I was superintendent was profanity and vulgarity. When we'd go out of region, we'd usually be traveling in a bus. I didn't want to listen to some kid's foul mouth. I didn't expect the drivers to listen to it either, because a lot of the drivers were female contract bus drivers. The crew knew that I didn't tolerate that kind of stuff. I didn't want to listen to the F-word 25 times in a sentence. I used to get so frustrated; I'd take my crew off the bus and say, "We'll get another bus." One has got to have respect for one's self and others.

Shawna Legarza (San Juan, 2002–2007)

We're only five years old, going on our sixth year, so I think we're getting a personality. A couple years ago, one of the guys on the crew who's my squad boss told me that he sees the crew getting my personality.

Our main philosophy is "work hard, play hard." I'm all about having fun, working hard, and being nice to each other, and we're kind of coming that way. But we're so young, [and] it takes at least ten years to get a reputation, build a good crew, and stuff like that.

I've always taught my guys to do whatever needs to be done around fire camp. This year, for example, we had a fire up in Wyoming. We couldn't do anything on the fire because it was so windy. We were back in camp, and the wind was blowing so hard that it blew over all the tents and all the outhouses. Papers and everything were going everywhere . . . , so we went over and helped them out: put up the porta-toilets, gathered up the paper, and helped out the team. Nobody else did that. I'm trying to teach my guys to be mindful of everybody, not just the people who you work for or work with, but who's around on the fire.

Mark Linane (Los Prietos/Los Padres, 1973–2001)

I would guess that the motto was "work hard, play hard" for a lot of those years. There was the expectation that family squabbles were family squabbles; you didn't have outbursts among the crew on the fireline or in front of other crews. You handled family squabbles back at the house, back at the truck. You spewed by how much line you put in, how successfully you burned a piece of line out, fired a piece of line out, how much mop-up you got done. . . . That's how you bragged about it. Then once you got back to base, back to your own watering hole, that's when you could call yourself the best hotshot crew in the world. Other than that, you weren't supposed to talk about it, though you thought it.

Rusty Witwer (Mendocino, 1978; Hobart/Tahoe, 1979–1995)

The badge of honor was not showering, kind of like Chena does now: "the dirty boys." I used to let them let their fire shirts get a bit greasy and stuff . . . , and other supes would drive me nuts with, "If you're clean then everybody thinks you're fresh, and you'll get an extra shift." I let them kind of go on the grungy side a little bit.

What I tried to stress with the crew is not to belittle any other crew or person, not to put any kind of jive on anybody else. Our motto was, "Stand on our line, not on our mouth." If we started getting folks who would do that, then they didn't stay on the crew very long. In other words, we weren't into that: vibing another bunch. A little bit of competition's healthy, but not to that point of belittling. Our intent was [to] keep our head down, just do the job, smile, go on, that type of thing.

We had a couth system, and people could fine each other, and I understand now that they can't do that. The reason that was started was so that everybody was a safety officer. If people started becoming vindictive about just busting somebody [who] busted them, then we had a court system that took care of that. The intent was that everybody looked out for each other. They could fine me. Some years I had the most fines of anybody. It kind of kept you on your toes a little bit.

Dave Matier (Midnight Sun, 1992–1997, 1999–2007, 2009–2010)

Hard-core. Low-maintenance, hard-core. And we work hard. That's about it.

Who do you hire?

Ted Mathiesen (Arroyo Grande Flight Crew, 1990–2007)

This year we're hiring two people only, brand-new people. We get a lot of phone calls. We encourage everyone to come out and face-to-face. That's huge. They need to do that. You can't just do it on the phone. We want guys who have a couple, three years' experience, who are trainable, teachable, obviously physically fit. Almost hate to say it, but present a good image. . . . We look for guys who are humble and really want to be here. After they come for an interview, there's always a follow-up call or two, and the overhead will get together, and we'll rate them.

Stan Stewart (Los Padres, 2000–2009)

We do have a lot of guys putting in. We try to get as many who are really interested to actually come and meet us face-to-face. We've got just a little two-page questionnaire we fill out with them with a variety of stuff: experience and phone numbers, special skills they have, what schools they've had, sports they've played. It's nice if they've done some team stuff. We ask them a couple questions on why they want to be there and what they add to the crew, so it makes them think a little bit. Plus, you can put a name with the face.

Your gut feelings are probably right: I'd say at least nine times out of ten or so you can look at somebody and talk to 'em for 10 or 15 minutes . . . , and you've got a pretty good clue. We don't hire anybody usually . . . who doesn't come in to see us. Unless they live across the country, their odds increase dramatically if they can make an appearance.

[What's a good answer when you ask what they can bring to the crew?]

First question is why you want to be there, and that's usually reputation . . . of the crew, and then sometimes it's for the money. . . . You hear a lot of different stuff: what can you add to the crew, teamwork, motivation, leadership, and all this other stuff, but you can tell where they're coming from by what they're saying, what their body language is, and a few of those other little things. . . . It actually seems to work. Puts them on the spot a little versus just asking them a name and a Social Security number; makes them think a little bit.

Greg Keller (Eldorado, 1985–1996; Modoc, 2000–2007)

I don't know if that's a good or a bad way, but your only way initially is how they sound and present themselves on the telephone. Then you ask for a résumé, and you look at what someone can do to represent themselves or their lives or their accomplishments.

What we really like is for someone to come by and see us. . . .When you can physically see someone, [they] start making impressions. Not to say you're always right, but you can see if they appear to be in good shape, and you can start telling things about their personality and their demeanor. You can look at their hands and see if they've worked, if there are calluses. You can ask a few questions and see how they respond, and how you think they might do in a group setting. It's a long process, but a lot of it has to do with who shows initiative. The person who shows the most initiative, and then if we can back up that person's prior experience with good performance ratings.

Kurt LaRue (Diamond Mountain, 1993–2001)

We started screening from their first phone call. I'd go through whatever hiring procedure we were using at the time. I almost invariably would ask them to send me an app, separate from the one they sent in to get on whatever roster we were using. [I asked them to] include a note that referenced their phone call to us. That was your first step in the screening process—can you follow basic orders?—and we just took it from there.

It helped enormously if the young person came by, said hi, shook hands, [and we] got to talk to them [about] what they expected, what we expected. I know the kids who come by always act like they're intruding on your time. Really, they're not: if you hire happy kids who are hard-working kids, your life goes well.

You hire dumb bastards, life is full of dumb bastard things happening, so it's good to see the kids. We would try and set up times and locations to see them as we traveled to meetings.

The other thing that I learned over the years . . . is not worrying about it as much as I did when I first got the job. Some of the kids, when they leave the crew, they say, "I was looking for work when I found this one." I could tell the kids, well, you know, I was looking for a crewman when I found you. (Laughs.)

Steve Karkanen (Lolo, 1990–2011)

We have an alternate program in the summertime. We take one person off each district, and they go through our critical training with us. Then we assign them a month period of time where they are number 21, and they go out with us. We get the chance to see how they work, and probably more importantly, they get to see what it's really like on a hotshot crew. We've hired a few people, sight unseen, off of districts, who come onto a hotshot crew with really good experience and good recommendations that totally fall apart. They don't operate very well in that environment at all.

Paul Musser (Flagstaff, 1990–2004)

There are a lot of people who show up and right off the bat tell me how great they are, what a good job they do, and how hard they work, "This is what I want on a job," and stuff like that. The ones who come in and say they will try as hard as they possibly can, and this is what they've done in the past, and they really want the opportunity, and they want to know what they can do to make themselves more desirable for the job, those are the people I want. The ones who already think they're God's gift to the job, I don't want.

If they've come from someplace else . . . , the first thing they have to do is prove they can do the job, and that's just by hard work and attitude and willingness to help. Like chores on the buggies and stuff like that: you see some people jumping in all the time and doing things and some people standing around talking and listening to Walkmans and stuff like that. Those people who are jumping in and trying to help and trying to learn are the ones who do better.

J. W. Allendorf (Wallowa–Whitman, 1980; Arrowhead 3, 1981)
A lot of it's just gut feeling. I think what I always looked for was somebody who was just a little bit on the ragged edge but had some definite leadership traits that showed through. Informal leaders others wanted to be around: he could get other people into trouble because he'd led 'em there—he or she took 'em there. Just full of piss and vinegar, hard worker, not always doing what you wanted them to do, but I think that's good too because that's where creativity comes from. I'd look for people who were not necessarily the well-behaved, always-squared-away types. Too many of those folks were putting on an act. I liked the people who were spontaneous, who were themselves, and who just demonstrated some leadership ability.

Fred Schoeffler (Payson, 1981–2007)
Generally, interested applicants who call and stop by to talk with us, so we have a name and a face, are preferred over just an application. Applicants who have good references, honest with integrity. Often hired former Boy Scouts, especially Eagle Scouts because I am one and I value their character. Physically fit: high school and/or college wrestlers and/or cross-country athletes. Generally speaking, big people eat too much, drink too much water, and generally don't do well in the heat; then again, it's good to have at least one big guy on the crew to lift the heavy stuff. Intelligent and woods-worthy; a good attitude. Willing to follow orders yet also make constructive suggestions when appropriate. A good, solid work ethic and willing to work hard. Finally, a sense of humor and commitment to the job and all that it entails.

Greg Vergari (Union, 1980–1987)

I said to my captains, "You ask three questions of everybody they put on the list for a reference: Did they get along with others at work? Are they physically fit for the job? Are they self-starters?" They applied for the job because they think they like fire, and many of them had fire experience, so you could ask that question too. But those are the magic questions; that's any individual who you'd want working for you.

I don't forget where I was coming from then, and it still sticks in my mind even today, because I'll ask: Are they nice individuals? . . . I mean, you could have some real fire-eaters out there, but if they can't get along with a stick, they make everybody mad, why put yourself through that burden? It was a hard lesson to learn . . . because I hired some animals, and it didn't turn out too good at the end.

Dave Matier (Midnight Sun, 1992–1997, 1999–2007, 2009–2010)

I look for people who are highly motivated, able to work by themselves without having to be supervised every minute of the day. Physically fit, intelligent. I personally prefer hiring people who have fire experience but not necessarily hotshot experience because I can't tell you how many times I've heard, "Well, we used to do it like this," and up there it's totally different.

Shawna Legarza (San Juan, 2002–2007)

We've got a program in Kansas where we bring one person straight out of school to our crew. Other than that, I will make sure that they have a little fire experience, and what it is, I don't mind. If it's engine, helitack, or hand crew, either way, but I encourage them to visit me in Durango and to come down and meet me and my assistant and sometimes the squad bosses if they're in the office.

I try to look for their basic personality characteristics and if I can ask them any morals-and-values kind of questions. We have a canned interview list, and it's not probably what you would find on other job sites or other crews. It dives a little deeper, like where they were from, what their morals and values are, where do they want to be in five years, where they want to go. Then I have little questions that I ask them to see how they react to it. A lot of personality traits, and if they're going to want to stick around for four or five years on the crew and buy into my philosophy.

Bob Wright (Sacramento, 1990–2002)

I always tried to find the person who was kind of the go-getter, the one who couldn't set still for five minutes, always had to do something. I didn't like smart-asses, but most hotshots are smart-asses anyway. I liked a kid who liked to work, and work hard, and then doesn't give you a bunch of crap. . . . Calling references: that helped, talking to people. Sometimes you just took a hunch: looking at [their application] the person may not have even spelled it right, but you just had a hunch in the back of your mind, "Well this kid may be okay. We'll give him a shot." Sometimes they didn't work out; sometimes they did.

Craig Workman (Black Mountain, 1988–2005)

I don't necessarily look at somebody who has a whole bunch of credentials. I look at somebody who really wants the job, who understands what the job is, even if they haven't ever been there, but they've taken the time to find out what it's like. I will ask them questions and find out if they even know what they're applying for. If they keep calling me, anytime, day or night, and stopping by the office if they can, and showing true interest, then that person is at the top of my list.

Rusty Witwer (Mendocino, 1978; Hobart/Tahoe, 1979–1995)
I wasn't a believer that I needed a hotshot crew that all had six years of experience. I personally believe that a portion of your crew could be GS-2s right off the street. In fact, I think that's kind of healthy to have a little bit of new blood into the system. I know it's only 10 percent of the crews now, but years ago, when people came to work for the Forest Service in the '60s, they started on a hotshot crew. If they did well there, then they were put on the engines because then we knew that they physically and mentally could put up to the challenges of wildland firefighting.

I always wanted a core of about 8 returnees, max of 10 or 12. The rest I wanted new, just to give people an opportunity. What I didn't want to have was 20 people who all thought they were more interested in how the fire was being run than actually what we were there for, which was to put 60 chains of line in. That is what we hire the crews to do, not to micromanage or second-guess incident command teams. In most cases, usually two to three, four years is max, in my opinion, at the same grade level on a crew. After that, they'll either be moving up the chain of command, or moving across into some of the other fields, or we can find somebody else, because it's not a career position. I guess I'm old-school on that.

Steve Dickenson (La Grande, 1990; Redmond, 1994)
I've worked with crews with people who have stayed, and they've earned their jobs, and you can't create openings. Sometimes the crew gets too comfortable. What I like about having new people on both hotshots and smokejumpers is those young people add a lot of energy, and then they push the old people because they're going to do some amazing great things. That will inspire your experienced people to not be left behind, to not be lazy, and to not rest on their past successes. They see people pushing them and see people doing well without the benefit of their background. It's a great dynamic.

Ben Charley (Horseshoe Meadow, 1974–1989)

I had a guy one time, from Massachusetts, a big college kid. He says, "I wanna work for you." I says, "Yeah, okay, I got an opening." "What do I have to do?" "Nothing. You do what I say, when I say, how I say." [The kid said,] "I don't want to work for you." Fine. I want somebody who's gonna take direction. (Laughs.) Evidently he didn't want to. . . . You've gotta tell 'em what to expect. . . . You gotta let 'em know what's going on, what they're in for.

Craig Lechleiter Explains How It's Different for Detail Crews

Most of the trainees came to Redding feeling like a bunch of prima-donnas, better-than-thou individuals. Not every detailer who came in here thought they walked on water, but it's something I had to deal with. It didn't take me long, and I would flat tell 'em several times the first week, "You're not hotshots yet. This is not a hotshot crew. The worst thing you can do is go to our first incident and act like you are. You're just gonna fall on your face. You may be able to run as fast as any other hotshots: in six weeks, you're gonna be able to run. You're gonna be able to do pullups and pushups. But you don't have a clue what it takes to be a hotshot crew. That's why you're here."

To get respect, we've got to demonstrate who we are to our family of hotshot crews. If we don't achieve that by the end of the year, we've failed. That's probably one of the biggest goals that I wanted to achieve: recognition from my peers. Knowing the other supes respected us: "Yeah, we'd like to work with Redding."

That's what you look for in a crew. Where do we fit in? Can we perform? Are we capable of building line, firing and holding that ground? Because all of our reputations are on it.

That's the best it can be. Telling those people the first week, "How are we gonna get there together?" was very powerful and challenging.

The reality of it all was 50 percent of the crew couldn't meet the physical demands of the job when they first arrived. Half of my women and half of my men couldn't do two pullups, pushups, or run. We were always in their face: "You're all gonna have to kick ass. If you can't, hopefully you haven't unpacked your red bag yet." I'd always tell 'em that: Don't unpack your red bag, because you will be required to perform before we hit the fireline. It was hard sending them home, but we had minimum standards that were required.

Richard Aguilar Cordially Invites You to Hell (Week)

We invited everybody in the center to participate in Hell Week. At the end, the first 20 would be the Type 1 [crew], and from there on we would build up the Type 2 crew. Then they would start putting in requests for camp crews, and we'd work on that one, too, if we had extra people.

The first day of Hell Week, just for them to qualify to participate, the first thing you would do is run a mile and a half in 11 minutes. Anybody who didn't make it was disqualified. Then we would turn around in the afternoon and we'd run ten and a half miles. New recruits could do it in an hour and 45 minutes, but the guys in their second year had to do it in an hour and 30 minutes.

The second day, we would go to the football field and form a circle around the football field and start doing calisthenics. The person who couldn't do all the pushups, he would immediately get up and run around the football field and come and try again. Jumping jacks, the same thing. We would do three and a half hours, nonstop. Then in the afternoon on Tuesday, we had a 16-mile hike. The first 12 miles was uphill, and then the last 4 miles we would drop down to Wolf Creek.

Then [for] the guys who were still with us Wednesday, we would already have an area where we would cut line . . . like around clear-cuts. We would start at eight o'clock in the morning. They would get two quarts of water, that's all. We would promise them a good lunch, but that lunch would never show up. We were checking also for the attitudes, and we would work straight, eight hours of line construction, nonstop. We would explain to them the truck got lost, that they couldn't get the lunches to us. The second day would be the same: one, two o'clock, no lunches. They wouldn't even complain, because they would lose their position. They would just quietly continue working.

On Friday, the people who still were with us would show up. At that time, we were testing to see how strong they were: if they could do 25 or more pushups in one minute, 25 or more sit-ups, and pullups—10 at a minimum. . . . The last thing we would do was a pack test. By then, we knew everybody who was there was going to make it. But that's what they called it. I didn't name it "Hell Week." They did. Because if people would ask them, "How was it today?" "Like hell, man!" (Laughs.)

Who do you promote?

Jim Cook (Arrowhead, 1981–1995; Boise, 1996–1998)
Somebody with initiative, somebody who's open to new ideas, somebody who shows passion and commitment—that's what I look for. I don't look for "yes" people. They've got to have passion and commitment. That means speaking up, but that means when the commander speaks—boom—I'm committed to this program;

we're going to make this work. I'm going to carry out what this person told me to carry out. Even though I had my opportunity to speak, the boss listened, the boss said this, I'm good with it, we're gonna make it work. That's commitment. That's the two-way respect that subordinate and superior leaders need to have. You need to listen to what your subordinate leaders have to say, but somebody's gotta make the call. After somebody makes the call, the subordinate's duty is to make it happen.

Dan Fiorito (Union, 1996–2006)
I want people who are thinkers. You could be the best sawyer, hardest-working line digger, or whatever, but if you are not thinking and trying to get the big picture, that is as far as you will go. I look for the crewmembers who want to do more than just put their heads down and work hard. For leadership positions, I need people who are looking at the situation at hand, figuring out how things are developing, and thinking about what to do next.

I also need people who want the responsibility that comes with leadership. I have known guys on hotshot crews who have worked on six or eight different crews over a 15- or 20-season career. They were awesome hotshots but they never wanted to do anything but dig line or run a chainsaw because they did not want the responsibility of leadership. Some people want to be leaders, but they don't have the skills or personality to be leaders. There is something about people who are going to be leaders: you can see it in them.

Kurt LaRue (Diamond Mountain, 1993–2001)
Performance is part of it. How well they blend into the crew. How well they work with the existing overhead and within the structure of the crew. Different crews have way different personalities and ways of doing things. We always looked on it like, if you don't like how this one's run, there are always 50 more out there, and you can go find one you like. Obviously, the people we

were lining up to promote were the ones who integrated into the system best. We did try and promote aggressively from within, thought it was a good reward.

We pretty much have told them—though we can't write it down—three years, up or out. At the end of an individual's third year, if you weren't somebody who we were going to make a squad leader, who we thought would make a squad leader, you were invited to look for employment opportunities elsewhere for the next year. Older crewmen, they get to know too many tricks in the system, and they tend to manipulate the younger crew-men too much, and that's your NCO class. They're setting the standard, so they have to be fully on board with how the crew operates. The overhead can tell the crew what the SOPs [standard operating procedures] and everything are, but the younger crewmen are looking at the older crewmen and seeing how they do things. There can be a lot of places where there's room for hypocrisy—say one thing and do another—and the kids pick up on that. If we didn't think that you had a future with us, at the end of your third year you could still get an excellent evaluation if you'd earned it, but we're not going to bring you back.

It's pretty easy to tell. You live with them long enough; you can tell which ones are going to supervise and which ones aren't. . . . Rookie crewmen, their sphere of consciousness is about two feet around 'em. It's a world of pain: my feet hurt, my back hurts. . . . They don't see much. As they start to expand out and survive through that phase, you can tell which ones you want around.

Steve Karkanen (Lolo, 1990–2011)
The guys who have the drive, the incentive. The ones who are really interested in this, who show that they have some kind of passion for it. The ones who do the best are the ones who jump into the training program right off the bat. They get involved in training new crew members, and you can see that right away. They'll start off, a couple years on the crew, kinda quiet, and then

they start teaching people: on-the-job training type stuff, with the chainsaw, or even simple things like swinging a tool, or just watching out for one another.

We'll pick up on that and give them the opportunity to get involved in the formal training when we do that the first part of the year or throughout the season when we do it, then give them as much opportunity as we can. We have all kinds of opportunities on some fires to let people go off and do their own things with a small group of people and see how they do. We try to give people as many of those chances as possible to go out and deal with the spot fires some place, work with the helicopter, or work with the engines, or whatever. If they're good, it shows.

J. W. Allendorf (Wallowa–Whitman, 1980; Arrowhead 3, 1981)

The folks who worked the hardest and set the example and who were always there. The tried and true. If you knew you were rolling out on an assignment, you've always got those folks who are there early checking the truck, making sure you've got everything you need. Those are the folks, if they had that leadership ability. Most of them did, because they cared—they cared about the other people. That's why they were there early. They weren't checking to see if they had it; they wanted to make sure the crew had it.

Fred Schoeffler (Payson, 1981–2007)

I pick those who have integrity and are good with people skills, especially communication. Good motivators and those who can think on their feet in order to get stuff done, and independent thinkers. Those who can get the job done safely, in good physical condition, possess common sense—a rare commodity these days. This job is not for everyone and not just anyone can be a supervisor or leader.

The initial hurdle is getting past the transition from crewmember—one of "the crew"—to a supervisor level, especially squad boss—one of "them." It's tough for most folks to make that switch to being a supervisor and having the respect of others. A key move was establishing the senior firefighter position because it eased and strengthened this transition.

Greg Vergari (Union, 1980–1987)

The folks who had the good of the whole in mind, the ones who wanted the crew to succeed, the ones I knew could and would become GS-9s and better, the ones who had a future in the business. If I was doing it again, I think I would make it GS-11s: the ones who would bump up into management.

Old supervisors told me this—this is not something I invented. I firmly believe the individual needs to be able to grow in the organization. Some folks can be perfectly happy at 50 years old and a GS-5. There's nothing wrong with that if they're happy doing that; that's fine. But a lot of people, they want a lot more in life. They want a little more security.

Dave Matier (Midnight Sun, 1992–1997, 1999–2007, 2009–2010)

I don't know if I can actually put a finger on who the people are who move up, . . . the ones who are motivated to learn, who are there for more than just a paycheck. It's real obvious once you get into the season—when you get to know these kids and such— which ones are looking to go beyond just running a Pulaski or running a chainsaw. They want the responsibility, and it comes out right away. I've been doing this long enough that it's easy to pick that stuff out.

I can't say that I have any particular method that I look for, because they're all different. It just sort of happens, and I've been pretty lucky, getting a good crop of them coming through all the time. It's definitely a revolving door, though, training them up, and then they go somewhere else.

Richard Aguilar (El Cariso, 1974; Wolf Creek, 1975–1997)

The life of a hotshot, unless he's going to be a leader, is two years. Two years, you get the best out of him. After two years, you better move him on because he'll say, "I have a lot more experience," and he starts delegating. That's not his job to delegate the work to other people. If you want [them] to stay, a foreman has to realize, "Hey, I need him as a lead sawyer," a special job, so he can continue. But some of them will go up as high as they're going to go and then they level off, and then soon they start declining and you do not get the best work.

Ron Bollier (Silver City, 1993–1995; Carson, 1996–1997; Fulton, 1998–2013)

Between the captains and myself, we'll watch, and we'll try and target individuals. Everybody's interested in wanting to move up. We'll watch the ones who have good common sense, make good decisions even when they think they're not making a decision. We'll throw them a question for some reason out of the blue, and see how they answer it. There're some who you can throw a question out of the blue . . . and they have no idea how to answer it. There're some who will throw an answer out right away. Then you'll find out that they continually rattle the answer out the right way every time. You just start targeting that group, then you start working with them and helping them.

Ron Regan (Del Rosa, 1977–1997)

You'll see one in probably 40 or 50 who is going to make this their career. [For] a lot of them, it's just a temporary position: get them through college, and they want to do something else. Firefighting is hard work, no doubt about it. It's an inspiration to see that individual, and you want to give him or her all the encouragement that you can as far as wanting to make a career out of it.

Craig Workman (Black Mountain, 1988–2005)

When I promote somebody on the crew, it's somebody who has really stood out, who has shown that they are dedicated, and they've put out that extra effort. People who work nine to five in the hotshot program aren't very successful. It takes more than that. It takes a commitment, and so that's the type of person I'm looking for when I promote them on up through the program.

Rusty Witwer (Mendocino, 1978; Hobart/Tahoe, 1979–1995)

Usually with the captains, I hired off-forest. I also looked at whether they had been a supervisor on a module before. I firmly believe that the hotshot captains need to have had some prior supervision, especially on an engine, initial attack, where they are the boss. They made the decisions on that IA until whoever showed up as the duty officer and had had a bit of practice in individual thinking before they came to the hotshots. When we would split, or farm out to different IAs, having that background was important to me.

What are your priorities before the first dispatch?

Greg Keller (Eldorado, 1985–1996; Modoc, 2000–2007)

My number one priority has always been physical fitness. We take an inordinate amount of time to prepare the crew physically, and I've always said that people either love or hate this job. There're very few people in the middle, and a lot of the people who have hated it have not been in good shape, and it's a miserable experience. . . . Even on your most miserable day, if you're in good shape, at the end of the day, once you get back to the trucks and get a cold water or a soda or get a meal, all of a sudden the kids are laughing. Six hours before, they were at literally the most miserable point in their lives.

Kurt LaRue (Diamond Mountain, 1993–2001)

Well, there are my priorities and what the agency requires. We have 40 hours before you take them out. I brought the crew on working ten-hour days so that I could get a decent PT program in with all the other stuff going on. We got classroom stuff out of the way, and then we took them up and just started cutting line and seeing who fit into what positions.

All of our orientation, all of our SOPs, all of our classroom stuff was loaded into PowerPoint and handouts, and everything was in a binder when they came on, and we'd go through the program. That went fairly quickly.

Once they started cutting line, the big discriminator was the big hill for PT. We had more people quit the crew over that than anything else, and that's what it was there to do. It served its purpose. . . . It's just over a mile and a quarter, and it's almost a dead-on 2,000-foot elevation gain. . . . You do it with gear every day, and you drag an EMT in the back to work on the ones who aren't doing so good. Usually just peer pressure takes care of getting everybody there. Most of them are a lot stronger than they think they are. That first day or two they get up there, and it takes them forever. They don't think they can ever do it, but it's part of the "tear down and build back up" process.

Richard Aguilar (El Cariso, 1974; Wolf Creek, 1975–1997)

Before we got the first dispatch, we would have a false alarm, start down the road, and then turn around and go back or stop somewhere and explain to them, "This is a false alarm." This is a time we can check the equipment. We would have a scale with us, and we would weigh the packs. Somebody would be way over, and we would check to see if they had enough socks and a jacket, if they forgot anything. We would check the tools, everything. That would put them on their toes, because when we got the first dispatch, they didn't know if it was a false alarm or the real thing, but they would be ready.

Charlie Caldwell (Redding, 1967–1986)

We had a situation one year, on the first day: . . . got our first dispatch while we were handing out fire pants. I said, "Shove 'em into your bag. We're going to a fire." My two foremen are standing here going, "We can't do this! We're not ready!" I said, "Oh, yeah. This is the way it works. This is good." They're going, "No, it ain't either! We don't have this and that." I said, "Throw the saws in the back." "We don't have any saw teams!" "We'll manage." On the way to the fire: "Know how to run a saw?" "Yeah." "Where have you run a saw?" We stuck him with another guy, whether he'd run a saw or not. (Laughs.) Get there, and you put out the fire, and I think it was the most memorable first day of doing anything for all those people.

Bob Wright (Sacramento, 1990–2002)

Most of the time I was thinking even before the crew got laid off about training for next year because you have an idea who you'll get back. After a fire, we'd talk: how to improve, what went wrong, what went good, and all that. I tried to get a plan: what we need to improve, work on, that we didn't do too good a job of the year before. I get that in place in writing, in my little notes and stuff, and get my training outline done.

If we were weak in the saw deal, we would do more saw training for the saw teams. Say I got the saw team back: I would break the saw down, and they would have relays. They would have the saw completely torn apart, they'd put it together, they'd cut line in brush with a swamper—100 yards or so—take it apart, that kind of stuff. How they cut and how they handled falling trees, but mainly just progression of line for the saws and how fast they could cut and do it safely.

If the line construction wasn't that good that year, we'd do a lot more line construction. Just anything we could've done better. Getting out of the truck, unloading to go to a fire for IA, we'd practice that. I'd pull up a stopwatch and watch how they got out, how they got their gear, how fast they could go. I'd give 'em what we were going to do, safety zones, what we were going to do before we got there, and how they passed that down in order. Firing out strips, firing out a piece of line, how did they line out. Because when I did it, I wanted it like that (snaps fingers). I didn't want to set there and explain it to them for an hour.

Greg Overacker (Stanislaus, 1979–2006)

When my crew is finally assembled and ready to go—just barely ready, we're on the boards and we're gonna take our first mission—we have a barbecue on the last day. That barbecue is done prior to the availability of the crew. . . . I want to see your significant others, your children, your wife, your grandmother, your father, whoever's around. . . . I want them to see who they're going to work for. Who's going to take care of their children. Who is going to be responsible for them. I want them to know who to call.

That's our job: bring them down and look into their eyes and realize that a mother and father, 40 years old, are entrusting you with their 18-year-old daughter. . . . You better know that that is your only job. Whether you can fight fire successfully or not remains to be seen. But you bring all the kids home, not just physically well, mentally well. Once you realize that, it makes your job a whole lot easier.

Mark Linane (Los Prietos/Los Padres, 1973–2001)

In the years we kept people working, I had firefighters come on early. I'd bring them on up to six weeks early, and we'd do a trail project in the wilderness. That was our team-building. We'd check work attitudes: we'd put in 12-hour days, we'd spike out and camp out overnight, and do that for about six weeks. We had some really, really tight crews. When we hit the line running, the cohesiveness was really tight. Everybody knew everybody's weaknesses, and around the campfire—nobody can hide around the campfire.

When we had that capability and we had the project money, we'd put them on early, and we had some really good crews.

Rusty Witwer (Mendocino, 1978; Hobart/Tahoe, 1979–1995)
Anybody who wasn't in school was rousted out of the unemployment lines and the ski lift lines about April 1. They came back to work, and we would plant anywhere from 2 to 600 acres of trees every spring. We would also slash anywhere from 4 to 600 acres of clear-cut blocks all summer. We would take on burning projects all fall. We would usually work the crew—especially in the heyday of logging on the west side of the Tahoe—from about April 1 to December 1.

I saw it in the production of our crews when we went to meaningful project work . . . because when we would go to our first fire . . . it was a party compared to what they had just gone through. Crews that were still breaking in their boots and had been on for a week were standing still when we went through 'em.

If you look at the fireline handbook—right or wrong—there is a chain production that's hard to attain, especially when you're underslinging or actually having to go back and forth because of fire runs. I'm an ops chief now on a Type 1 team, and when I put a hotshot crew there, I expect production rates to be better than what I see on other crews. When it's time to throw dirt, it's time to throw dirt, and we don't fly or drive people halfway across the United States to put in ten chains of line.

What expectations do you have for the crew by season's end?

Stan Stewart (Los Padres, 2000–2009)
I guess the idea is to do the best you have with what you have. Out of the 30 or so years, we've been pretty strong most of them. We've had a couple years that . . . they stuck us with some real crap, and we just made the best crap we could out of it. Can't

make cookies out of dog shit: all you get is dog shit cookies. If we can hire our own people, we don't normally have that problem. A couple years, back in Consent Decree times, there were times when we got shoved X amount of this and this and this, and then they weren't the top of this and this and that flavors of the month, and we weren't as good as other years. You do the best you can with what you have. I think that's the key: you want to train the heck out of 'em so they learn something if they're there for one year or ten, and they can move on and go somewhere else. You want the best product you can get out of them. They came to work. We strive to be the best, and that's all there is to it.

Kurt LaRue (Diamond Mountain, 1993–2001)

What I'm looking for mainly is a crew that's efficient, has good morale, has pride in what they're doing. I would say the two big words are efficiency and pride. They kind of run together. Willing to take on whatever job comes up. Hopefully, as they're working together, they're teaching each other and they're learning what they need to learn from the program itself. They're also learning to meet standards: you show up a certain time, you have your gear. That's part of the "efficient" end of it.

Steve Karkanen (Lolo, 1990–2011)

Probably the biggest expectation I have is that everybody comes back with all their fingers and toes, and with a good attitude. To me, that's the most important thing: everybody goes out and works hard, works safe, and has a productive summer and comes back feeling like they've accomplished something.

Brit Rosso (Arrowhead, 1996–2006)

I guess my expectation would be to build the best team, the best crew that I can, and even if we have some underachievers, some underperformers, we're going to put the emphasis on helping those people along. I obviously would like to see a crew that is synergistic. That is, there's no infighting; everyone's jelling well. In every season, if it's a long season, there are always going to be little things. I mean, we've all been there, but every year I try to help the crew develop into something that's better than the last one. Sometimes we achieve, and sometimes we don't.

Paul Musser (Flagstaff, 1990–2004)

They're never the same. Every crew is different as far as what they can or can't do. I've had some crews over the years, especially in the earlier desert years—'92 and '93—that could cut line in the desert, fast. . . . Since '94 we haven't really hit desert fires. In the years that we get quite a few timber fires, the sawyers get pretty good at falling trees, but we don't fall very many trees anymore.

Every crew has its own weaknesses and strengths, so you just go with what you get, and that changes every year. We're a little bit more stable now that we have seven career people on the crew. Even at that, you're changing the rest of it. We had four people off the crew take career positions last year. Lost another three with seasonal hiring the way it is. It takes so long to hire anyone that we seldom ever fill in and get filled up. That's one of the bigger challenges right now: keeping enough people around so you can actually go.

J. W. Allendorf (Wallowa–Whitman, 1980; Arrowhead 3, 1981)

I had set expectations in terms of production, and pretty much that was it. At the time when I was a superintendent, the way the 5100 manual[11] read was that a Type 1 crew could produce 20

---

[11] "Overview of the Forest Service Directive System," US Forest Service, last modified November 3, 1997, http://www.fs.fed.us/im/directives/dughtml/overview.html. The fire management section of the Forest Service Manual, which "codifies all policy, practice, and procedure."

chains of completed hand line in an MM fuel type in one hour. We'd go out and flag off one chain 20 times, and every one of us cut one chain, instead of with a crew. And that got people's attention as to how much work it is to cut one chain of line in one hour in an MM fuel type, where you're bucking up jimjammed lodgepole with a Pulaski. As long as the crew could meet that very basic minimum—because I knew they'd always exceed it once they saw what the minimum was—that was it.

As far as personalities and that kind of thing, I didn't try to put them in any kind of a mold. I always felt that it was healthy for the crew to have a mixture of personalities. You have to have a couple of wild men in there, and you have to have your Professor Peabodys. That's just the way it is. They're all good for each other, and it's funny how so many of your opposites end up being the best friends.

Dave Matier (Midnight Sun, 1992–1997, 1999–2007, 2009–2010)

I don't really have any set guidelines—just my personality and how I approach the job. Professional attitude is real important to me, how we work. I tell my guys straight up that they'll probably work harder doing project work than we do on fires because customer service is a big thing, especially when you detail down to California. We're on fires most of the time, but the times we do project work, it's real important to me that we put out a good product. They're paying big money to have us down here, and I want to make sure that they get their money's worth, even if it's only a short amount of time.

Shawna Legarza (San Juan, 2002–2007)

Every year, at the beginning of the year, they have to write down five personal goals, and they have to write five goals for the crew. At the end of the season, they have to write down five things that they accomplished and five things they want done for the crew next year. . . . I've saved all that over the years, and it's pretty cool.

My main thing that I stress on the crew is to be steady all year so we don't have the peaks and valleys. When they're hard-charging at the beginning of the year, and we haven't gone on a fire, they're all antsy to go. . . . We'll have our debrief that evening, and I'll bring up a scenario from the year previous, like a really hard fire assignment . . . and we'll talk about it. . . . Whether they realize it or not, that makes them relax a little bit about going out again. I tell them, "There're always going to be fires. Enjoy your time now. You can't get back yesterday, so just take your time now and enjoy where you're at."

When it comes around about August, we talk about a lot of stuff then. I bring up those goals and stuff for them and what they want to accomplish, and I really touch base with every crewmember. I'll go and talk to whatever crewmember anytime I want on the line and sit down and visit with them and kind of see how they're doing—what do they think about life, what are they going to do this wintertime . . . try to get 'em out of that boredom-burnout role so we can get back to the team goal of steady-freddy all year.

Craig Workman (Black Mountain, 1988–2005)
It changes every year. Probably after the first couple days, then I have a better idea of where it's going to be. I actually try not to come in with a perceived idea of where these guys are going to be. I let them try to show me. Then I won't be expecting things they can't provide, and they won't be disappointed in me, because expectations are our own things, and that's not good if you're expecting [something] of somebody else.

Ted Mathiesen (Arroyo Grande Flight Crew, 1990–2007)
We just want people who will give 100 percent and try to keep up and so forth, and show improvement. It is a physical job, so

we want guys and girls who can do it—and we've always been successful. Everybody doesn't have to be first. We don't all have to finish the race in a tie.

Last year we had an apprentice here who's a good example: the last run of the year, we had a 15-mile run. He was a big guy. He'd lost probably 30 pounds through the year. He was always kind of last in the pack. On the 15-mile run, he smoked four or five guys, beating them all here. He had heart. He had it in here, and he had a mental attitude, and he wasn't giving up. That's the kind of guys we look for. . . . Nobody's here by accident, and we want everyone to be successful. We go through the time and effort of recruiting and hiring and training—we certainly don't want to break them.

Charlie Caldwell (Redding, 1967–1986)

[Did you want everyone to be able to do the same things?]
No, I don't think so. I gave that a lot of thought, and I'm thinking that the personalities on each crew determined what that crew was going to be like. Every year, it was never the same. . . . People would say to me—people who were on the crew, "How would you like to pick out the best people from each year and make a crew out of them?" I said, "No. I'd still have a weak link." [They'd think:] "Crazy old man." You do. I don't care if you picked your top two people out of every year and made a crew out of them. You're still going to have a couple weak links.

What are your best practices for training?

Stan Stewart (Los Padres, 2000–2009)
We had Tom Taylor chat with us last year.[12] He was with Paul [Musser]; we were over in Sedona, and they showed up. We were just hanging out, so he actually just came out and scratched

---

[12] Tom Taylor is a survivor of the 2001 Thirtymile fire.

stuff in the dirt—kind of a basic sand table—and did the whole thing kind of one-on-one with the guys. It was cool. They got about two hours straight from him. Pretty straight stuff, made 'em think a little bit. Did the actual classroom stuff when we got home, and then we walked through it later on in the year, so it worked pretty good in the respect that you actually see it.

Greg Keller (Eldorado, 1985–1996; Modoc, 2000–2007)

The single biggest drill that I like to do with the crew is shelter deployment practice, and we have individual deployment practice as well as group deployment practice. We spend a great deal of time doing group deployment practices and having the saws work in a pattern where they start from the middle, and everything gets thrown. They come around in a circle or in a circular motion, and they come back in and start again, and then the hand tools start working in behind the saws: scraping, working from the middle to the outside, and practicing with that in the event that we ever had to go into a crew deployment.

What we've done for years and years with my line construction is that we very seldom ever scrape less than a four-foot scrape. . . . Sometimes I think we overbuild the line, but I always want to ensure that what we've done is good. On occasion, given fire behavior and fuel types, we'll do less, but on a fire in average fuels . . . we generally scrape a minimum of a four-foot line with six, eight, ten feet of saw cut. . . . Worst-case scenario, we're bringing our deployment zone with us, and a four-foot-wide line allows us a place to put the fire shelter.

Steve Karkanen (Lolo, 1990–2011)

The first time the crew comes in and sees the sand table, it's fun to watch because their eyes are rolling and they're going, "Oh God, what's this all about?" Then we give somebody an assignment. We typically have it all laid out for them, and we pull them off to the side and give them a little briefing: "You're the IC on this deal, and that's your crew out there. You go tell 'em what's going on." All of a sudden they get really serious, and they get scared. . . . It's just the perfect opportunity to practice their ability to give briefings and make decisions. It's fun, and it's safe.

One of the things we do that's really helped me out a lot over the years is getting a lot of our second- and third- and fourth-year firefighters more involved in our training. . . . I lay the sideboards, and I let them put the outlines together and do all the training and give them as much of that hands-on experience as you can get. Then they decide at that point in time whether they like it or not, because when they go on in their career they'll have to do that. Some people simply just can't do it, and they back off and say, "Well, I'm just going to be a firefighter. I don't care about the rest of this stuff."

Craig Lechleiter (Redding, 1986–2002)

We had what we called "the shadow program." Each week I selected a different person on the crew as a crew boss trainee, and that person would shadow me wherever I went. Not so much on the compound here, but as soon as we had a resource order, they were involved in all the decision-making and interactions. That got high reviews from the crew over the years. Usually in a week, depending on fire assignments, I would transition from one shadow to another. It took a lot of thought who we selected for the shadow role. You had to earn it one way or another. If you didn't show the right characteristics as we progressed through the season, you weren't going to get an opportunity. In my mind, there's no way we're going to waste our time on someone who's not worthy.

The shadow assignments were great. I had one person with me, and we'd discussed issues for hours, driving or sitting on a rock. We'd fight every battle you could think of. That was probably the most fun. I think the most productive and enjoyable time was that shadow experience for me. Give me enough time with an individual and I could cure anything.

ONCE YOU'RE THERE • 119

Successful superintendents and captains remind their employees every day, somehow, that, "You're being evaluated every day." After three months, we would conduct their first quarterly review. To be told, "You're not meeting our expectations," was an eye-opener to personnel. . . . Counseling was our middle name.

They were continually reminded they were being evaluated on how they interacted with me and the captains and each other. If you can't live up to our expectations—which are your home unit's expectations also—you don't fit in. And some people just don't fit in. Unfortunately, it was our job to determine that. There can't be any surprises. You've gotta tell them every day how they're progressing. Thank goodness for computers. We had to go into a database and write something on them, every one of them, so that we had documentation. The task books really helped.

On the fireline we would just talk, talk, talk, and analyze every aspect. Crews would walk by us and say, "My God, they're not working again. They're just talking." That was a big part of our program. Our purpose was to get through to these potential managers that something just happened, good or bad. Conducting after-action reviews was an ongoing process. No matter what it was, I would tell them the fire environment is an extension of our classroom. No matter where we are, it's an extension of our classroom.

Greg Overacker (Stanislaus, 1979–2006)

Your briefing needs to be effective. They're the most serious part of your operation, so don't brief too much. When you brief, have rules of briefing. There's not a lot of throat-clearing, farting, or anything else. There is absolute attention: you must validate that your information is being received. It's important to understand that it might be the last time you ever talk to all of your personnel. You would hate to think that anything you allowed in that briefing—distraction, playfulness, lack of understanding, lack of validation—might have contributed to or not provided them with the information to be successful in survival that day.

A kid talks in my briefing, first thing I ask is, "You have a question? Do you have something to share with us that's important?" Usually the answer is, "I don't have a question, and I don't have anything to share." If you want to stay on this crew, be quiet while we're briefing. There will be questions. There will be a test. Someday you'll be standing here. Anyway, it's a very serious time.

I guess the thing I say most about my training practices: physically practice and put up scenarios that allow your people to understand and engage what they'll be coming up to. Make it as real as possible. Sit down and take the time with your background to make a situation that you've seen; put them out with the radios; go through it on the ground. Troubleshooting a radio. Losing somebody on the line. When we run a drill, for instance, for shelters, most of the time doesn't everybody expect the supervisors to be standing right there? Sure. After we run a couple of drills, guess what happens: the captains disappear, and so do I. The drill starts, and we never show up. Does the drill go on or not? I guess you're waiting to see. Because it needs to. Make it real.

Charlie Caldwell (Redding, 1967–1986)

Post-fire critiques carry a lot more weight than people realize. There's no use coming back from a fire and you clean everything up and shine it on. You need to have that post-fire critique for everybody's sake, including your own. I've come back, post-fire critique, and people have brought up stuff, and I say, "Yeah, maybe I should've done that. You're probably right." In the heat of the battle, sometimes you don't.

I've had people come back and look at me and say, "That was bullshit, having to run from that fire and then go back and hit it again, and then run again, and then go back and hit it again, and run again, and run back into the burn." What? What was wrong with it? You certainly respect the force of nature, don't you? Look at where we went. Then I get on the chalkboard and draw a line, saying, "This is where we were at. This is when that started, right on the top of the ridge. Look where we built line, little bit at a time. (Laughs.)

[Author relates Craig Workman's story about being required by Caldwell to teach climbing.]

That's beautiful to hear, and I'll tell you why that's beautiful to hear: most of the calls I've gotten back, of all the guys who have been a member of the Redding Hotshot Crew through the years, including the foremen, saying, "That instructor training is the best thing you ever did for me" . . . I didn't do it, you did. Just made it available.

There were guys who cried. There were guys who hated it. Those guys hated me for it, but you've got to do it. You take some Indian kid off the reservation in Arizona, he couldn't do it: "I'll go home. I'll go back. I can't do it." I finally got him to sit down in my office: "Talk to me about yourself, what you do. Where do you live, what do you do?" He always had a sharp knife. I said, "Sharpen your own knives?" He goes, "Yeah." "You pretty good at it?" "Yeah," and I looked at his knife, because I'm a knife sharpener. I looked at it, and I said, "Good job. What do you think about using this for a subject for instructor training?" It worked. People were just totally amazed what he came up with. By the time he did all his research and all the instruction, it was great.

Ron Bollier (Silver City, 1993–1995; Carson, 1996–1997; Fulton, 1998–2013)

For the last three years we've been doing some intra-crew training. We all like to take a crew boss off the crew and put them in charge of the crew for a day and give them training that way. Three years ago, we decided to take it a little bit further, and we've been doing it for six years now: we build full overhead teams. There are three teams within the crew. . . . The seasonals all fill the roles as a superintendent, as a captain, squad leaders, and they take the fire from start to finish. I get an order in the middle of the night, I call that person and say, "Here's your order: this is it." They call the whole crew, get them to the station, get them here, and we'll go to the fire. They take the fire over from start to finish, to demob, to walking out, to driving it back into the station. . . . Each team gets about three or four assignments a summer.

At first it was kind of tough because the other crew members took it as a joke until they were put in the position. All of a sudden a light bulb would come on, and they would come to us and say, "Hey, they're not doing what I said." . . . I said, "Didn't you just do that to them when they were in charge?" . . . Then we'd have a big group talk and really discuss that this is what we're going to do, and this is how the program is going to work. You're going to get well-rounded, and you're going to know everybody's job on this crew.

We may get stuck on a tool somewhere, but our captains shadow. We still do the same amount of production; we still do everything the same. What it has eliminated is my second- and third-year crewmen in the back of the line going, "This is a bunch of BS. Why aren't we doing this?" . . . There's no pissing and moaning in the back of the line anymore. They all have a focus and have a vision of what our job is out there. They all have a goal, and they all know what we're trying to do, and they all know a little bit about everybody's job. It has built so much strength within the crew that it's incredible.

[Would you make a second-year person the leader of a team?]
We don't pick the teams: the crew picks the teams by themselves. We leave the room, we come back, and they say, "Okay, here's our three superintendents, and here're our sets of captains." Then those captains will pick the squad leaders they want. We

have really no input on that, and they can actually pick the first-year crewmember as a captain.

We don't come out of the gate running like that: we go as normal structure. They get to see how everything works, get their feet wet, we go to four or five fires, and maybe we'll start.

[Do you ever call time out because it's too big of an assignment?]
Oh, yeah. We watch 'em really close. When we first started doing it three years ago, it was really a slow process. They were checking it out. They were getting their feet wet. . . . There are a lot of times we get on fires—depending on what the fire behavior is—we don't do it. Or we turn them loose, and we do have instances where they can get overwhelmed and complexity starts happening where we'll shut it down, and we'll step back into the positions. We'll fix it . . . , tell them what's going on and how it should work, and then turn them loose again. . . . They're all doing well enough at it now that they do pretty well. They may do things a little premature, but that's not bad either. I don't think we've ever had them wait too long to do something.

What marks do you leave on your people?

Jim Cook (Arrowhead, 1981–1995; Boise, 1996–1998)
I think probably the first thing, and it's even been mentioned to me by the smokejumpers . . . is they never compromise escape and safety. It's one of those things: if I don't have it, I don't do it. I think the second thing is, "We before me." Another thing, particularly with my subordinate supervisors and those I was mentoring along, is quiet confidence: show me, don't tell me.

Stan Stewart (Los Padres, 2000–2009)
Good ones I don't think we have that much to do with, really. I think they're already there. We probably help just round some things and formulate a lot of that stuff for them, but a lot of that stuff's already there. Mom and Dad did a good job somewhere

along the line. I don't think we can take credit for making these wonderful human beings out of guys who were with us for a couple years. They were probably like that when they got there. They just got a little more knowledge of wildland fire, and some teamwork skills, and some other stuff they might not have had.

Steve Karkanen (Lolo, 1990–2011)

If there's any mark I try to leave on my folks, it's that they try to learn how to deal with problem people who are working for them, and—which I think can be even more important—people who are making bad decisions who are supervising them. That's really difficult for people to deal with, and then to do it in a way that's respectful. It took me quite a few years, and I made a lot of mistakes in terms of dealing with people—both at home and on fires—figuring out a way to tell them they were doing something stupid in a nice way.

Brit Rosso (Arrowhead, 1996–2006)

The marks that I leave on them are personal accountability, holding others accountable, providing direction, and taking charge when there is no one in charge: not circumventing the system but not standing by idly and watching things deteriorate.

Having the respect for your subordinate leaders and your employees, not treating them like pieces of machinery. There's a delicate balance between, "You're just a Pulaski motor," and, "This is a human being." . . . High standards, too: setting high standards but not unattainable standards.

Paul Musser (Flagstaff, 1990–2004)

I am fairly strict as far as I want things done right, and that's the only way they're done—as far as I'm concerned—is done right. I don't like half-assed stuff, and I don't like stuff left hanging. I want it finished: face it head-on, get it done.

J. W. Allendorf (Wallowa–Whitman, 1980; Arrowhead 3, 1981)

Being direct in their communications and their opinions, as well as having fun when you can have fun. Having a good sense of humor.

I've always encouraged people to enjoy their job. Enjoy your life, enjoy your job, and be honest. I think almost everybody I've worked with and tried to promote is the same way: forthright about their opinions of the agency and some of the screw-ups that we continue to make for God knows what reason.

Craig Lechleiter (Redding, 1986–2002)

I would hope the people I worked with came away with a level of professional ethics: that you can be dirty and work hard, but you're still a professional. My biggest theme was "remember who you are." I got that from Charlie. I'll always give him credit for that: remember who you are. Did he mention that? . . . When I was here in '75, that's where I first heard it. Remember who you are, whether you're going out to get drunk in Redding or you're going to mop up 300 feet of line. Remember who you represent. I carried that all the way through my life.

Charlie Caldwell (Redding, 1967–1986)

Through the years, there were a lot of calls back from fire control officers and district rangers saying, "What did you do to my guy?" [I said] "I didn't really do anything, just kinda opened the door, and what they're doing is kind of a self-motivation thing." They're going, "Well, okay, but I'll tell you what, he just got a QSI [quality step increase], and he volunteers for everything. He's running the crew, and he's got everybody out doing exercises."

Ron Bollier (Silver City, 1993–1995; Carson, 1996–1997; Fulton, 1998–2013)

What I would like them to have learned when they leave me is how to survive in the environment, whether it be in the fire environment or in the agency itself. Administration-wise, administration duties: how it works and what their job is. They know their job, learn their job, and to be able to teach their job to somebody else. And be successful wherever they go.

Shawna Legarza (San Juan, 2002–2007)

I hope that when this crew keeps continuing on, five years from now, down the road, that we can continue with the reputation we have whether I'm here or not: just working hard and being social to everybody—on the team mode and not being all stuck up or whatever. Talking to the ops people and talking to the safety people. Talking to the safety guy when he comes down the line, and stuff like that. That's what I hope for.

Craig Workman (Black Mountain, 1988–2005)

I would hope that they go off with a very strong feeling of self-worth and effectiveness, and that they honestly believe that whatever they're doing at the moment is the most important thing to be done. They could be washing dishes: at that moment; it's the most important thing. Then the next step that they go on to, that's the next important thing. I would hope that they live with that throughout their career.

Greg Overacker (Stanislaus, 1979–2006)

It's hard to tell. So far I've had a lot of success. I'm very concerned when a young man or woman leaves my organization . . . that not only do they take with them who we are and what we're about—hard work, family values, all of that stuff . . . not only that, but that they not rub it in anybody's face; they use those skills to help that new organization that they're with, become part of that organization. Leave our T-shirts and hats in the drawer. When you're gone, you're done. If your only claim to fame is our hat, it's not yourself, you've got a problem.

I would like our people to leave a mark of excellence. Everybody will tell you that that's what we all hope for. I think a quality person who is accepted based on their performance and liked for their friendliness and openness is what's important to me. They will bring me opportunities again for the rest of my people tomorrow. They are the ones who open my doors. If I send somebody someplace that's just a screwup, they won't be back, and, unfortunately, it'll impact a lot of people.

Mark Linane (Los Prietos/Los Padres, 1973–2001)
I would hope that they had a good experience, that they got the basics, the fundamentals down. For a firefighter, they could throw dirt. That's one of those batting-practice skills, the fundamentals, that our folks could always throw dirt. That was a key function: they could become very dirty and very skilled.

Sawyers were good sawyers, safe sawyers, aggressive sawyers. Work harder, not smarter. If you only needed to trench one yucca instead of the whole hillside, you were smart enough to figure that out. Good recognition of changing fire behavior, at least the signals that were coming up.

Good safety, but more safety from the standpoint of there are consequences for doing stupid things. It's gonna cost you time off; it's gonna cost you pain; it's gonna cost me paperwork. Don't get hurt—there's a consequence, and you're probably going to suffer more than I will, so pay attention to safety.

I've dealt with explosives, so I was a stickler for procedure on real hazardous things, because there are no old, bold blasters—there are only old, smart, follow-by-the-book, follow-by-the-numbers blasters. We were probably the only hotshot crew in the nation that did fireline explosives, so everybody was really pretty safety conscious from the standpoint of when you're doing something really hazardous, there's a risk you can take, but you follow by the book. Follow by the numbers on procedural kinds of things; otherwise, you're going to go tits up.

What are the toughest things to teach?

Jim Cook (Arrowhead, 1981–1995; Boise, 1996–1998)

The toughest thing to get people to do and to bring along and to mentor is situational awareness: the ability to think like fire, and to instill the important indicators that are out there. We joked about "Look Up, Look Down, Look Around," but that was literally a group of superintendents, well-tanked at one o'clock in the morning, who penciled that out on a piece of paper because they were really tired of people coming back from S-390 ["Introduction to Fire Behavior Calculations" course] going, "So, what's important?" . . . Literally, I have not used a nomogram since I took S-390, and that was in 1980. Why would I? That has nothing to do with my job. I don't have time to do nomograms. It's a qualitative skill—being aware, distilling the important pieces of information, and keeping them in your frame of consciousness.

Supervisory: the "power paradox." I know because it took me a long time to learn that you gain power by giving it away. It goes along with that value of respect. You don't get respect from people until you give it. You treat people like adults, they're going to respond like adults. You treat them like kids, they're going to act like kids. That's an insecure leadership, new leader thing that everyone has to get over, and that's a tough thing to bring people through. The faster you can bring them through that and show them the benefit of going to the next step, the better. It's tough because when you first get into that role you want everything done your way, and you want it done right because you don't want to look like a knucklehead.

Dan Fiorito (Union, 1996–2006)

The toughest thing is to get people to think about what they are doing. "Situational awareness" is the new buzzword. It is the same thing that we have always tried to do. The first fire order I ever learned was, "Know what your fire is doing at all times—observe personally and use scouts." If you can see the big picture and get other people to see the big picture, you will be way ahead in the game. It doesn't matter if you're on a two-person initial attack lightning fire or if you're going down to a Biscuit fire, which was 500,000 acres. You have got to try to get as much information as you can about what is going on around you, and what the plan is.

Probably the biggest thing that I have to get people to understand is to not get tunnel vision and just get into their own workspace. You can hire the greatest, most in-shape people, and they will dig line and go for days and not complain, but if they are not thinking about what the next step is and somebody has to be there to tell them, "OK, you did A, now do B"—I mean, it's not rocket science.

Ted Mathiesen (Arroyo Grande Flight Crew, 1990–2007)

Being humble is probably the toughest. . . . Be humble, especially when you're working around other crews. Don't get the holier-than-thou attitude, that kind of thing. There are good crews, there are bad crews, there are in-between crews. We're all there trying to do the same job, but there are some that are going to be better. When we go through a piece of line, say, on initial attack, that's our signature on the ground. The crews coming behind us, they're going to see it. That's where the talking is.

When we assembled this crew and went to the larger crew in 2001, everyone was competing: all these new MEL [Most Efficient Level] crews were going on and so forth. I was fortunate enough to be able to get people from all over the state and even out of region. I assembled people who all brought a little something, a little bit different perspective to the table. I think it made our crew that much better, instead of the same old, we're-gonna-get-all-LP-people. It really helped.

I don't care whose idea it is: it doesn't matter from what crew it comes. If we can use it to make our program better, we're going to do it. I've seen a lot of supervisors who, I've even worked for [supervisors] who are very closed-minded, and this-is-the-way-we-do-it-here, blah, blah, blah. They really punish themselves, hurt themselves, hurt their program by doing that. It's a great big world out there.

Greg Keller (Eldorado, 1985–1996; Modoc, 2000–2007)

I think you have to lead by example. If you lead by example, people will absorb and pick that up, and they'll be inspired to follow or work hard for you. I think you have to instill in them the pride of what "hotshots" means, and if they can buy off on that, they will go out and work beyond levels they thought they were capable of.

Most people who come to work for us have never been tested. They've never worked in the yard, they've never worked for private industry where they've . . . collapsed, fallen down, where they've worked to the point of exhaustion, to the point where they've thrown up and become physically sick. Few jobs will push a person to that level, to find their limits. What we want to do is find that person's limit and pull back just a fraction, . . . so they don't go over the edge, so they don't go down. But people find out about themselves, and what they can and can't do.

Number one and foremost is teaching people what they don't know. What I mean by that is they don't know what they don't know. The way to find that out is simply by experience, by being on the fireline and being in pressure situations; and being able to recognize . . . and interpret fire weather, fuels, and topography and how they're going to interact with each other is hard to teach.

I've also found that firefighters, by and large, are very aware, very intent on their surroundings when the fire is up and moving.

They will pay attention; orders will flow very smoothly and crisply. They want to know where their safety zones and their escape routes are, and if you haven't given them in a matter of minutes they'll ask for them again. . . . My big concern about teaching them things is: when the fire's not up and big, they tend to let their guard down.

On a fire just last summer we hiked up over a ridgetop, and the fire was located in a bowl below us. The hair immediately stood up—what hair I have left—on my head and my neck, and I looked at my foreman, and I said, "I don't like this," and he goes, "Boy, I don't either." Escape routes didn't look good, safety zones looked even less good, but not one person on the crew was concerned because the fire wasn't doing anything. . . . I stopped, and I said, "Well, let's go down in the hole," and everybody just went, "Yep, yep, yep, ready to go," and I said, "Is anybody concerned about this today?" Not one person was concerned, so we sat down and had a lesson, right on the spot there. I said, "Folks, this is the most dangerous fire we've been on all year." They all looked around and were puzzled at that, because it wasn't showing anything yet.

Kurt LaRue (Diamond Mountain, 1993–2001)
When you first get the younger ones, getting them through the first end of it—the physical end of it—to get them to see what they're actually capable of. If you hire people who don't have some form of sports background or who grew up working on a ranch or that type of work ethic, there are a lot of them who go up that hill a couple times and then they quit. You know from looking at them and talking to them that if they'd stick with it, they could make it; they quit because of mental weakness. They don't quit because they physically couldn't; they don't believe they can—the job's too much for them. That's one of the things you try and work into them or instill into them. One of the hardest things to get into some of them is: you're capable of a lot more than you think you are.

One of the other things it's hard to get instilled into them: the transition from being one of the crewmen to being one of the supervisors—from "I'm one of the buddies" to "Now I'm one of the bosses." That's a hard transition to help a kid through. I noticed our success rate was much better where we could, if the individual had been a crewman in past times, bring them on that spring from day one as a squad leader coming in. It was really hard for kids to promote in mid-season.

Art Torrez (Vista Grande, 1994–2004)

The fire behavior portion of it—that just comes with time and experience: just let them know that they need to be patient, that you don't need to jump the gun on any one decision; take the time and analyze before you engage. I think that's the biggest thing, because when you're at that younger age, you've got that adrenaline rush to where you want to be aggressive. There's nothing wrong with being aggressive, but you need to make sure that the right decision is made.

We're from Southern California, and we have a diverse work-force: all the different cultures, folks from the inner city. I guess [it's] being patient with the different work ethics and being able to take the time to show them the right way to accomplish the task at hand.

Paul Musser (Flagstaff, 1990–2004)

Anymore, attitude has become so important, probably more important than skills. We don't dig as much line as we used to. We don't put in the long hose lays that we used to. We do more stuff on roads. There's more buggy time. There's more sitting-around time, more in-camp time. For years, hotshot crews [believed] that it didn't really matter what happened anyplace else: what happened when you cut line was what mattered. That's one thing that's swapped over the years: it really doesn't matter if you can cut line. It matters if you can do all the other things.

I think that one of the harder things to teach them is that it's not just the physical part of the job. . . . You have to learn to live with a group of people for six months in very tight quarters. . . . That's the hardest thing: to bring them together and get them to work as a group.

The line location, the fire behavior stuff, it takes more time. Some of the sawing skills. The one thing I've seen over the years is that people don't have the experience with small engines like they did years ago. When I was a kid growing up, you had to be able to work on motors to keep things running. You didn't take them to shops. . . . We've really lost the skills of being able to work on small motors, so those are things that you have to teach. In the early '90s we were carrying extra cylinders and things like that with us, and we rebuilt saws while we were out on the road. Anymore, we don't mess with it. It goes to the shop, and the shop fixes it.

Barry Callenberger (Palomar, 1979–1982; Eldorado, 1982–1988)

I think the hardest thing is getting everybody to realize that you're not an independent person. You have independent thoughts, but you have to work together as a team. . . . Bringing the crew together into a cohesive group or organization is probably the hardest thing to do. I always encouraged the crew to work as a unit from the squad boss down, and then they knew who they worked for. Teamwork is probably key, and that's when you either knew you had a good crew or didn't have a good crew. If they didn't get along together and work together, the crew was going to be tough that year.

Greg Vergari (Union, 1980–1987)

I have to say this in the right context. It's putting down the tool and supervising, not getting bogged down in tactics to the point your crew is not being watched over. Now that I've said that, I think we have gone overboard. I see superintendents sitting on their butts in a pickup across the canyon from their crews. I can understand that at times you need that kind of big picture and no one else is doing this. What I'm talking about is almost an SOP for some supes and, you know, I think that's bullshit. Your job is with the crew, being a leader, not some inflated sack that is too good to be in the bush with the kids. A leader is one who shares his troops' hardships.

Dave Matier (Midnight Sun, 1992–1997, 1999–2007, 2009–2010)

A lot of them get attitudes from whatever they've been doing before. I take this job seriously, and I know that a lot of people consider me a hard-ass because I do things that I just think are the right thing to do: not wearing hats in buildings, looking professional, keeping your shirts tucked in. As far as their personal appearance, that's their deal, and I don't have any problem with that, but the way we look, the way we act in the public view—my dad was in the military, and so I guess some of that probably came from that. Eighteen years I was living on military bases, so I didn't need to join up to find out what it was all about.

Dennis Baldridge (Laguna, 1990–2009)

The tough part is that a young supervisor usually has a lot more faith and trust that they're going to do exactly what he thinks they're going to do. You have go out and tell them to do this, and you go back and check every once in a while that they can do it. . . . If you just tell them once and then walk away, it doesn't always get done, because they're young too.

Usually, the new supervisor, you have to give them the room to make some mistakes, to try it because that's the way they're going to learn. Try not to keep saying, "I told you so." They forget what it was like when they were a crewman. It's not that they're trying to get away with stuff, but they're not focused from the same direction that the supervisor is on getting things done.

Lance Honda (Redmond, 1992–1997; Prineville, 1997–2009)

I taught language arts. Language arts is communication, and that's a skill. Whether it's reading, writing, or speaking, that's where the success is in terms of relationships, whether it's professional or personal. . . . If you're able to write who you are, what you want, where you want to go, how you feel, you're going to be a success. . . . Those are life skills that are important. In a leader or supervisor, they're doubly important.

Charlie Caldwell (Redding, 1967–1986)

Respect goes a long way. There are people who don't respect fire, and I think that will affect your supervision.

Stuff that I want to keep instilling in the kids is the basics: the 10 Standards, the 13 Situations.[13] Be alert; pay attention to what's going on around you. There're some newer things that have helped us teach those: the LCES and Look Up/Look Down, situational awareness. We've put terms to things we used to talk about differently. I just want them to know the basics and pay attention, because there's so much legislation that's going on now that's telling us how to do our job that really doesn't need to be there.

Ron Bollier (Silver City, 1993–1995; Carson, 1996–1997; Fulton, 1998–2013)

How the system works. Teaching them that they can be the best fireman in the world but if they don't have the system worked

---

[13] The 18 Watch Out Situations began in the 1960s as "The 13 Situations That Shout Watch Out"; five more were added in 1987. Jennifer A. Ziegler, "13 Situations That Shout Watch Out," *Wildfire Today*, February 26, 2009, https://wildfiretoday.com/2009/2/26/13-situations-that-shout-watch-out/.

out and the administration end of how it works—all the ins and outs—they're going to struggle and fight and not be as desirable in the long run because they fight the system. They need to learn how to use the system, to use it to [their] advantage.

Shawna Legarza (San Juan, 2002–2007)

If you're a squad boss, make sure that you let your crewmembers know that you care about them. I don't think that happens enough. I think that in our job we're breaking into the human factors, touchy-feely stuff, but a lot of people have a hard time with that. They're not willing to engage one another.

I have my overhead do stuff that they don't even realize they're doing, accomplishing a [goal] through the human factor thing, and they don't even know it. For an example, a couple years ago, I had one of my assistants and one of my squadies—they didn't fight, but they didn't get along. They didn't go out of their way to say, "Hey, how is your day going?" I had an issue with that because the assistant, the foreman, is supposed to supervise the squadie.

We had an assignment to go to Washington on a fire, and I told my assistant, "You and one squadie and one senior firefighter are gonna drive together." . . . I said, "Before you get to Washington, I want to know where this person was born, where they lived, what's their favorite food, blah, blah, blah." I made my assistant talk to the person he had a problem with and find out all this stuff, and by the time they got to Washington they were buddy-buddy. . . . Then they were really good friends, and they got along, and the flow of the crew went really good. It was just that one little thing—I could see that there was tension. There wasn't, like, a bad tension, and I don't know if anybody realized it or not on the crew, but I could see it.

Bob Wright (Sacramento, 1990–2002)

It seems to me that they're not aggressive enough anymore. You can be aggressive and still be safe. Flow charts, go-no-go charts, all that crap. Seems like it gets to a certain point where it's, "Well, we're done. We can't do anything."

You always have three plans, no matter what you're doing. Especially when you're doing IA, you always have a first plan of attack, your second, your third. If the first one doesn't work, you go to the second one. You can transition without thinking about it too much. Same with the third. After the third, then you have to do some head-scratching. Even if it's a big fire, three different things, even on my section of line, what I'd do, unless the overhead says something different. Lot of times, these overhead teams, after first plan, they're done. They have to go to a planning session, figure it out another two or three shifts before they get their shit together.

Craig Workman (Black Mountain, 1988–2005)
My whole feeling for young supervisors is to keep it simple, and to keep focus, and to narrow down. Don't spread out. . . . With hotshot crews, we have the idea that we need to do a lot of things at once. Once you get a crew that's established and you have a good, strong core of people, you can spread out and do a lot of different things. But before you do that, you need to narrow it down and keep it very basic and simple. I think you'll be able to keep out of trouble much easier that way.

Mark Linane (Los Prietos/Los Padres, 1973–2001)
For fire behavior, probably the weather. Keeping their situational awareness, recognizing the weather changes. Frontal systems—those small, imperceptible changes can change the whole dynamics of that situation in a heartbeat. The little drop in humidity, little increase in wind, a drought year—recognizing those little tiny things that can change and how much it can impact your planned operation.

Probably the other thing that's tough to teach—and it takes time and adaptability and flexibility—is learning when you go by the book for line construction and when you can cut it down, when you have to increase it, and the hows and whys. It takes some time and experience to know when you can string line in and when you have to put ten-blade line in and it'll hold, or when you could have a twelve-lane freeway and it still doesn't matter. Again, that's an experience-based thing. Big tree falling—not everybody can do it. It's one of those jobs where not everybody's a C-faller, not everybody's a B-faller. Some folks have it, some folks don't.

Greg Overacker (Stanislaus, 1979–2006)

Supervision—they need to learn how to separate it from leadership and understand there's a big difference between them. . . . You need to also teach them that supervision is a privilege—bang, straight off the bat.

What to teach them about fire? Don't be in a hurry. . . . When you first run to the beach, when you're young and you've never seen the ocean living in Sonora, California, [and] the only thing you've ever seen is a stock feeding pond, [and] now you find yourself at the Pacific Ocean, and as the water backs off the beach, you chase it out. Next thing you know, you're standing up to your knees in kelp and seaweed, and your new shoes are ruined. Well, you just dry out the shoes, but in fire, if you run up that close, and you don't know what's going to happen, it'll burn your legs off up to your knees and probably kill you. We don't have a lot of room for error.

I think one of the things that scares me in fire is that we engage fire with a tactic that works—that may not be worst-case scenario that day, for that activity, and that tactic would not work under a more extreme condition—but now that you've seen that tactic work, you need to realize that if the fire was a little more extreme, the tactic would be no good. You would've failed, probably put you in harm's way. You need to teach people to be really, really aware that they don't build a false tactic. Remember how fragile we are. Remember [that] what you're doing in extreme conditions may not happen with the rest of your people unless you take control of them. If you're gonna push the envelope, for whatever reason, you'd better be prepared for the consequences of that envelope and know how to get out.

Never compromise your safety [by] remaining engaged in a failing tactic. It happens all the time: too late, not enough horsepower, whatever, but don't ever compromise their safety. A lot of people think that because you have a failed tactic you may have put your people in harm's way. It's not true: they're two separate situations. Don't ever put your people in harm's way. Set up a worst-case scenario, a realistic worst-case scenario. You're not going to have a tornado that day, so don't think about tornadoes, but you do have to think about how hot will it get, what's the most extreme wind direction I could get, what would it do if it got into that fuel? Paint the picture. Will my tactic be successful? Maybe, maybe not, but at any time, will my people be in harm's way? If the answer is yes, questionable, change the tactic. Get some room, back up.

Situational awareness, how do I make you understand that? Well, not everybody's been fighting fire, but a lot of people have children. You don't leave your young daughter or young son alone and let them wander around the house and put their fingers in the plugs. You don't let them fall down the stairs, and you don't leave the bleach under the sink. You sanitize their environment to ensure that still they can learn, but that they'll survive. You also sanitize it so you don't have to be with them 24-7; you can actually lay down and not worry. They even make little machines that listen to them in the other room.

Eventually take your daughter by her hand—she's three years old, or your son—and you take them outside. You never take your hand off them because there's a dog out there, there's a stranger out there, there's a car out there. . . . You haven't even taught them anything; they don't have any intel. Now you give them knowledge. They're still in harm's way because they can't outrun the dog . . . , and they can't get away from the stranger, and if they chase their ball into the street, they're dead.

They not only need to recognize the situation but also the need to be able to respond to it appropriately. In some cases, since you can't always control the dog, the answer is to go back in the house. When you go to the street to cross the crosswalk, you don't just walk out in the crosswalk—you wait until the light turns green. Not only does the light turn green, you look both ways to ensure that everybody is slowing down. Then, to really prove to your mother and father that you're capable, you also take your little sister down there and show her how to do it, too.

That's the same environment we're dropping our firefighters in. How can you go fight fire with a young firefighter? You can't just not let 'em fight fire. They can't know everything. When you get them up to a reasonable level, you put them with their older brother or their older sister. You won't be there with them. Now you're entrusting your youngest one to your oldest one, and he or she is told, "You will take care of your sister or brother. You will bring her home tonight—happy, in one piece, okay? No dogs, nobody steals her, no cars run over her or him." Why can't they comprehend the same thing in fire? What makes you think that you can say, "Okay, Billy, be-careful-out-there-there's-a-dog-stay-out-of-the-street-and-watch-out-for-strangers-have-fun." They'd be lucky if they survived it.

How do you monitor your crew for fatigue through long shifts and a long season?

Bob Bennett (Horseshoe Meadow, 1989–2006)
A lot of it's the attitude. Are they in good moods, bad moods? . . . You've got your normal kidding that goes on in the crew, but when some of it gets to be more destructive, and you can see people getting more sensitive at times, you see them bickering

more, the way they use their tools. . . . You can even look in their eyes, and you can tell at times.

Sometimes as a superintendent, or even the captains, we tend to be mission-oriented at times. You have to listen to the squad leaders or even listen to the guys sometimes. They'll tell you. They'll bring up, "You know, we're not feeling good." . . . You watch 'em. You can tell when they're fresh, and you can see their performance starting to slip. . . . Maybe you'll see them not eating as much. Injuries, small injuries: they might get sprains or something like that. Sometimes they'll want to keep going, and sometimes you have to be the boss: "No, you aren't going to do this today. You'll sit in the crew truck," or, "You'll sharpen tools," or, "You're going to the hospital."

Greg Keller (Eldorado, 1985–1996; Modoc, 2000–2007)

I've come from the old school. Sometimes the kids, they say they're tired, and I think they think they're tired. I said, "Folks, you haven't even gotten to the limits yet," so I'm struggling a little bit with that, as being an old-timer and a dinosaur. . . . The first couple days of a fire, you'd work literally around the clock, sleep in the dirt, get up, and go at it again. Today, when someone tells me they're tired, I struggle with that just a little bit, but, again, it's all relative. They've never worked those kinds of shifts, so now a 14-day assignment is a long assignment, and to actually go out and work for 12, 13, 14 hours appears to them to be long. I do keep an eye on it, but I also think they have more to give. They just don't quite know it yet. They haven't been pushed to the limit.

I do watch their behaviors. I watch their faces. I watch how they interact. I watch how a person will snap at someone or not snap at someone. That's the hard part: having 19 people, to understand which person is signifying what thing about them, and when they've had enough or when they're physically tired. One person may become animated and agitated where another person could be withdrawn, and you don't know: is he just sleeping or is he withdrawn?

It takes a while to know the crew, and that's what I've found in this second career: that I have to spend much more time watching, observing, listening than I did in the past. In the past, they might come right out and tell me they've had enough. The crew now, I think they're a little more detached because they see this old person with gray hair and wrinkles and stuff, and they don't feel like they can sit down and chat with me as they once did maybe 15 or 20 years ago.

Kurt LaRue (Diamond Mountain, 1993–2001)

I think one of the things that helps you through fatigue is a set routine. I realize the books say you want to remain flexible and vary for every contingency, and to a point all of that is good. Now we don't go out for very long at all: 14 days and you're back. As I was saying earlier, we didn't have as many shifts per fire back then. But in '94 we were out 53 days. I can go back to some earlier ones where we were out comparable to that. It didn't happen a lot, but it happens sometimes.

One of the things that I worked on was trying to get rid of what I called "preventable conflicts" on the crew. Some crews you see walking in from line shift, and 200 yards from the truck at the end of the day [you hear], "Are we going to do the tools here, or are we going to go into camp and eat first?" These kinds of discussions going on are what I call preventable conflict because as soon as the question comes up, some are going to want to go eat, some are going to do tools. Somebody's going to be a loser no matter what you pick to do. . . . We tried to keep the routine down to the same every day: you hit the trucks, tools, gas, and water. Everything's ready for tomorrow's shift, then we drive in and eat and release. It's the same every time, and I think knowing what's happening next and what is expected helps manage fatigue.

How do you tell when your crew is tired? You start to notice the little things. The ding rate starts to go up: not the really big injuries, but little "head not in the game" injuries. A couple years ago, we reached a point where I finally just called it a season. We were working on the Big Bar fire, and I started noticing a string of just little stupid things happening. A guy sits down to eat his lunch, and when he goes to get up, he cuts his hand on his bar. Pushes himself up [on it], not enough for stitches or anything. That's just one example. There were a myriad of small things that were starting to happen, and they just come from people getting tired. You also ask them: "How's everybody doing?" Hopefully, they answer. (Laughs)

There's the sundial method for telling if they're tired on the shift you're on. . . . You're lined out, and you're walking along, and the supe runs into another supe. You're making a plan somewhere, and the kids all sit down or they all covey up under a tree somewhere while the overhead's making a plan. Or maybe you're just going to stage while you see what the fire's going to do for an hour or two before you cut line. If your crew all sits down underneath the tree in the shade and the shade moves, and they keep getting up and moving over to stay in it, they're fine. They're just sleeping. If they just lay there and it's a 109 and the shade moves and they stay laying on their backs in the sun with their tongues out and the flies crawling all over them and they don't move, they're probably really tired. They probably need a break. (Laughing.)

J. W. Allendorf (Wallowa–Whitman, 1980; Arrowhead 3, 1981)
I based it on general morale and productivity. If I saw either falling, I knew I needed to start taking some measures. Some people don't handle stress as well in the long term, and long, extended shifts or even just time away from home—and sometimes more so for married folks—can start to sour their attitude. You know how that is: like the old saw about one bad apple in the barrel,

it can spread through a crew. If I saw that, immediately I would take people like that aside and go, "Hey, here's what's happening: it ain't gonna fly. We've got a week to go. Can you hang, or do you need to go?"

I'd talk to people. I knew who was honest. They always wanted to appear "up," so I knew who I could ask, "Hey, what kind of shape are folks really in?" If I saw people sitting around licking their wounds and sticking stuff on their blisters . . . more than normal, I knew it was time to do something.

Fred Schoeffler (Payson, 1981–2007)

I believe that the 14-day fire assignments are a God-send. At least we know we'll be moving on to another fire or home within two weeks. I'm thankful that we no longer have the 30-day and 21-day assignments unless we choose to do so.

In 1987, when Northern California was all on fire, we worked well over 1,000 hours of overtime—1,200, if I remember correctly, mostly on the dreaded Klamath National Forest—and we were toast. These were the days of the 30-day dispatches. Many folks got really sick with bronchitis, pneumonia, mutant cruds, and worse. We had folks sick all through the winter. . . . I knew of other firefighters who actually broke ribs from intense coughing.

After that season, Marty Rose and I decided that those kinds of hours weren't worth it anymore. We started taking an extra day or so between assignments and progressively adding days off as the season progressed, even up to four or five days, depending on the assignments. We figured that even a few hundred less hours of overtime was worth it—both tax-wise and fatigue-wise—and it was worth it over the following years. We also found that rarely did anyone complain about taking extra days off between fire assignments. Moreover, I felt we were able to offer IMTs [incident management teams] an IHC that was well-rested in order to give them our usual 110 percent effort. We also found that we had fewer injuries and illnesses.

A major ingredient related to fatigue management that is not considered enough is the impact of carbon monoxide poisoning. I believe that this adversely affects more firefighters and over-head than many want to admit, especially in certain fire regions with heavy fuels, prone to heavy inversions, like Northern California. And then there's the seemingly incessant habit of placing incident command posts, fire camps, and helibases in meadows and other low-lying areas rife with inversions and carbon mon-oxide. I have refused to stay in several fire camps because of the known CO poisoning and potential.

Fire seasons are marathon events, and we usually only have a month or so to prepare for them. Make the most of the time you have to prepare because it is pretty short, and utilize the time between fire assignments to run, bike, or hike in order to con-tinue to improve or maintain your fitness levels and, of course, to purge those lungs.

Ken Jordan (Sierra, 1998–2014)

That's a proactive thing that we drill into their heads from day one, preseason letter: you will be tired toward the end of the sea-son. You will be away from your family; it's going to affect you emotionally. You're going to have problems at home, and we just have to deal with that. You get everything out of the way during the winter, and that's one of the blessings that we have as a tem-porary workforce. You get everything taken care of; you spend time with your family. You do everything you can, non-fire, but expect to be consistent all the way through fire season.

I've had people come to me: "Ken, Ken, the morale of the crew is at its all-time low." That's usually, like, four people: the "thermometer people," I call them. I said, "Oh, it is?" "Yes. You have to do something about it." I said, "Okay, tell those guys to bring up their morale or they're never coming back to this crew." (Laughs.) They go, "What?" "It's their job, I told them at the beginning. It's their job to keep their morale up, and if their morale is not good right now and they don't bring it back up, then they're not coming back, because we can't have that." "Okay, but—" I said, "Hey, it's in your hands now. You've got a week. No whining, get back to work." (Laughs.)

We make sure, mentally, they're ready. We do that a lot on Family Day, too, and we involve the families: "Expect your guy, or your husband, or your wife, or your significant other to be gone all fire season. Just expect that. If you're not good with that, we need to get somebody else." I send that out in the preseason letter: "If this doesn't fit into your lifestyle, then it's time to go," and they sign it, and they send it back to me, and if I ever had to, I'd wave it in front of their face.

Ron Regan (Del Rosa, 1977–1997)

That was a strain. It was tough on everyone. I said, "Okay, when this thing is over with, we're going to have a good time, and we'll do something different." We spent quite a bit of time on the Marble Cone fire, and when we came back, we swung off to the beach and let the crew hit the water for a while and took lunch there. It's things like that: they know throughout the summer that stuff like that's going to happen on our crew, and that's to keep their morale and the spirit going.

Shawna Legarza (San Juan, 2002–2007)

As a supervisor, I can realize that sometimes I'll get irritated easily, and then I'll know that it's a long shift or late in the year. Then I have to just be careful and relax and make sure that I'm not being too critical of the guys.

I love those shifts, man. I used to love those in the old days, and I really like to talk about them. I still talk about them with the guys—that the harder, the better. The best part of the season's from August on, and I challenge my guys. I go, "Come on . . . are you gonna be a hotshot or not? Buck up. How hard is that? I've been doing this for how many years? You guys can hack it out for two days." I kind of joke with them a little bit on that, but I challenge them to enjoy the harder shifts.

That's not easy with everybody, because some people don't like that. . . . We call it "PMA": positive mental attitude. Whenever we hear any kind of negative jokes or conversations going on, we always go, "PMA, PMA," and that kind of clicks that person out of that. But, yeah, I like the long shifts. We don't get 'em enough anymore.

This last year is a good example: September this last year, when we went back to California, we were driving for three days to get there. I think if you spend too much time with somebody, you'll kind of get on each other's nerves a little bit. I know that, so I'll try to rotate the buggies, just for the drive. I'll make them all sit with somebody else: "You're going in there, and you're going in there," and then they're watching different videos, watching different DVDs, and playing card games. We'll do that for one day: mix it up. One day my saw boss will ride with me, or one of the rookies will ride with me, or whatever.

Usually in July . . . we'll take four days off. . . . They all look forward to that. . . . They'll have a group get-together. . . , and I don't go to it. I tell them that they can't talk to any of their buddies in fire. They can't listen to their cell phone; they can't watch the news, none of that. They cannot think about fire: that's their goal. . . . That helps, for sure.

Doing details in the middle of the summer has helped also. A couple people rotated through this last year doing helitack. Some of the guys who have been with me since '02, this last year is when they did big rotations of details so that they didn't get burned out.

Then, just keeping every day that we work still fun. . . . On a fire in Wyoming this year, I took the chainsaw and I cut some pondos down. . . . They couldn't watch: I and the saw boss cut them down for my "C." . . . I nailed these two trees, and the next day the whole crew comes back out, checking it out. . . . It's a big thing for them to come check out the stump that the supe cut down. To them it's like, "Wow, we didn't know you could run a chainsaw."

You have to make it fun, because the work can be so hard and so mundane. . . . Make sure they get stuff done professionally, but balance it out.

Dave Matier (Midnight Sun, 1992–1997, 1999–2007, 2009–2010)

The end of September, it's like the alarm bell goes off: time to go home and be a couch potato. Time to keep them focused on what you're doing, but not drive them into the ground, either. . . . When you're doing project work, give them ten minutes longer for lunch and stuff like that, just to break it up. You have sawyers on fires; during project work, everyone runs a saw. Everyone stacks sticks; everyone gets that experience. Plus, the same guys aren't running the saw, and they get a break. Everybody gets a little more comfortable doing other things.

Bob Wright (Sacramento, 1990–2002)

In the old days, we'd run 30, 60 days out on the line, running from fire to fire, with no days off. Even when we were without any fires, we'd run 30 days without a day off. I had a lot of girl-friends and wives who used to call me up, cuss me. I had one pull a knife on me one night because she was so mad her boyfriend wouldn't get to go home. (Laughs.)

You're like a father, or a mother, so just mother 'em. They may not like it. [You tell them,] "You're staying in today because you don't feel too good." They argue with you, but after a while they realize that you're trying to take care of them. If you do that, you're going to get more back from them. . . . They know if you're BS'ing them. If you really care about 'em, it'll come back tenfold for you. Guarantee it. Every time.

How do you ensure your own decision-making is still good when you are tired?

Greg Vergari (Union, 1980–1987)

Some type of fatigue management is needed. We had none when I was running a crew except when someone went nuts over your time sheet. Something needed to be done, but I'm not sure we're where we need to be now. I think it is better than nothing, though. My decision-making came by taking five and regrouping when the assignment changed. I would reread the rules of engagement over and over, again and again, asking, "Were my mitigations solid enough to ensure no one was going to get hurt?"

Dave Matier (Midnight Sun, 1992–1997, 1999–2007, 2009–2010)

I don't party. On my R&R, I don't go out and do whatever. I do what I need to do, and at fire camps I don't stay up and chat. I eat, I go to bed. Eat, work, and sleep: that's what I do during the season. I don't do things that are going to make it hard for me to function, like liquor. But that's just me. I try and stay in shape year-round so that at the end of the year when the grind starts to wear on you, you're still able to go at it and keep a clear head. I take that seriously because [of the] 19 people I'm responsible for, and I want everybody to come home. I don't want to have to call somebody's parents.

Mark Linane (Los Prietos/Los Padres, 1973–2001)

Myself or one of my captains went back to the trucks to catch a nap so that during prime time in the afternoon one of us would be sharp. Situational awareness changes, so that's how we dealt with that. Management used to hammer us for being fatigued and tired, and then I'd go into fire camp and watch the overhead team, who were supposedly rested and fresh, especially on those run-and-gun fires in '88. There was no relief for them and no sleep, and they were making really stupid decisions. I was recognizing what lack of sleep was doing to their operations.

When the crew is beginning to wind down on night shift—four in the morning on a heavy line cut—production's down, the troops are just shot. I'm shot. We'd pull everybody back in the black, into a safety zone, and sleep for a couple hours; then get up just before daylight, have a bite to eat, and cut till we either got relieved or they said get out of there. Another thing we did when we were fatigued to make things work better: we'd camp out drivers and let them sleep. It's kind of against the rules, but we had safe, alert drivers. It's Skunk Works[14], but it works.

There are a lot of old tricks we used to have before we had all the rules. You were expected to use some common sense, some ingenuity, some creativity to stay fresh and alert. . . . Sometimes we'd rest one squad, put one squad down, and have the other one mopping up. If it was hot enough and there was enough activity, we could put one squad down and let them sleep for two or three or four hours, with the other squad patrolling, then wake 'em up and switch.

Back in the '60s and the '70s, hotshots just did hotline. We never did these massive mop-up shifts. They'd pound you real hard, punching line in until it got tied, and then they'd give you either one shift or two where they said mop up, but all they'd want you to do is space out and kind of kick it on the line, just in case something happened. It was operations' and the line bosses' expectation that no, you weren't going to mop up much. They'd want you to rest up a bit, nap out a bit. Kick it, and then if something happened you were ready to jump up. That's all gone away.

---

[14] Mark Linane's personal shorthand for an "ends, not means" approach to problem-solving. Skunk Works used to be a secret division of Lockheed Martin Corporation that later became famous for their innovative, unconventional approaches to problem-solving while designing, engineering, and producing aircraft for the US military.

We don't teach anybody anymore the concept of mitigating fatigue. . . . I guess that's because it's not easy to manage.

Jim Cook (Arrowhead, 1981–1995; Boise, 1996–1998)
In a short-term sense, fatigue at the end of a shift, you can always ask your number two to be a devil's advocate: "Buck, what's wrong with this? Tell me, are you all right with this?" If you hire guys who aren't afraid to speak their piece, that's a good tool. If you hire a yes-man, don't worry about asking.

When I see the humor go out of them, when I see them quit asking questions, I know they're shot. Those are what I call my little canary in the mine.

Rusty Witwer (Mendocino, 1978; Hobart/Tahoe, 1979–1995)
[On taking care of yourself later on in your career.]
In myself, I started feeling it about 40, 41 years old. I was a walker and a runner. When I was younger, usually finished in the top third—in the top three when I was real young. All of a sudden, I couldn't keep up. I was falling back a few steps. There wouldn't be enough food, so I'd let the crew eat, and then we'd do a good, healthy hike out. We were coming out of the Salmon River—I think I was, like, 42 or 43—and I went, "Wait a minute. I'm not that old. This can't be happening to me." Then I realized I hadn't eaten anything. So, the next day, I ate everything, and we took the same walk out, and I kept up. It was hitting me that I had to tend to my fuel and body better and pay attention to it as I got older. That helped me with fatigue.

Greg Keller (Eldorado, 1985–1996; Modoc, 2000–2007)
The air attack called me early in the morning and informed me that some thunderclouds were building off to a given direction, and I thanked him. I asked him if he wouldn't keep me apprised of the situation, and as the day wore on, I forgot that conversation. . . . I was standing with my foreman, and I had my sleeves

rolled up. I felt a drop of water on my arm, and my foreman said, "Did you feel that?" and I said, "Yeah. I don't remember a helicopter going by," thinking it was the water that drips off a bucket going by, and he goes, "I didn't either." It was the thunder cell that had developed above our firing operation and, obscured by the smoke we had, it was now starting to collapse. I missed the indicator. I forgot the information in the morning, and I think that was true due 100 percent to fatigue.

How do you handle pressure from above?

Steve Karkanen (Lolo, 1990–2011)

They need to stand their ground, but they also have to be able to communicate their reasons why they don't want to do something. One of the biggest mistakes I see some of the younger supes make right now is just being real arrogant or standoffish or just flat-out saying, "No, we're not going to do that," without providing good reasons. Or, on the other side of the spectrum, doing something to try to prove themselves. That will get somebody in trouble at some point in time.

It's scary right now because there are so many new crews, and there are a lot of crews out there that are doing things that certainly I wouldn't do right now. I took a lot of risks when I was a younger supe . . . things that I would never do now. I've got the perspective now of having been out there for 16 years as a superintendent and having seen what can happen.

Paul Musser (Flagstaff, 1990–2004)

If you're afraid to say no, or if you're afraid you're going to make somebody upset, then you can't do your job. Most of the hotshot organization is not afraid to voice their opinion. Most of the organization is not afraid to stand up and just say no. There are a few around who waffle on that a little bit, and then there are also a few around who are still a little braver or gutsier than others. (Laughs.)

That's also just a change with time that you go through. I can remember myself on a fire wanting to take a squad down in to go after this one piece. It was in grass, and it was burning hot, and the supe's like, "Well, it doesn't look that good," and I said, "Well, it's all grass. If it comes after us, we'll just light it off and then jump in the black, and then we'll just keep going." He said, "Nope." I wouldn't let one of my people do that, but there are still some supes who are in that experience range who will say, "Yeah, we can cut it that close and we'll still be all right"—99 percent of the time they are.

There was a study done a few years ago: the people most likely to get burnt are [in] the first few years—two or three years—and then the [ones with] ten to fifteen years because they think they've got it all down and know so much that they can really hold onto it. Then, when you get to the 15 to 20-plus years, then you become more cautious.

Fred Schoeffler (Payson, 1981–2007)

Speak up and let the appropriate people know when things aren't right or need to be corrected. This certainly includes those fire-line assignments that are not safe or not smart. Use your best communication skills; use the "turn down" protocol, or whatever else to get your point across. If you accept something as right and it's not, then you acquiesce and accept it and, even worse, you become part of the problem. If you get reassigned to "Division Siberia" or demobed from the fire, so what? You are a Type 1 IHC, and you'll be grabbed up and reassigned to another fire soon enough. Do the right thing.

Dennis Baldridge (Laguna, 1990–2009)

It's just paying attention to the basics, and if somebody's pushing them, they need to start asking the questions: "Why do I have to go do that right now? I'm not sure that I've got everything in place." Push back, ask the questions, try to justify why it's so important. Sometimes that's hard because we can be intimidated by management. It's a lot easier for a younger person, a younger supervisor, to be intimidated than it is for those of us who have been around for a while. We don't take it as easy. I think a good thing we can do is marry up those newer supervisors with an experienced supervisor, get them out working together so they can talk and learn from each other.

Shawna Legarza (San Juan, 2002–2007)

If they ever feel unsure about stuff, and they feel that they're being pressured into getting something done, the best thing to do is find options. The people who we work for, the ops people or whomever, they really want to get it done a certain way. We run into this on every fire that we go on: they want to get something done a certain way, and you know that it can't get done that way, so you make some options for them. Then you present those options to the folks who you're working for, and you talk about each single option. Within your idea of how you think you should get it done, it's in one of those options, and then you can talk about all those options with a division or the ops. You can persuade them to take your option, and if they don't like those other options—if they don't like your option—then they have to find some other options. If you don't feel comfortable with it, don't do it. It's as simple as that.

Last year we went to the hurricane assignment down in Texas, and I was taking a class at the University of Nevada, Las Vegas. My assistant called me on the phone one day, and he's, like, "Hey, Legs, they're trying to pressure us into cutting out these power lines, but it's not safe because no one will tell me that the power lines are on or off. I don't know what to do. I need to get it cut, but they won't confirm that the power's on or off." I go, "If no one can tell you that the power is turned off, then don't do the assignment. It's as simple as that. If it's not safe, then don't do it."

I think that if a young superintendent doesn't feel comfortable with something, talk to your peers out there, talk to the other supes, get some options. But if you're all alone . . . and you don't feel comfortable doing it, then don't do it, because there isn't any house or land or anything worth anybody's lives out there. Just cut it off and back down, back away.

Bob Wright (Sacramento, 1990–2002)
First thing, the safety of your crew is most important. If you're getting pressured, if there's another, older supe there or somebody with more experience, talk to them if you can. If not, and you don't feel it's right, just say, "Hey, I just don't feel comfortable in doing this." . . . Explain to them, and if they push, just say, "Hey, I'm done. I'm pulling out," and then do it. Be big enough to accept the consequences if you get in trouble, but, hey, at least your crew's alive.

Guys who get pushed into that—doing something stupid—get in a lot of trouble. Those people who are doing it to them, they're the ones who need to be out of there. You get these kids who are afraid: "Oh, my crew's going to get a reputation of being bad." . . . They need to get over that and do what's best for them.
[Sometimes crews think they need to prove themselves . . .]
That happens. Then a lot of the supes will say, "Hey, you better think about this. We're not going in there, and this is why." If they're stupid enough to do that, then you want to watch out for them. Try to stop them if you can, but like you said, a lot of times you can't because [they say], "We're as good as or better than the hotshots." Sometimes a hotshot crew will do it because they're a new crew and they want to prove themselves. That's not the way to prove yourself. You prove yourself by being smart and by doing the right thing.

On the Rodeo fire, Bennett and I went over there and they didn't have safety zone one. They've got these guys firing; we didn't have a place to go. The burn was no good. We wouldn't do it. We said, "Heck with it. We ain't doing it." Then they had this crew from California, they were in there doing it. Bennett confronted them that night, and he chewed some butt. He said, "What are you doing? You didn't have a safety zone. You're head-firing this thing, and you guys couldn't have had anywhere to go. You couldn't turn the truck around: it was all high-crown road, big bar ditches. . . . You're out here firing this out, and you lost it anyway. What are you doing?" He chewed their butt, and finally the guy said, "Yeah, yeah, yeah," and that way he learned. He could've gotten some people hurt. Finally, we went in there, and they had to build us a friggin' safety zone. We fired it out, and it was done, and nobody got hurt. But they were lucky: lucky that Bennett was there and talked to them and told them, because he knew the guy.

Brit Rosso (Arrowhead, 1996–2006)

Years ago, when I was a foreman, my superintendent had a family emergency and had to leave the crew. I was a young leader. We were in a situation where we detailed somewhere down here in Arizona, and the commanders or the management said, "Supe's gone. We're going to take advantage of the crew now."

The next morning . . . it was pouring rain, and the guy came charging in. He said, "Okay, here's what we're gonna do, you guys grab your saws off your trucks, we're going to go out and build this fence line." . . . I was giving a briefing to the crew. . . . We're on his dirt, and he knows he's in charge. I glance over at the crew, and their eyes are all this big, and they're looking at me like, "This is the test," watching me. . . . I think that guy expected me to say, "Okay, we're ready to go." I had to think about it, and I stopped. My gut was saying, "No, no, don't do it. This is wrong."

I said, "My name's Brit. I'm the foreman; I've got the crew right now. Let me just grab some paperwork." I got him out of that environment because I didn't want to try and deal with it in front of the whole crew. . . . It was a stall tactic for me, and it gave me time to think about, "How do I deal with this?" I went over there and sat down, and I talked to him calmly, and we worked things out where we used their saws. I said, "Look, we're going to do this project for you. Our primary mission for being here is fire suppression. It's raining today, but if you provide the saws, we'll come out there and work. I'm not going to work the crew in pouring rain, but if the rain lets up, I don't mind getting a little wet banging around in the bushes. I'm not going to beat the hell out of the guys in the rain: it's just too hazardous, walking around on the buckskin logs and everything." [He said,] "Okay, I see that."

I think part of it boils down to that leadership thing: do you have the raw material, born versus learned? It's a school of hard knocks. It really is, because you're going to try a tactic or a style, and it'll work—or kind of work—and you're then going to try another one, and it's going to backfire in your face: "Okay, take that one off the list. That one didn't work."

Dan Fiorito and Union Stick to Their Guns and Get It Done

We had a good fire in 2001. We were assigned with the La Grande Hotshots, a couple of BLM engines, and a Type 3 BLM helicopter on a fire in the Painted Hills near John Day, Oregon. It was a Type 3 incident of about 10,000 acres in the piñon-juniper fuel type. The La Grande supe and I took a flight and got a plan together to work the fire in some rugged country and tie into the John Day River. The plan was that Union was going to fly in to the river and work up toward La Grande; I was going to act as a lookout above my crew in the black. I was flown in with the first load and dropped off on the north edge of the black above the river. The Type 3 helicopter could only carry three firefighters at a time, so it was going to take a while to shuttle the crew to the bottom of the fire. We got our assistant superintendent and a couple of crewmembers delivered to the river about the time the fire blew up. The rest of the crew went and tied in with La Grande and worked with them. The fire moved pretty well through the flashy fuels, and within an hour after I landed on the fire's edge, I was a mile inside the black.

Our plan of anchoring at the river and flanking up the hill to where La Grande was working didn't work out quite the way we had envisioned it. The helicopter came and picked up the crewmembers on the river, and I hiked up to the road about a mile up the ridge from my lookout spot. We all regrouped and started burning off the road system. We burned for the next three days. We had six miles burned out along the river and the road system. We would burn as late as we could into the night, and about midnight or one o'clock in the morning the humidity would come up, and we would stop burning.

Wherever we stopped burning for that shift, we would park the crew carriers and put the crew down to sleep. My assistant superintendent and I would go out and scout the roads for the next day's burning. By the time we would get back, the crew would already be asleep and we would just kick the seats back and crash out in our vehicle. The next morning we would get the crew up, eat, and start burning as soon as we could. This went on for three shifts, and it was a great time: just burning and holding.

On the fourth morning, about five o'clock, I was sleeping in the cab of my truck when I was awakened by a bunch of noise. I looked out of the window and was surprised to see several contract engines and crews along with a division supervisor. I thought, "Who ordered these guys?" It turned out that a Type 2 IMT had assumed command of the fire and nobody had bothered to tell us.

We only had a mile of road to burn to tie the fire into the road. The wind was wrong for this last bit of burning. We had saved this part of the fire for last because the road switchbacked into this drainage, and it was the toughest part of the burn. The ops chief from the IMT came up and started looking around. The fire had died out up on the ridge above the road and left a large unburned area of several hundred acres. The ops chief wanted to go direct on this pocket of unburned that ran up the ridge for about a mile above the road and along the road at the bottom for about a mile. To go direct along the fire's edge would have taken the two hot-shot crews a day or two to cold trail and mop up. The mile of road, we figured, would take an hour to burn when the conditions were right. We wanted to wait for the conditions to turn in our favor; the ops chief wanted to go direct.

We talked for a while about our options, and the ops chief was convinced that his plan was the way to go. I told him that we had been burning along this road for three days, and we knew that the winds were going to turn in our favor just before dark when the drainage got shaded out. It took a lot of negotiation on our part to convince the ops chief to wait it out and finish the burn, as he was impatient and wanted us to get to work on his plan of going direct. We waited, and about five o'clock the wind quit, the drainage got shaded, and we finished the burn by six o'clock.

Sometimes you have to stick to your guns and wait for the fire behavior and weather to turn so you can do the right thing. You cannot let overhead try to intimidate you into taking an assignment that puts the crew at risk or does not make sense.

Someone's in over their head on an assignment. What should they do?

Jim Cook (Arrowhead, 1981–1995; Boise, 1996–1998)

I know early in my career, when I was in over my head, I was hesitant to ask. I know I wouldn't ask, but I would slow up. I was, like, "I have to stop and check it out." Early on, I didn't have a lot of good guidance about what was important, and I was starting a crew with a new agency in Southern California, which is probably the most competitive environment for hotshot crews. I think I made a lot of decisions based on ego that were probably not good decisions.

I recently had a discussion with one of the kids (laughs)— he's the fire planner for Alaska now—and I said, "You know, you guys put up with a lot of shit from me that ten years later I wouldn't have done," and he goes, "But you know, Jim, we always knew that our safety was your number one concern." That was an eye-opening thing to me. They knew that I would never compromise that, so they compensated for my other weaknesses based on that. Crewmembers are a lot sharper and smarter than a lot of supervisors give them credit for, and they pick up on that kind of stuff. They will compensate for your weaknesses if you take care of the critical things that they view as being the most important.

Paul Musser (Flagstaff, 1990–2004)

That's the problem: most of them are not going to realize when they're in trouble. When they do realize that, they need to try to gather as much information as they can from as many people as they can, and that may very well be crewmen. There're a lot of crewmen out there who have more experience than over-head. . . . There're a lot of crewmen who even after two or three years, because they're sitting back and learning and watching and stuff like that, they can figure those situations out pretty quickly.

[They should] gather as much information as they can and not be afraid to back up and just get out of there. That's what's hard for a lot of people. When you talk about not feeling comfortable with the situation and you need to back up and reevaluate the situation, as soon as people start doing that, then you've got another group that's saying the only reason they're doing that is because they don't want to work. They're using safety as a crutch so they don't have to work. It always will be a big fight throughout the whole organization.

Everybody's line of safety is going to be different. Until you've gained enough experience and enough confidence, [say], "It doesn't matter where your line is. This is mine." We were in California last year, and five nights in a row operations asked me to do this assignment. I said, "No, we're not gonna do it." The first night it was, "Well, we'll go and look at it," and after that it was, "No, we won't do that," and every night he'd ask. Then he called the branch director: "Well, you go explain it to him so he'll do it." I'd call the branch director: "I already said no. It's a done deal."

That's a thing that happens to a lot of especially younger supervisors: they [overhead] are going to work their way through the crews and supervisors until they find somebody who will do it. I spent extra time on the first day when we came back down so I could talk to every day-shift supervisor and tell them what was up there and what the assignment was and not to do it, just so none of them made a mistake and said they would.

It happens to everybody that you get in over your head. I mean, that's pretty easy to do out there sometimes. You just have to sit back, reevaluate everything, and don't just act or react. Figure out exactly what you want to do, what the course of action is, and where you want to end up at the end of the day. You just need to sit back and think about those things, and stand by what your decision is. Don't let someone else sucker you into it, which happens all the time. It still happens to me. I'll get out there and someone will say, "Yeah, I'm doing this, and it's good. There's no problem; come on in," . . . I'll be, like, "What are you talking about?"

What do you want to tell people from a Type 1 team member's perspective?

Greg Vergari (Union, 1980–1987)

First, there is nothing different from the management of incidents in my opinion: I have been on many Type 2 fires that were just as complicated as a so-called Type 1 fire. If anyone on these teams thinks they are better because they are on a Type 1 team, then they might be inflated blowhards—just maybe. . . . That said, what I have to say from a Type 1 team member's perspective—I appreciate it when you: give me your all; see the right thing to do and do it instead of the easy thing to do; come up to me, say hello, and help me/us have the best assignment we can; take care of the others around you or even just watch out for them because you are who you are; don't get herd-bound; and act like the men and women you are: professional!

Rusty Witwer (Mendocino, 1978; Hobart/Tahoe, 1979–1995)

I think the tendency for people to want to complete something by the end of their shift is probably the most serious mistake. If it's a big fire—which is why we go on them—you eat a bit of the elephant every day. If we don't finish something and we've got line halfway up the hill, that's line halfway up the hill that—if we get a weather change or another shift that can come in behind you—we've lucked out and we've got 15 more [people] who can pick up from what you've done. In other words, anchor. There's nothing wrong with putting a piece of line in—whether or not your mind thinks it's going to . . . get this fire wrapped up in six days—that's not a bad thing. I think many supervisors are trying to tunnel-vision: "Well, this won't do any good because it's gonna jump the drainage or across the canyon." It's a piece of line that holds, that we can then evaluate and maybe get 20 percent of this fire wrapped so that we can go a different scenario.

The other thing, too, is that there's nothing wrong with two plans of attack happening at once. In other words, direct and indirect. I've had superintendents come up to me who go, "Why are you having us do this when you're building an indirect line on the next ridge?" Well, because if yours doesn't work, we'll have four days of a backup plan B in. In other words, focus on the plan that you've been assigned to and realize that as long as it's safe, and you might not complete it, it's still part of the plan, because weather changes. . . . I'm a firm believer that weather changes every three days. I've seen too many examples where even our FBAs [fire behavior analysts] who give us a seven- or eight-day forecast are wrong. It's hard to forecast, according to our weather people, more than three days. What might be hammering you a bit right now could potentially be the way to go three days from now. I guess that's my pitch: we think it's going to take eight to ten days to work around this scenario. Let's stay with the plan, unless there's a reason for it to be unsafe. If it's unsafe, let's take a look at it. But nonproductive? Let us worry about that part.

Half-a-million-dollar programs that we fly around the country, or drive around the country, that don't put fires out after a while are going to get questioned, and I just think we need to realize that that's what we're there for—to build handline. That's why we tool you up, that's why we get you there. It isn't just to grab a drip torch and go to the nearest road and start firing. I'll be honest with you: anybody can fire a road if the weather's with you.

I really think that we all need to be asking ourselves when we do decline an assignment or whatnot, or come up with an alternate plan: is it in synch with the big picture, and is it going to work? The hotshots have to realize that you're just part of a cog of a big incident, and you're going to have a piece of that, but you aren't wrapping the whole thing up.

PART FOUR

LESSONS LEARNED

This is the premise of the entire book, but here are some of the hardest knocks, the closest calls, and the toughest of times. Let the supes' hard-earned experience help you and everyone else you work with.

What was the experience of "getting religion" like?

It's called "getting religion," "being scared straight," "coming to Jesus," and others. Nearly everyone has an experience in their career that helps define them as a firefighter, especially their attitudes toward escape and safety. Paul Gleason put the finishing touches on LCES after one of his experiences on the Dude fire in 1990, where six firefighters lost their lives. Jim Cook and Craig Lechleiter describe the process, and others describe their actual experiences.

Jim Cook (Arrowhead, 1981–1995; Boise, 1996–1998)

I told them all [his overhead] the sports car analogy. It took me a long time to go through it. When you're a young person and you get a sports car—a brand new, shiny sports car—what do you do with it the first couple times you go drive it? You're going to drive it, like, "Oh, . . . " (mimics hesitant driver). The next time you're, like, "Hey, this thing drives pretty good," and you'll be catching a few gears and seeing how fast it corners, and you keep pushing the corners a little harder and a little harder. You keep pushing the envelope. The first couple times you're going to be a little cautious, and pretty quickly you're going to start pushing the envelope. If you're lucky, what happens? You spin out, you get back on the road, and you say, "Now I know where the envelope is," and you pull back a bit.

Supervisors in the fire business, that's the curve they go through. When they first get a crew, they're timid. They want to make sure they don't do anything wrong, don't want to scratch it. Then you're going, "Hey, these guys can cut line pretty good. Hey, these guys can cut downhill pretty good. These guys can really light up some fire." You get pretty aggressive, and pretty soon you have a situation—what I call getting religion. I got that term from Rusty Witwer. I always tell my subordinates, "You're gonna go through that curve. You can't help it. It's part of your learning process. Just make your aggressive moves incrementally, find where the envelope is, and then come back. You're going to have a religious experience. Everybody does."

Craig Lechleiter (Redding, 1986–2002)

Everyone goes through an ego-humbling phase throughout their lives. I tell people, just think about it: every time you promote, you get to a level of performance where you feel, "Hey, I do have the confidence now. My self-esteem's up, I can do this, and I don't need my supervisor around here anymore." As you evolve to that position in life, you say, "You know, you can leave now, boss. I can do this better than you can." That's when you begin to have conflict with your boss.

Just when you think you know it all, something will happen: something significant will happen on the fireline. You realize your decision-making wasn't all that tuned up to where you thought it was. Something significant gets by you, something critical, and you see your first-line supervisor catch it. Your supervisor has that way of getting you to humble yourself. You realize there's a lot more to this job.

You then understand how much you really need your boss, and you say, "Hmm. Don't go anywhere. I need you." Then it gets worse—you don't want him to go at all. You realize you're not going to have as much fun after they leave. But then it happens—[your boss leaves] and you find yourself starting all over again.

The intimidation of being a superintendent was overwhelming for me. I didn't share it with anybody. Every time I promoted in my career, I went through that process. That kind of stuck with me all these years. I anticipate it in people who work for me. I tell them, "You're gonna get there. You're going to get to the point where you don't give a shit about me anymore, and you're going to want me out of here. It's normal to feel that way. Don't worry, you'll be ready for my job. Trust me."

Bob Bennett (Horseshoe Meadow, 1989–2006)

It was a fire that I and [Jim] Cook were on. I was the scout out in front of us. It was when I was a captain and we were in Arizona. We had bailed off the hill, downhill line construction, and a cell came over. . . . Everything was looking good, and we were right on the edge until the cell came over and blew shit all over the place. We were basically off the side of the hill: our crew and Arrowhead. Cook is yelling at me, and I'm running around on the side of this hill trying to find some place to get to. Finally, I find a place, and I go, "Okay, I've got a place. Just follow the flag line." The fire's crashing up the hill, and we get the line tied in. Cook comes up the hill, and he goes, "Goddammit! This ain't no goddamn safety zone!" I go, "Cook, yeah," and he goes, "Bullshit." All we had to do was walk a little farther, and then we ran into a better one. But it was one of those things, just going, "Oooohh—this could've been close. This could've been disaster."

I think probably the second one was going in on South Canyon about three days after the fatalities and picking up saw parts and stuff off the line. Just being there, seeing where they were putting the flowers on where everybody fell. Just being there and looking down and going, "Why'd they do this?" . . . Being there and then reading the reports and some of that stuff, physically being there a few days after everything happened. You could see where everything was at, what the terrain's like. I go, how many times have I done this in my career? We went on a fire right after that; they asked us to do something, and I said no. I go, "Nope, this ain't the place to be."

I can remember back in the early '70s, when I was a squad leader and a captain, and pushing that envelope maybe a little bit too far, and nothing ever happened. I think that probably did make me go, "Man, we did a lotta stupid shit"—just being able to relate that back to your crew, saying, "Hey, this why we're pulling out of here now," or, "This is why we're not going to commit or engage with this now."

Steve Karkanen (Lolo, 1990–2011)

I think I got religion early on in my career, even before I was a superintendent. I got involved in a burnover on the Butte fire. I rode it out in a safety zone. . . . We still had to deal with an ugly situation for eight hours: we were trapped. It was a crown fire, 300-foot flame lengths rolling around us. We were stuck in a good spot, thankfully, but it was uncomfortable; and it was a situation where we were told by a strike team leader that we would be fine, when the reality of it was, had we had our act together and had good lookouts posted, we could've driven or walked away and within 15 minutes been completely out of the fire area. There was no reason for us to have been there, for any of those folks to have been there. From that day on, I swore that I would never put the people who I was responsible for—and I was just a firefighter at the time, in 1985—I never wanted to be in that position where I was going to be burned over. Never.

Brit Rosso (Arrowhead, 1996–2006)
I feel that it's necessary for all supervisors and leaders, to "get religion." I even talk about it. I'll talk about it with my foremen: I'll say, "You can tell he hasn't got religion." You can call religion a reality check, the "scared straight," whatever it is, but I don't want everyone to have to go through the actual experience, because it sucks. But I'll never forget it, and I share it with my folks. I give them my "virtual religion," we'll call it: the opportunity to share that experience but not share the horror and the trauma that goes along with it. Religion by proxy, there you go.

It was about 15 years ago, but I'll remember it for the rest of my career, even though I was just a dirt-thrower back then. . . . Our superintendent at that time, even today I try and put myself in his position . . . back then, and I think, "Holy moly . . . I almost killed my whole crew." As a sawyer, you're doing that fight-or-flight for yourself, you're looking out for others, but when you're the crew leader, the supervisor, the squad leader, now all of a sudden you're in charge.

That's the whole thing about the error chain and the point of no return—that was one of the few times that I've ever been in a situation where we crossed the point of no return. The only thing . . . that kept us from becoming a fatality report versus we're still here was luck. The wind was in our favor and everything worked out, and now it's our religion versus a report sitting on a shelf.

Shawna Legarza (San Juan, 2002–2007)
I had a "coming to Jesus" experience as a supe three years ago in New Mexico. I learned a lot from it, and it has definitely changed the way I make decisions on fires. Or not make decisions. . . . It was my third year as a supe and my gut instinct said, "No, don't do it," and I was the only person in the crowd that was saying,

"No, don't do it," and everybody else said, "Yeah." They did it, and then stuff went bad.

I learned from that to take my gut instinct and make sure people hear it, and if they don't hear it, then I can tell them they can find someone else to do the job. I think it takes a while to get to that level, to feel confident to say that. Five, six years ago, I probably wouldn't have done that: I would've just gone with it. This time it got me caught, and I usually don't go with the group. I'm usually very independent, but it hasn't been in a life-or-death kind of thing—so then I went with the group and it got bad. Now I know that if I don't like going with the group, I'm not going to go with the group.

Dennis Baldridge (Laguna, 1990–2009)

We were on a piece of line, and it went down into a little drainage that you had to walk maybe 100 feet—into the drainage, up the drainage, and back up on the edge. We knew there was a crew up ahead, and we knew there were rocks that were probably going to roll, but the idea was that, one at a time . . . we would be able to get through. I made it to the other side and had my first sawyer coming through. He just barely makes it when a rock rolls down. Oh, shit. Well, that was good—that was close, but the chances of that happening again are really slim. The second guy comes across, and he has to jump over the rock that rolls down. I went, "Okay, that's it. That's too doggone close. We're not gonna do it." I'd just put not only myself but two other people at risk. We knew the risk; we just didn't think it was as high as it was. Luckily, nobody was hurt. It was, like, "Okay, let's see what else we can do. There's got to be a different way to get to where we need to go."

That's probably my biggest fear: that somebody gets hurt seriously or dies on my watch. That's part of the crew boss or superintendent's responsibilities. They don't talk about it a whole lot, but it's always there. . . . Those little times when it got close like that it's, like, "Oh, man, that's telling me something. Let's not do that again." You have to be reminded every once in a while. You got religion, but you need to get reminded every once in a while.

Ron Bollier (Silver City, 1993–1995; Carson, 1996–1997; Fulton, 1998–2013)

When did I get religion? There were two times in my career, I think, that were a real eye-opener, the first time being on the LP crew. . . . We got in a pretty tight situation on the Painted Cave fire. We initial-attacked it, and we had to end up firing a piece down Highway 154 into Santa Barbara; and if you don't know any of the history, it went, like, seven miles in two and a half hours. I mean, it just smoked—downhill. It burned 600 homes in probably an hour and a half. We had some sundowners blowing down the front country of Santa Barbara; it basically burnt to the ocean.

If you know San Marcos Pass, it's kind of the high point, just above the beach. The fire started about three-quarters of the way up, wind-driven, had about 50-, 60-mile-an-hour winds on it, and all we could do was start firing the road to try and keep it below the road and from going back up into the forest. It was all shoving downhill, so we started firing. Then we started flanking it, but we kept it north of Highway 154. If it got on the south side, it would've gotten into Sycamore Canyon. We basically kept it channeled down into the city.

We started firing just as fast as you could drive in the crew trucks, and the guys would run behind the crew trucks with drip torches. It was beating us down the hill. We got on one of the turns, and it pinched us off. The fire came up on the downhill side of us, in the front, laid over the crew truck. All this took maybe a total of ten minutes. First it would hit the front, and we'd back up. I was a driver. You had to follow the double yellow lines on the road. We'd back up, and then it would hit us from the rear, so we'd pull up, and then it would hit us from the front. There was no visibility. Then it hit us all at once, jumped the road, and with the wind on it, it came right back down on us, so it double-pounded us.

Was it a reality check? Yeah, it was a reality check. The tires caught fire on the vehicle. When you start getting to that point, you're pretty close. All our gear on top caught fire, guys in the back having a rough time of it. Could we have done something different? Would we have done something different? Probably not. What we did was good sound tactics. Were we doing good? Yeah, we were effective. How did it beat us? Abnormal weather conditions. It beat us down the hill and, unfortunately, cut us off.

Everybody came out no scratches, no scrapes. Probably a good thing we were there: there were [members of the] public behind us in their own vehicles who probably would not have done very well. We had to get out, put their vehicles out—they were on fire. If we hadn't been there and put their vehicles out, they probably wouldn't have made it because their vehicles would've caught fire and they would've gotten out and run to who knows where.

Greg Overacker (Stanislaus, 1979–2006)
[Nineteen] eighty-eight. Got involved in a near-miss burnover. . . . We had a couple guys get mildly burned: here and there on the arm, a little bit on the face. Mostly radiant heat, no direct flame contact. I realized on that very day, "You've already been a superintendent since '79. A superintendent almost ten years." Strong overhead team with me. . . . It was my greatest day of awakening. From that day on, I used that situation to strengthen myself and my crew. On that day, I knew I was vulnerable, and I knew everybody else with me was, too. I've never forgotten that, ever—like it was yesterday, 14 years ago. Yesterday.

That made me a stronger, better superintendent. I now understand that we need to teach our people so rapidly that when the Big Dog wants to move, let it. It's going to anyway. Don't get stupid with it. If there's something you can do, do it—safely. If there's not, enjoy the afternoon. That's my day of religion, when I thought I had lost or hurt some of my personnel.

Craig Workman (Black Mountain, 1988–2005)

I think every year you get a little bit of religion, but I got my first religion when I was running a Type 2 crew, way back when, on the Modoc. We went to a fire; it was about a year and a half after I'd been with Redding. Redding was on this fire, and I ran into [Charlie] Caldwell. He said, "Hey, we're running a big burnout. Would you like to come up and work with us?" I really wanted to do this, and the crew I had really wasn't up for the task. We went and did it. We survived, but it really wasn't a good experience for the people who were there. I think I really learned at that time to start gauging the limitations of the people you have . . . and very early find what those limitations are. Don't push them too hard, because you can do more damage than good.

Art Torrez (Vista Grande, 1994–2004)

I think probably everyone has been in that position. It's a real eye-opener; it's a real rude awakening. . . . [You] have moments when you feel you can accomplish something, and just like that, you realize things have changed that quickly, that you may have rushed into something just because you were trying to be a little too aggressive.

   We were on a fire on the San Bernardino—it was the Verbenia fire—and we were supposed to go direct in this really steep country. We were making a push, going direct on it, and things started heating up a little bit below us, so we decided we were going to abandon that plan and try and fire it off the creek bottom we were anchored [on]. We're taking it slow, and taking it slow, and all of a sudden we're seeing it's getting active in the upper part of the canyon. If I could do it differently again today, I probably would not have committed the entire crew in there because it was a touchy situation. We accomplished what we wanted to do, but it was a very tense situation where that fire was coming down a lot faster than we really wanted it to. It was something that'll always stick in my mind—that maybe I should've had a backup plan where I didn't need everybody up in there, but all of us were committed. It got warm.

Ron Regan (Del Rosa, 1977–1997)

There were a couple of times up on the Gifford Pinchot. One year we were up there and I was out ahead of the crew, scouting. This large snag fell over, and the crew was probably within 50 feet of it. It actually was a green tree, a big green cedar, and it was burning at the base. I had just come up on it, and it went over, just like that. If the crew had been there five minutes sooner, it would've taken out half of them at least. The fire behavior wasn't a problem, but things like that just frighten the hell out of you. I used to pray to God that we would make it home: every shift, bring them all, nobody left behind.

Getting religion isn't always about fire behavior.

Barry Callenberger (Palomar, 1979–1982; Eldorado, 1982–1988)

I made probably the biggest mistake in my career. I was a superintendent and we were having drug problems, where a couple guys were doing drugs on the crew. It wasn't so overt where I could see it all the time, but I thought it was becoming a problem. . . . It got to a point where it was potentially a serious problem, so I called in law enforcement on the crew. . . . I don't necessarily totally regret having to bring in law enforcement to try to deal with it, but I regretted the kind of law enforcement that came in, and it was kind of the old-school cop thing. They brought in a task force to interview everybody on the crew, and they really put some of the crew folks on the spot, to the point where they upset them enough that they were scared because [law enforcement] wanted them to turn in the other crewmembers. I didn't want to deal with it that way.

It ended up not being as big a problem as the foremen and I had thought it was, and it only [involved] a couple of guys. We ended up terminating one of them. But it had an impact on the rest of the crew. We had destroyed their trust. After a month or so, it started going away, and I think we regained that trust that we had lost. But I made the decision—it wasn't my foremen's decision, although I did talk to them about it. When you break that trust, it really hurts the crew's effectiveness. Toward the end, it came back, it came around, it was all right. The person who went had to go. . . . I think the folks it had a positive impact on were the good folks anyway, [those who] were being exposed to it who didn't want to be exposed to it.

All in all, it worked out, but I just didn't like the way it was handled by law enforcement. It was all Forest Service law enforcement, but there were a couple heavy-handed law enforcement guys who came in. They searched the barracks. They went through everybody's locker, searched the place. The only reason this guy got terminated was I think they found marijuana in his locker, but it definitely put the damper on things. It definitely let the crews who came afterwards know that it wasn't tolerated, so I don't regret that.

Craig Lechleiter (Redding, 1986–2002)

One experience that I had was 1990, Dude fire. Standing there with my "shadow," looking over the rim, observing the most extreme fire behavior you could think of. Area ignition of five to ten acres—whoosh—gone in a minute or less. The whole time, you're looking at people dying and you don't know it. You don't know it's happening. There's nothing you could have done to prevent it.

There were other situations where I personally got too separated from the crew, scouting. I liked to get back and see the big picture, be the L (lookout) in "LCES," and allow the captains to orchestrate the crew. I felt instrumental in making sure nothing snuck up on them. You know those big, long whip antennas? The one I had that night, the cap on the end was missing, so it had this bare wire up there. I remember a lightning bolt hitting in the area I was in, and in a moment the tip of that antenna turned blue. It was about the color of bright neon light. It looked like a ghost, or I did. I remember saying, "You dumbass. What are you doing out on this rock?" Just then a lightning bolt hit near me, and I'm telling you, what a crack that bolt made. This guy was gone. I realized how close I came to getting hammered.

Greg Keller Meets Rax and Dodges the Mine Fire

I'll tell a story where I learned that you have to be aware of things yourself. Superintendent was somewhere else; the foreman was somewhere else. We were cutting behind Fulton, and we had tied into their line. The assignment was to leapfrog, and we tied into the back of Fulton. As a squad boss, I walked up to the saw teams and said, "What are you guys doing?" They said, "Well, we're sitting here," and I said, "Get out in front. Bump up!" They said, "There's a big guy up there. Won't let us come through." "What do you mean there's a big guy? I'll take care of this." I'm walking up a fairly steep hill, and when I get up there, there's a guy standing on a rock up there. I'm looking up, and he is a big guy. I walk up, and this is my first meeting with Greg Overacker. Never met the man before, never saw him before. I said, "Hey, pal, why don't you guys take five and pull over so we can bump through?" With a wad of tobacco juice that came out and landed on my boot top, in a big, gruff voice he says, "Fulton don't cut behind nobody!" (Laughs.) I went, "Oh, okay."

I went back down the hill, and they said, "What are we gonna do?" and I said, "I dunno." I'm looking around for a foreman or superintendent to take charge of this. What happened in the process of not taking a leap out in front of them was the Elsinore front winds took over—this fire was the Mine fire on the Cleveland [National] Forest by Lake Elsinore—and the fire went from a small fire, a few smokes here and there, to a raging inferno in a matter of seconds. It was all we could do to run, rush, a free-for-all flight downhill, trying to get into something that resembled a safety zone.

Fortunately, the fire had made a pass below us and we were able to get into the burned-out area. It was so hot you had to scrape down so your feet could stand on it. That, to this day, has been the closest call I've ever had by fire. I've always said Greg Overacker saved my life by being an ass-hole. I've told him this story, and he always goes, "So that was you," and I said, "Yeah, so that was you." From that started a lifelong friendship that I've had with the man, . . . but had he allowed us to take a leap out in front, we'd have been in 12-, 13-foot-high brush. We'd have had plenty of time to get out way in front and take a leap, and we would've had no way to get back when the Elsinore front kicked in.[15,16]

Mark Linane and LP Survive the Pacoima Fire

I don't know if I "got religion" per se, but we had a huge lesson learned. . . . We went to the Pacoima fire in 1974 or '75. It was on the Angeles, and we had a downhill line construction to burn out this dozer line. We started down

[15] Bill Sandborg, whose interview appears in Part 7, was Overacker's supe at Fulton; he also mentions this fire and the Elsinore front winds in his answer to question no. 22.

[16] "Firing Highway 33 with the General," *Wildfire* (June 1997). Another Keller anecdote about Greg "Rax" Overacker.

at nighttime; it was 100-year-old brush. It wasn't real hot; the sun was setting down on the coast. We began firing that line, and they told me we had a lookout from LA County down below. There was a Forest Service division or operations guy and an engine up on top. We had a hose lay coming down supporting us.

I sent scouts out right away to make sure the line was completed, because everybody said it was complete. We got down there and found that there were a couple of X spots where dozers had just punched a road around the ridgetop but there was no line there. By the same process, they hadn't put any safety zones in. We had a couple dozers with us: an Angeles fire dozer operator and another Angeles engineer. I said, "Okay, we'll send some guys down, and we'll open up at least a firing line down that ridge and get those dozers started putting a safety zone in."

I had a short squad firing down, pretty big fire behavior because it was in pretty big brush, 100 years old, and a lot of kindling. As we were bringing fire down . . . we spotted a spot [fire] down below us. . . . Had some guys scattered, up watching the firing that's coming down. All of a sudden, this huge ball of fire comes out of the bottom of the drainage, from way the fuck down below us, with no warning there was any spot. Either the LA County guy couldn't communicate, didn't see it, or left his post, I don't know. But I learned after that never to trust anybody. . . . The fire laid over the top of the line, just sheeted across the line that was above.

I had a young captain/foreman with me who only had about three seasons in. He was hollering at the guys to run back up the hill, and I'm, like, "Negative. You motherfuckers get back down here right now and get on the off-hill side."

Everybody came, got down, and the fire just laid over the top of us. We had to get almost on the edge of the green. The fire laid over the top of the line, rolled across the top of us.

I got all the guys back up the hill, except I had one lookout who was on top: he was in place. Got everybody else down to the safety zone, and the guys who were down below us, got them to the safety zone. Then the fire made three flashovers, and this heavy fuel exploded three times. Each time it exploded it would lay fire across, and then it got the other side of it, so we had fire around both sides of us. I guess we had maybe a 100-foot safety zone, probably 100 foot in diameter. Maybe seven blades, ten blades, is what we had time to put in. Got behind the dozers, and we sat that out.

Everybody thought we were dead because this thing just exploded and laid over top of us. I just stood behind the dozers, swapping back and forth with the dozer operators. After the first flashover, Perv says, "Should I get the guys into shelters?" and I said, "Yeah." They didn't need 'em, and they probably would've survived without 'em, but we put 'em in their shelters.

After we marched out of there, I had everybody fold their shelters up. Everybody was pretty shaky. Got to the top of the hill, and I knew the engine captain up there. He goes, "What the fuck are you guys doing here? You guys should be dead. We thought you were all dead." I said, "Nah, piece of cake."

We got down, washed our clothes, and got rip-roaringly drunk. We thought we were going to be off and get sent home. I got awakened about four o'clock in the morning, after we got in about two. I said, "What the fuck you guys doing wakin' us up?" "They want you back again." I'm going,

"Oh, fuck." Where do they put us but two ridges over, other dozers punching down line, and now we're doing it one more time, the same goddamn game: downhill line construction, burning. But we had hose support and air tankers, and we got it done. I had to do some serious talking to get the crew to do it.

Then we got home and one guy quit. He was a Vietnam vet, still a good friend. Turned out to be a great fireman later on, but he'd had a couple near misses in 'Nam, and it scared the shit out of him. About a year later [he came] back with us, and then he turned out to be one of the best firemen there ever was.

It was a scare from my foreman making a bad call and having to countermand his order, and I chewed his ass because he thought he was pretty hot. When I brought everybody back down afterwards, he goes, "Supe, I can't thank you enough. I fucked up and made a bad decision." I said, "Yeah, you did. You almost got some people killed, son. Next time when I tell you to do something, I want it done, now."

Lessons learned out of it: 1) I never trusted anybody unless I really knew 'em, like one of my compadres from the hotshot crew, Jim [Cook] or a few other guys, but after they'd scouted, they'd said everything was A-OK—Fred [Schoeffler]'s another guy I trust, from Payson—either myself or my own scouts who I knew, scouting the line; 2) if there was some lookout over there I didn't know or didn't trust, we didn't do it until I got one of my trusted cohorts that we could communicate with. That lasted the rest of my career. My trust level of others I didn't know became very, very small.

J. W. Allendorf Recalls the Pacoima Fire

We got burned over on the Pacoima fire in '75. It was a nasty deal. It really scared the shit out of me. In fact, it almost made me quit fighting fire. We were working a downhill piece of line on the Pacoima fire; it was the first ICS [Incident Command System] test fire. I'll never forget it, because here we'd been talking all this FIRESCOPE,[17] ICS, and all this bullshit; I was just starting to figure out the large fire organization stuff, sector bosses, and all that, when we switched into this ICS. The Pacoima fire was going to be the first test fire to see how it worked. It was all fucked up and only because we didn't have common communications. That's one of the things they laid out in the very beginning with FIRESCOPE: we needed to have common communications between agencies, and it was the one thing that didn't get done. All the window-dressing was done: everybody had their little nametags . . . but the thing we needed the most, the common communications, we didn't have.

Here we were, a couple days into the fire, building line downhill, and if I remember right, it was off the Mendenhall truck route, right up there in Pacoima Canyon. . . . We were late getting out there because logistics was all screwed up. We got out there late on the assignment, and we're building line downhill, off the Mendenhall truck road, to an unknown road in the bottom, an LA County road. The fire was burning like a bastard, even at night, and it was real old brush:

---

[17] FIRESCOPE is the acronym for Firefighting Resources of California Organized for Potential Emergencies, the project that developed the Incident Command and Multi-Agency Command Systems after the especially severe 1970 fire season in California. "Some Highlights of the Evolution of the Incident Command System as Developed by FIRESCOPE," FIRESCOPE California, last modified May 29, 2019, https://firescope.caloes.ca.gov/SiteCollectionDocuments/Some Highlights of the Evolution of the ICS.pdf.

decadent, nasty stuff. It spotted easily, a lot of dead in the mix. We had burned out the saddle above us, and a bunch of engines were up there to pump a hose lay the inmates were laying. We had burned it out, throwing napalm canisters to get it clean, and then we were moving down the ridge with the intent of just firing it all the way down and taking the edge off with napalm—never any real expectation of the fire making a hard run.

Late in the game, we started getting a whole lot of fire activity. Linane got a call on the radio that LA County was working a spot fire, not in the mouth of the canyon but across the road, down below us. All this was third-hand, coming to him on our frequency. You had a couple wingnuts standing in camp: one guy would talk to LA County, and then he'd talk to the Forest Service guy, and he'd relay; there were no direct communications. It came to Mark that they had this fire on the other side of the road, and they had it contained and knocked down and to keep on firing and keep on moving. We had two dozers pushing line.

All of a sudden everything went to shit, and we started getting spot fires all over the country. . . . I got separated from the crew while working a spot, and I ended up making about a three-quarter-of-a-mile run by myself uphill to where the engines were. The crew was sheltered up behind the dozers, and I would keep stopping and looking. I wanted to be with them. That was the scariest thing: being away from them.

I was running up this dozer line, and the fire would lay over the dozer line, and I'd lay down behind the dozer berms. We had fire shelters, and they were the big ol' huge things. I never considered just deploying it and sitting it out, which I could've done easily there; I kept on running. Kind of a funny deal because I ended up with a kind of bowl haircut from losing hair around my hard hat. I got up to the trucks and could see down where the crew was. The fire was just rolling around them. I felt really bad that I wasn't with them, and I didn't feel safe up where I was, for no reason. I don't know why, but I didn't feel good.

It was a real tough thing for me to overcome that because it scared me so bad, and I think it was having been away from the crew that caused the fear. I almost quit after that. I talked to Mark, and I told him—he knew it, too—and he talked to me about going downhill on fires. I was real shaky about it after that on all the fires through the rest of the season. I think that was in July or early August. Mark told me, "You gotta make up your mind what you're gonna do. You gotta either get back on this horse, or get off it and stay off." . . . I stuck around, and then the following year I got an appointment as a 13/13, but it was on an engine.

What are the hazardous attitudes that firefighters have? What essential attitudes should they adopt?

Jim Cook (Arrowhead, 1981–1995; Boise, 1996–1998)
I did that from two perspectives. One, from a firefighter's: terrible twos. Every kid that worked for me, 99 percent of them became the "terrible twos." I told those guys [his overhead], "When they come back next year, you gotta come down on them because they're going to know everything, and they'll be sure they tell the new kids they know everything. Hammer the terrible twos out of them." When you get a kid back for the third year, they're awesome employees.

Kurt LaRue (Diamond Mountain, 1993–2001)
The learning curve: you start out, and you don't know anything, so everything's an experience and a lesson. Then you start to get

a little experience and you can predict, "That clump of trees over there is going to burn," and sure enough, it does. . . . Pretty soon, and still early on, experience-wise, it's getting to where you're predicting stuff pretty regularly, and you start to think "I'm getting good at this." The more this happens and the longer you go without failure or surprise, the higher you get, not on the wisdom side of the learning curve, but on the arrogance side of the curve: "I've seen it, been it, done it."

Then one day something will happen: you had no idea that whole canyon was going to go off or the fire would move in that direction. For me, this is when we start to understand we aren't as smart as we thought we were. We don't know as much and can't predict everything as well as we have been telling ourselves we can. This is my version of the downside of the learning curve—when you start to see you aren't as smart as you thought you were. At this point, people have seen enough to quit getting more arrogant and to begin to get wiser. I do think once you start on the downside of the curve you get more cautious. You start to plan more, not for fire behavior—which has a 90 percent chance of happening—but more for what we will do if the 10 percent chance of fire "misbehavior" happens.

I think the biggest hazardous attitude I see is people who are still on the upside of the curve in fire management positions. They haven't had a failure, or what you called the religious moment, and they are 12 feet tall and bulletproof. All of their experience so far tells them they have seen it all, and often their computer programs are reinforcing these views. They don't have the experience with fire misbehavior to understand how fast things can go bad and how irrevocable fireline decisions are.

You see it in some of our recent accidents and fatalities, where groups may have noticed they were in situations which aren't good, but the it-can't-happen-to-me syndrome—because it never has happened to them—kicks in. They see things going wrong but don't come up with a new strategy; they just keep changing their tactics. You can't tell them they're being arrogant because they don't know they're being arrogant. All of their experience to date just tells them they're dialed in, and they and their computer have it down to a clean, safe percentage.

I think this attitude has crept into fire pretty hard the past couple years. To an increasing degree, we have let people with this lack of first-hand fire misbehavior experience—people still on the upside of the curve—weight their political considerations too heavily in how we go about things. We're basing too much of our tactical and strategic planning on a political need rather than the physical reality that's in front of [us].

It was a lot easier to be a crew boss when I started in the late '70s because we cut a direct line on everything we went to. Your tactic was to get as close as you can to the fire and start cutting line. If it goes bad, we'll scurry off into the black. It was pretty basic, pretty easy. There weren't as many things to be looking for since we were always on an edge then. Now we have the kids back X amount of chains indirect, and when you're burning, you are asked not to burn all the canopy down: "Kinda underburn it a little bit."

I think there's an attitude in fire: an attitude people have that everything they've done so far has worked for them, and they will make this assignment work too. I don't think they realize how many times they're setting themselves up for reburn, no place to go when there are spots, or way out in the green where there's no type of active fire to provide a dead edge to go to.

Fred Schoeffler (Payson, 1981–2007)

Arrogance and egotism are hazardous attitudes. . . . In the last several years, it sure seems that many of the IMTs are threatened by the competence and experience of the more experienced hotshot superintendents. I don't really care if the operations section chief or my division supervisor is less experienced than I am. I thought we were all on the same side, with the same goals, just trying to get the job done safely and efficiently, and go to as many fires each season as possible.

Know-it-alls are fairly dangerous. I recall one IHC superintendent instructing S-290, "Intermediate Fire Behavior." Throughout the course, questions were broached about this fire behavior or that. His comments were generally, "Don't worry about that. I've been fighting fire for a long time now, and I've never seen that before." You'd better be learning something new on every fire and from every fireline and/or crew supervisor, and even from crewmembers.

"Group Think" is another hazardous attitude. This is also known, in my opinion, as the "team player" concept, where one has to go along in order to get along. This is very dangerous and does not encourage others to speak up when there is disagreement or when other viewpoints need to be expressed and discussed.

[Essential attitudes are] maintaining the basics, no matter what position you hold or who you are—or think you are; adhering to the 10 Standard Orders and LCES while doing one's best to mitigate the 18 Watch Out Situations; being as safe as possible at all times while still being able to do the job effectively and efficiently; following Gordon Graham's maxim that "what is predictable is preventable"; . . . adhering to and making sure you follow all just safety rules and regulations, starting with the basics, then ensure that your crew does the same, in everything—whether it's seat belts, PPE [personal protective equipment], eye protection, ear protection, Nomex® in good condition, driving, whatever. You may not like it, but you must set the example every time.

Having sincere compassion for your people is essential. I will always remember a distraught and saddened father who lost his daughter in a fatal Northern California firefighting accident telling a roomful of hotshots and other fireline supervisors how important it was for us to take our supervisory roles seriously because we were responsible for their children's safety. As parents, they trusted us to do just that. That continues to affect me to this day.

Passion for getting the job done right the first time: something I learned from my first Forest Service supervisor. Every time we have to do something again, then we're only moving forward by half.

Dave Matier (Midnight Sun, 1992–1997, 1999–2007, 2009–2010)

They think that they know it all. I can look at how long it took me to get to where I am before I was a superintendent. I look at how long it took me to get strike team leader [qualified], and I'm not advocating that somebody take that long, but I do think that the longer you do this—and if you're open to learning—the better it is.

The opportunities are a lot greater now than when I started to move up. Just getting an appointment: I was in fire about eight, nine years before I got an appointment. Part of that is why I don't work for the Forest Service anymore, but I think that's great. I'm happy for them that the opportunities are there, that they don't have to go through what I did to get an appointment or just move up in the ranks and stuff. [They] do a good job for me, and I'm willing to give them any and all opportunities that are available to me.

I think a lot of them, their head gets a little too big and they don't realize that there's more to it than getting classroom training and getting qualified. It's more being out there and doing it. The ones who realize that, those are the ones who do good for me—he ones who aren't real stuck on themselves. I think the essential attitudes are hard work no matter where you're at and not forgetting where you came from.

Ben Charley (Horseshoe Meadow, 1974–1989)

Treat your people like human beings. I always treated my guys just like I'd want to be treated. I'd give 'em a hard time, but they'd come through. I made 'em work, but after we'd come home I'd say, "Okay guys, first store, I'll buy you guys ice cream"; rewards: just saying, "You guys work for me, hey, I'll treat you good."

What I've always done is keep my people informed, so they'll know what's going on. I come from a briefing and before we hit the line I tell them, "Okay, here's what we're looking at, guys; here's what they want." I think if you don't keep your people informed, they're not going to really want to follow you. It's not a one-man job. It's all 20 people. I firmly believe in that. You know the guys who come out and say, "Okay, let's go. Get your gear, let's go," and away you go. The guys look back, and they say, "Where are we going? What are we gonna do?" You put yourself into that guy on the tail end, that last McLeod, he's gonna say, "What's going on?"

When I started out in fire, if you were a sector boss, you walked your line three times. That was prerequisite. Your shift, you walked your line three times. I believe in that very, very strongly. Your relief, when he comes on, you're going to tell him where it's at, and he'll know what you're talking about. Don't rely on your people. I never did believe in that. I'd never sit in the truck. Maybe my last year I did, but before that I was always out on the line with the guys. You can't teach 'em anything with a vehicle, but you can out there in the field. I didn't want to go out and say, "Go do this; do that," without my knowing what's going on.

What are the best examples you've seen of rare or extreme fire behavior?

Jim Cook (Arrowhead, 1981–1995; Boise, 1996–1998)
I wrote four things down: 1985 on the Wheeler fire. The first night we showed up, we did total defensive firing operations along highways and county roads and stuff. I had guys pulling horses out of corrals—total anarchy, bedlam, and chaos. A great

time. (Laughs.) The next day, we came back to the heliport. I think it's at the airstrip in Ojai. . . . All I remember is seeing that things were going south in a big hurry, so we pulled people into the airstrip area. We got to watch fire crown through an orange orchard. That was pretty spectacular. . . . You know what an orange orchard looks like—there's nothing on the ground, the trees are all pruned up. Right through it.

The other one I have: 1988 at Canyon Creek. . . . We were with LP, and we were in the middle of a fire that ran 180,000 acres in eight hours. I think it's still the largest fire run recorded in North American history. We were tinkin' away, not thinking anything about it. We parked our rigs seven miles away . . . guys locked the rigs and put the keys on the leaf spring. Figured seven miles away, don't know who's going to be there. We had to radio through two human relays and tell everyone where the keys on our rigs were so they could move them because they were going to be burned when this thing eventually made it through there.

We had to be evacuated on a big Puma: they were just shoving people on this ship and shoving them on until they couldn't put any more on and then flying them out. That was precautionary, probably, because we were in a 40-acre scree in high mountain scrub. We're watching three major columns converge right over our heads. That was pretty impressive.

Marre fire, 1993—again a Santa Ana fire. It had developed into this fuels/plume-dominated fire with two columns that stood up through a mild Santa Ana. You could tell the Santa Ana was pushing through the columns because it was making lenticular clouds between the two columns. I got a picture of that. That was cool.

Hotelling, 1987 on the Klamath. The fire had pretty much been inversioned in for days, weeks. . . . They had us and Redding going down, cutting line. It was burning in the litter. Chasing this thing way down deep in this V-canyon . . . under the inversion the thing had flame lengths about this big [about one foot], and it was pretty easy to track. We just had a lot of edge. We couldn't figure out what was going on on the other side. . . . I said, "I'm going to go and drive around to the other side and see if there's somebody coming off the other side of the drainage."

I drive around the ridge and I'm looking out, and there's this thumb sticking up: a column above the inversion, just starting to bubble up. I called up and I said, "Lanky [Craig Lechleiter], there's this column that's starting to poke through," and I called Buck [his assistant, Dan Buckley], and I said, "You guys get out of there. I want you up on the ridge, and I want you to come around to the safety zone," and, "Lanky, I don't think this is a good assignment."

There was definitely some disagreement with the powers that be, but the disagreement only lasted about an hour, because the whole drainage went up. That was one of those things: nothing could've happened all day. It could've just gone down. But I saw that thing poking up, and I said, "That hasn't happened before."

Greg Keller (Eldorado, 1985–1996; Modoc, 2000–2007)

Bill Bowman is a retired FMO from the Eldorado, and he was a Type 1 incident commander. He told Rax and I one day that in his career he had never seen a burnout or backfire operation as big as the one on the Wheeler fire. For day after day, we had fire literally rolling away from itself and just consuming large tracts of land. I would have to say that firing operation and that fire behavior on the Wheeler for a sustained period was probably the most intense I had ever seen.

The Marre fire: I saw a couple of occasions where the fuels in front of the flame front vaporized before the flames got there.

Brit Rosso (Arrowhead, 1996–2006)

I'll just rattle off the top three. Maybe not in this order of priority, but the ones that jump out. [Nineteen] eighty-eight, Canyon Creek fire, Montana, Scapegoat Wilderness: we saw the fire jump the Blackfoot River, and it was basically doing what we felt was just shy of area ignition, when it gets to the point where everything is just going up at once, spontaneously.

When we were trying to backfire this thing, we had one hotshot—our fastest person—on one drip torch and one supervisor—I don't want to say running, but moving at a very fast pace—along a dozer line, spot-lighting about every 50 feet in mature lodgepole. That fire moved into the forest, and at about 20 or 30 feet in was completely up in the canopy and moving away from us with just a drip of juice about every 50 feet.

The main fire, when it came up, . . . might have been three-quarters of a mile away from us when it came up this main ridge. We saw an air tanker fly over it and do a salvo drop. The whole drop came out—it didn't even hit the ground—and got sucked up in the vortex of the column; the drop just swirled up. We're feeling the radiant heat pretty good a half to three-quarters of a mile away.

That same year, '88, another fire in Montana . . . three in the morning, from camp, where it's spotting a mile ahead of itself in timber, running downhill at night, under drought conditions. That was fairly impressive.

This last year [2002], on the Rodeo-Chedeski fire, I saw good fire behavior. We knew it was dry; we knew all those things, but to really see it. I had heard from previous supes who had been out to R3 earlier in the year in the P-pine belts saying, 'Hey, watch it." . . . What impressed me was the short duration in which the fire transitioned from a fairly mild backing fire to an extremely aggressive, spotting-ahead-of-itself, head fire with just a mild wind shift of three to four miles an hour. That turned it from a fairly benign backing fire to an extremely aggressive head fire spotting out ahead of itself and taking out whole drainages in less than a minute all the way around us.

Also this last year, down on the Cleveland National Forest, where the live fuels were running in the mid-40s in the chaparral: burning manzanita at night, six- to ten-foot tall chaparral at night where you usually can't get the stuff to burn. We were lighting at two, three, four in the morning, just spot-lighting it in the sticks and the dirt and the leaves underneath it; and it was standing up and consuming it, taking it down to one- to two-foot stobs—something that is difficult to do in the daytime, without a lot of slope or wind in our favor.

Paul Musser (Flagstaff, 1990–2004)

One of my first years with the Forest Service, we were on the Stanislaus. Back in those days, you made stands. They had us lined up along the Cherry Road—this was all 200-foot-tall timber. You could just hear it coming off in the distance, coming through the tops. You could hear it five, ten, maybe fifteen minutes before it ever got there. You hear it roaring, and it's getting darker, and it's getting darker, and it's getting darker. We'd pretreated it with a lot of retardant and stuff like that, and the Cherry Road's pretty wide. When it hit us finally, it was everybody going in and picking up all the spots. Just remembering the sound of it coming toward you and knowing it was coming. . . .

[On how important it is to ask the locals about their fire behavior.] You look at the way South Canyon burned—because it ran in Gambel oak. It never runs in Gambel oak, but you talk to the local people: the month before, they'd had an escaped burn that had nuked Gambel oak. That's one of the things you would need to tell somebody.

We kill hotshots where hotshots don't go very often. When you look at that canyon at South Canyon, from there you can look just down the road and there's Battlement Creek, where Mormon Lake burned up. It's a place in that canyon where hotshots don't fight fire very much because usually it won't burn. But when it does burn, we seem to get into some trouble.

Fred Schoeffler (Payson, 1981–2007)

A fire behavior phenomenon I've seen increase in the last several years is downhill, downslope, or down-canyon runs, notwithstanding sundowners and conditions like that. When you see this kind of fire behavior, it's time to have a safe place nearby to go or be in that good safe area. The topography and terrain should give you at least some indicators of this. Always talk to and heed the locals and what they tell you about weather, especially winds and associated fire behavior. So many firefighters ignore this Watch Out to their detriment.

Always pay attention to the smoke and smoke columns and heed their warnings to you. Generally, the fire will follow the smoke. I remember on the Sadler fire in Nevada there were these odd puffs of smoke that would pull to one area for hours early in the shift. Then later, when fire behavior increased, the fire went exactly where the smoke had been traveling. I saw this type of phenomenon on the B&B Complex in Oregon, too, resulting in radical downhill and down-canyon fire behavior days later.

Sagebrush is wicked stuff. Range fires in this fuel type almost always exhibit radical fire behavior and almost always have the potential for extremely dangerous fire behavior. These fires can be a lot of fun, but you've got to keep your head in the game and pay attention, especially during burnouts—even small ones—and particularly as fire behavior increases. There are many incident reports, burnovers, burn injuries, shelter deployments, and burned vehicles in this fuel type. Study them and talk with the firefighters, crews, and overhead who work in these fuel types and regions.

During burnout operations, there are times to go balls to the wall and get it done, particularly in light fuels like grass. There are other times in heavier fuels [that] it's better to stop for short periods if you won't lose your pull, let your progressive safety zone cool off a bit, then move on again. Burning operations can be some of the most dangerous fire behavior times, so pay attention and regulate your heat and such accordingly. Don't be the trigger to set the whole thing off. Anybody can burn. Burning responsibly is the key.

It's amazing what drastic and intense fire behavior can be generated with the use of aerial ignition and yet cannot be duplicated on the ground by conventional firing methods. I call it "aerial-induced fire behavior." It's included in the [Payson Hotshot Crew's] "19th Watch Out": "death from above." I'll agree that there are times to pour it on and get with it. More often, though—in fact, most times—aerial ignition needs to be slow and deliberate, with patience being the key word. There are some really skilled aerial ignition firing bosses who can do this. However, I can recount numerous aerial-induced fire behavior incidents, including prescribed burns, in every region and in every fuel type that went awry because of lack of insight, forethought, or patience while ignoring both current and expected fire behavior, and finally ignoring and/or unaware of current or predicted weather. Several of these were very close calls and could be classified as near misses, not to mention all-out firestorms.

Alignment, using Doug Campbell's Prediction System terminology, is an excellent tool for a cumulative phenomenon that must be heeded. It's relatively easy to predict when this will occur and when to safely and tactically pull off an operation and, when it's time, discontinue tactics and pull out to safety. It's fairly straightforward looking back at all the burnover and fatality fires and being able to see the alignment that should have been recognized and heeded. When things are in alignment, it's time to be on your toes with a nearby good, safe place to go. Always take heed during burnout operations when there is alignment.

Ron Bollier (Silver City, 1993–1995; Carson, 1996–1997; Fulton, 1998–2013)

The Grand Prix had awesome fire behavior. You just knew it had a life of its own. Usually you can go to a fire and you can look at it, and you can deal with it. This one, you looked at it, and you go, "God, how do we trick this thing?" . . . It's not, "We'll go in here, put it in, tie it off here, and then we'll burn this." It's . . . how can we trick it and run it up on the hill, and when can we pick our opportunity to do something like that? . . . How can we keep it up on the hill the longest we can before it comes back down into the city again? . . . We put line in going up into nowhere, just to hold it up on the hill. The kids who are working for you, they're wondering, "What the heck are we doing?" . . . Everything we're doing is going against everything we taught them, and that's not how it should work. But you do what you have to do in that situation.

Ron Regan (Del Rosa, 1977–1997)

Montana in '73 was an eye-opener. It was very wind-driven and fuel-loaded. The Dry Falls fire was the name of it. Burned about 5,000 acres from about one o'clock in the afternoon till sundown. It was pretty explosive.

The fire here in 2003, in October, the Old fire, was intense fire behavior, burning downhill, and wind-driven by a Santa Ana in eucalyptus and ryegrass and palm trees. Every palm tree in the north in San Bernardino, I think, burned. It was very intense fire behavior. It had been a ten-year drought, and the fuel load wasn't severely heavy because we'd had other fires, but the intensity of that fire, once it got into the structures, spotting from one to the other—we had embers the size of briquettes flying through the air off those palm trees, going into attics and torching other houses.

Bob Wright (Sacramento, 1990–2002)

One was the Snake Bones fire in 1987. . . . I think it was July or June. It was felled and bucked timber. The pilings started—they didn't clean the tail block. The fire started there, and it ran up and burned up the yarder, and the loader, and everything.

We were only 40 miles away, if that far. We weren't the first crew there. There was a road at the bottom, and there was a road that went up top.

There were 400-foot flames above the 250-foot Doug firs, and the Doug firs were six foot on the stump. Four, five, six foot on the stump. It was ripping Doug fir stumps out of the ground, this thing was cranking so much.

We pulled up at the bottom and anchored on the west side in an old reprod unit—second growth, real small timber. We started flanking it because the fire was heading off to the northeast, so we could work the flank. It was logging slash, thinning slash, we were in. . . . We put a 40-foot swath through there in the timber, and a six-foot handline, because it needed [that] to hold it. We started working that until we got to the top of the ridge that next morning. Then we started firing. The next night it rained, and everything was pretty much mop-up.

They've got pictures in our district of a Forest Service truck: it looks like a little Tinkertoy in a clear-cut, where the fire was going through those clear-cuts. The ground was shaking. I've never seen old growth burn . . . like that. I've seen it burn hot, but not like that. In fact, it was so hot [that] all our Sigg bottles on the line were splitting. I got rid of those Sigg bottles after that. I went to plastic Nalgenes. (Laughs.)

Steve Dickenson (La Grande, 1990; Redmond, 1994)
When you're in chaparral in the South Zone [of Region 5], you've got these topographic breaks, which can make it a lot more complicated, but horizontal roll. Everything's the same height, and everything's available in the same place. It happens in the lodgepole of Michigan and Minnesota, too. Fire will burn so fast, and it will leave an edge that you can lay a straightedge on. A six-mile horizontal roll is something I've wanted to see that I never have [seen]. A key indicator for any firefighter is, doesn't matter if it's 40 [feet high], doesn't matter if it's 6. If it's homogeneous—if it's the same throughout its matrix—that's as dangerous a fuel bed as anything, I don't care if it's bricks or chamise or otay cypress. . . . That arrangement, that availability, that continuity in there—if it's

homogeneous, that's where the power of the fire takes over. That's something to always be aware of: the structure of that fuel bed.

That happened to them at Thirtymile—that's how that fire took off. There's a little chunk of fir in there that's just 16 feet high, and if you go up there and look at that bend in the road, right before the deployment site, there it is: the whole dynamic of getting that thing moving, not being able to get the heat out of those steep canyons. That heat's rising, and it's cooling. It's cooler, it's heavier, it's wanting to fall back, but the heat underneath is still trying to push. But this is heat, this isn't smoke; there's some particulate and stuff, but it can't get out of those canyons. It's going to lay, and it went horizontal. That's why it got those guys and they didn't get burned. . . . When that energy laid down, it was going up the pipe—going out the venturi.

Mark Linane (Los Prietos/Los Padres, 1973–2001)
Under Santa Ana conditions, when you've got battling winds— [this is what] caught the guys on the Loop fire. You really need to pay attention when you've had an offshore wind that's pushing down into the coast in the morning, and it's getting to be about ten o'clock, and you're still chasing it down this way. The wind is going to take a change, and you need to be heads-up for that change.

Rusty Witwer (Mendocino, 1978; Hobart/Tahoe, 1979–1995)
The religion in the subalpine fir is: don't even think about taking a drip torch and doing any burning in subalpine fir. It doesn't work. You can't get it to go at ten in the morning, and it won't burn at night. The only time you can get it to carry is when it wants to go. . . . We fired [Bill] Sandborg's famous catline in Yellowstone, drove the fire with a 60-degree-layover column into the black—not one layover, not one ember. As soon as the column dissipated the next day, it was 25 to 100 spot fires outside the line, and it was all gone.

Subalpine fir, in my opinion, [is] the scariest fuel type in the system. It's not the brush of Southern California or Northern California. . . . As long as you treat brush as liquid gasoline and you've got one foot in the black, you'll be fine. When you try to go indirect in the subalpine fir, it very rarely works. If you can get it into a pine stand, a different fuel type where you can get more of an underburn and less residual spotting potential, you're better off. The stuff is designed to burn—it's designed to burn by spotting—and even with the wind at your back, you're not going to be very successful. You just need to be patient in subalpine fir. Stay on the edge. Plumb it, line it, hold onto it between one and five o'clock in the afternoon, spike, get back after it when the RH [relative humidity] gets above 25 percent, and chuck away at it. You're not going to make an easy kill in subalpine fir, in my opinion.

I used to teach the crew diurnals all the time. . . . It's real easy to fight fires based on the time of day in the Sierras because the wind will go against the water during the day and with the water at night, because the water runs from east to west, downhill. The only place I've seen that not occur is on a chunk of the Snake River, where it hooks north to south, and it runs with the water during the day and against it at night. But for most cases, water flows downhill to a valley, valley heats up, so your canyon winds come up against the water during the day and then flow down at night. Also, in a combination with the canyon winds, you've got the slope winds, and obviously we all know they go upslope during the day and downslope at night.

When I flew into a new shift on a fire, I would look down and figure out which way the water was flowing, and then I was tickled during the day if I was where the water was hitting me in the legs because it told me I had the wind at my back, versus being on the upper stream side, where I'd have the up-canyon winds in my face. When I would have the up-canyons in my face—without any forecast or with frontal winds coming through, or passage or foehn winds, or upper level disturbances—that just immediately put my hair and my antennas up.

Art Torrez (Vista Grande, 1994–2004)

Marble Cone fire, on Cone Peak, 1977. Our assignment was to fire out the dozer line on North Coast Ridge Road. Everything's going smooth; next thing you know, things are picking up. We actually saw flocks of birds being sucked in: there was so much energy going in that it sucked these birds into the flame. Then we began to realize that there was a lot of energy going on.

Something that I had seen a long time ago out at Pocatello, Idaho: we had hotline, and we were going through sage fields, and we heard this noise. We were half a chain from tying in, and we started hearing this humming noise. Everybody's looking, like, "What's that noise?" About that time, a fire whirl comes out, right about where we're at, a real rude awakening.

South Dakota, 2003, I heard that noise again. Our assignment was to go ahead and hold the fire from crossing the dozer line. . . . I had my crew committed, two dozers committed, constructing line, and I heard that sound again. Right away I started looking, and there's fire on the plateau up above, and you could see that something was lining up to happen. I had pulled my group out, and they were all wondering what was going on because it wasn't real obvious. But it was a gut feeling of mine, and it wasn't more than five or ten minutes later [that] we had fire whirls dancing down that mesa that came off and overran our line.

Lance Honda (Redmond, 1992–1997; Prineville, 1997–2009)

Vertical fire is good, horizontal fire is bad. You don't think in terms of fire, but energy. High heat kills, so when the energy is going straight up, that's not necessarily a bad thing. It means the fire's not moving very fast, and the energy is going up as opposed to away from people or not at their level. . . . Horizontal fire means that fire is moving fast somewhere, whether it's away from you, toward you, or at right angles from you, or just at a distance. That's important . . . because if the wind shifts and you've got horizontal fire coming toward you, you've got all that energy. . . . When it starts going sideways or horizontally, then that's not good.

What are the most important lessons you've learned, maybe the hard way?

Dan Fiorito (Union, 1996–2006)

The biggest mistakes I have made, and the ones I learned the most from, were the times I got my head down and lost my situational awareness. It is easy to get tunnel vision and lose sight of the big picture. Earlier in my career there were times when I would get tunnel vision focusing on some important task, and I would look up and find myself in a bad situation. Being aware of your surroundings on the fireline is probably the best way to keep yourself from making the mistakes that a lot of us made early in our careers.

Ron Bollier (Silver City, 1993–1995; Carson, 1996–1997; Fulton, 1998–2013)

Biggest one on supervision is not listening. Don't be so pig-headed that you don't listen. Because you can be in charge and not be in charge, you have to listen to who's working for you. When you first get in charge it's like, "I don't care what anybody says—especially the people who work for me." You're going to falter, and you're going to stumble. It's going to be hard. If you have a good set of values and what you believe in, you can learn from the people who are working for you by listening to them. It might not be what you want to do, but if you can still make it fit in your values, they're telling you what you're doing wrong. You just have to be able to hear it. If you choose not to hear it, then that's a big mistake. A couple years it took me—of not hearing— to decide I needed to hear a little more.

Greg Overacker (Stanislaus, 1979–2006)

Probably pretty much everything. I keep buying taller boots so I stop beating the crap out of the front of my legs. I'd like to think that experience teaches you . . . how costly things can be, not to take things for granted. Probably my personal life has been most impacted. Two or three wonderful relationships have been lost. Maybe don't get so focused on this job that you can't take care of what's real. . . . There's nothing more scary than a single superintendent with nothing going on. He never wants to go home. He doesn't care if you have a friend in the world. He just wants to fight fire. You have to remember: those are people. You've got to take them home to ensure that everything's going to be okay.

Bob Bennett (Horseshoe Meadow, 1989–2006)

In Yellowstone in '87 we were dropped off by the bus, and the bus left. We were holding the road, and the fire was burning parallel with the road. I remember talking to the engine captain and going, "God, I hope this wind doesn't switch." As soon as that word left my mouth, the wind shifts and here comes this 200-foot wall of flame toward us. . . . I go, "Where's the goddamn bus?" We started running up the road, and luckily they brought some pickups back. We all jumped in the trucks, but it was one of those, "Oh my God, what did I do? Where's the bus?" and the bus wasn't there.

The reason we didn't have the bus was they had two crews on one bus, and they dropped us off and took the bus away with the other part of the crew. I just went, "No more." Never again will I be in a place where I don't have a bus or something where there wasn't a safety zone. That's when I was a captain. I just went, "Oh, this sucks." It melted the pavement where we were.

Ben Charley (Horseshoe Meadow, 1974–1989)

Go to the local people and find out what's going on in their country as far as the winds, what happens at certain times of the day.

That's something that's really important. I found that out. I lost about 600 acres. (Laughs.) I didn't feel very good about it because I half killed my guys trying to pick it up. We picked it up finally but almost killed my people who had to do it. That's the thing: I didn't ask, and they [the locals] knew it because, when I got back down to the bottom of the hill, they said, "You know, this happens all the time. This wind does this." I didn't find out what was going on. [After that] I'd go out and say, "What happens here? Does anything happen between here and there? What's it do?"

Ken Jordan (Sierra, 1998–2014)

I'd say what I did bad mostly was the drinking thing. I was totally into that and harassing new crewmen. . . . Nowadays, like I said, you don't want to fight battles—it distracts you from the job at hand. Anything you can do to avoid fighting those battles, you be proactive about it. Before, I wasn't. I was in people's faces. I was encouraging drinking as a crew. Just everything opposite of what I do now, and I learned from that. I made huge mistakes in those areas.

Not involving the family, my family. Never, ever called my family from a fire. Never. I just didn't do it. Now I try to make it a daily thing. We've got stinkin' cell phones. Let the guys use their cell phone, as long as it's not glued to their ear when we need them. Those were the biggest mistakes that I've learned from. And I'm still learning. I know when I screw up.

Paul Musser Becomes Just a Little More of a Skeptic

On the Wheeler fire we had about a 12-mile piece of line to fire. We were firing, coming down the line, and we wanted to get fire established on the next ridge over so it could run. I'd been a captain on the crew for three or four years at that time. We got down in there, and we were looking, and there was this grassy area down in the bottom of the drainage. It went all the way around the edge of the drainage, and it looked real good—kind of looked like an old road. I talked to the supe, and I said we needed to get some fire established down in there so it didn't shoot across or something like that.

The fire behavior officer came up and he said, "That's an old road that comes out of the bottom. You can take a squad down in there and you can light the edge of that and come out the bottom." "You sure?" "Yeah, I've been down there, scouted it out; it looks good. It'll take you right out the bottom, and you've got no problems."

The crew was going to be firing out along the top, so we were going to be under them. We just had to hook the front of it and make it out before they did. I say, "Are you sure?" "Yep. You can go ahead and take a squad down in there and light that." I said, "Nope, I take one other of my choice. Two of us down in there, and that's all," so I picked one of the sawyers off the crew.

We got down in there, started lighting the other side, and it definitely got the results we wanted. It ripped and then just started sucking everything the crew was lighting right over top of us. We got it pretty well-established, and we were watching, and it was starting to come over top of us pretty good. We said, it's time to start bringing it around the corner and get out. We lit around the corner and it was just a wall of brush—no road. I called Barry [Callenberger], and I said, "Hey, there's no road. It's a wall of brush. We're stuck." At this point, we were looking at fighting brush and trying to get out of there, and of course everything was coming over top of us.

Luckily, our forest helicopter happened to be on the fire, and a very good friend of mine was in it. The forest helicopter flew up the drainage to the bottom, and he hovered over top of us and down the canyon a little ways. He backed down the canyon, and he just kept yelling, "Right side of that bush. Left side of that bush. Right side of this bush." He just picked us a trail down the canyon until we finally got to one point, and then he said, "Okay, turn right, and get to the top of the ridge." We ran up to the top of the ridge.

By then we were just laying flat on the catline. We were a little bit tired. The fire behavior officer came by . . . , and he just looked at us. I said a few things to him. He walked off, and we never saw him again. I guess he just went back into camp and got demobed or something. Everybody gets suckered in sometimes. I didn't walk down the canyon and check it. I went by what somebody else was saying.

Kurt LaRue Lights Himself Off the Edge

It would be early in my time through Fulton: we're burning a line around a horseshoe-shaped canyon. We're burning at night. Things are going well. No big problem; getting a decent buffer in. It's not a huge canyon, but it's decent sized; got a lot of brush and crud in it. Bill [Sandborg] sent me down to go burn the bottom of the canyon to add depth to our firing and clean things up.

What we've got is a line that comes around the ridgetops with a drainage running down through the middle of the horseshoe with the crew burning the rim off. We've got a buffer backing in. I did interior burning like this a lot: I would walk in to the bottom of the canyon, up to where the fire was, behind where guys were burning, and I'd start burning the bottom, just lighting the bottom off, and just slick it off and make it nice and clean. Easy to do, not a problem.

Bill had always talked about taking somebody with me, but nobody else wanted to go down in the canyon that night. You have to put a pair of chaps on or your legs get all torn up in the brush. I got geared up and went down there with my fusees, doing my thing.

I'm be-bopping along, just happy, dumb, and fat, lighting both sides of the canyon. I step around some bushes I had lit right behind me with fusees in grass and chamise, and I find I had burned to the top of about a 30-foot drop in the rocks. I'm looking around, and it just scares the living hell out of me.

I ended up falling. I tried to crawl down and ended up falling. I got singed from the embers lighting the fuels below me and was limping about and all that good stuff. Of course, I was too embarrassed to tell anyone I got hurt doing it; you just keep doing your thing and get back to the trucks.

That has stayed with me till today. If you burned interior you still had to carry your tool, and you always worked in a group of two. I'm sure my kids got tired of the lecture over the years: you're not working out there to stand next to each other and bullshit. One of you is supposed to be out walking in front of the other one so this doesn't happen to you. They say, "Yeah, yeah," and then they go wander off in there and burn and learn their own lessons.

What mistakes do you see other supervisors making on and off the fireline?

Steve Karkanen (Lolo, 1990–2011)

People need to be mentored and not forgotten about, not just left to their own devices. That's tough, in the fire world, for a person to be hired on in a career position and then not be mentored and brought along. They need to have somebody there who has a better set of skills keeping an eye on that person and keeping them focused in the right direction. . . .

Greg Vergari (Union, 1980–1987)

I saw people treating their crew like they were second-graders, like they were kids, and leadership did this all the time—not spending enough time with people to make them better firefighters, not showing them what their mistakes were and how to do it right. I have to say that in the past few years I have seen the crews doing a lot better. I see a lot of professionalism today. I didn't feel that way in the '90s, but today I see crews being well-managed for the most part.

Ted Mathiesen (Arroyo Grande Flight Crew, 1990–2007)

One of the biggies is not knowing what you don't know, and having an ego, and continuing on with it anyway. . . . I'm part of the investigation team on the Tuolumne fire, and one of the biggies that's coming out of that is not recognizing what you don't know and trying to carry out a high-risk tactic—downhill, indirect line construction—having never done it before, and knowing that it can be done but not having those slides there, and not knowing how to do it, and saying, "Wait a minute. I need some advice," or, "I need some help," [as opposed to] just having the cocky attitude, "Well, we're gonna do it anyway."

Another one I'm seeing more and more is the hesitancy to engage. In the old days—and I'm not saying it was the right way—but it was, "We're going to go to work, and this is what we're going to do." Guys aren't being aggressive like that anymore. . . . There's always productive work that can be done. It may not be the objective, but there's still work that can be done. I see people going, "Here's the objective, but we're not going to do it, so we're going to sit." I don't think that's right, but it's hard to second-guess them. What are you going to say? If they say," Well, it's all about safety," how are you going to countermand that? You can't.

Craig Lechleiter (Redding, 1986–2002)

I think people with power, people with authority, they can give direction whether it's right or wrong. . . . They don't realize the impact they have on other human beings. Whether it's on the fireline or in this building [the Forest Service Northern Operations Center], if they don't reason before they speak or act or delegate—I've seen them hurt lots of people, career-wise.

It's not just your parents who build your self-esteem; it's your supervisor. Your second-line supervisor can bring you to your knees if you get any smell, sniff, indicator, [that] they don't trust your judgement. . . . Not that I was exposed to that, but I had my moments. I've seen other people who will just destroy people— to suicide. Unfortunately, I've seen quite a few people who have worked for me or around me kill themselves.

People, in a different sense, can take out a whole crew because they compromise procedure. This is a process: you don't go unless you've done your risk assessment. It's easy: be patient, take your time. But no, operations section chiefs will intimidate division group supervisors into doing stuff they would never do, and they're not even on scene. In some management team meeting, they come up with some strategy: "How are we gonna do this? Okay, we've got the tactics. Let's go do it." They don't think. They disconnect somehow. That was so frustrating to me over the years, how disconnected those people would get—they implement this plan and then kill somebody and not take responsibility for it.

People with power: watch out. I tell my crew, watch them. You've got to get your situational awareness on your supervisor. Being a hotshot superintendent is the most fun because you have to adapt to a management team. You've got to adapt to a division group supervisor you don't even know. You've got to influence an operational team or a management team to change their strat-egy because you know it isn't going to work: "You don't have the fireground to make this work. You don't have the weather." I used to get so upset with people, and I still do, but now I control it a little bit more. I just say no. It took me a long time to be able to say, "No. I'm not going." In front of my peers and the crew.

Stan Stewart (Los Padres, 2000–2009)

A lot of people get out there, and they're looking around, and they're seeing this much of the picture [a little piece], and this much of the picture [a different little piece]. I still blame a lot of the fatality stuff on lack of knowledge: they're just not get-ting the picture. Saw a lot of heads-down structure firefighting on the Cedar [fire] that was incredible. Just like, "What are you guys doing?" Lot of tunnel vision and not seeing what's going on around them. A lot of those were guys who shouldn't have been there in the first place—wrong engines in the wrong place.

Probably the biggest ones: guys who are too damn lazy—where they're hanging out, getting ready to retire—so they don't train, or they send their guys over to us to train because they don't want to do it. We get a lot of guys from the engines who we've taught, and they're good hands, but they've never had any-thing. We had one kid last year who'd had three seasons who said he got more out of our critical package than he'd had in three years. What've you been doing for the last three years? That's a huge part of your job: you're supposed to be educating them.

Kurt LaRue (Diamond Mountain, 1993–2001)

The most serious mistake I see is from a safety point of view: more and more supervisors are getting away from basic fire sup-pression and trying to fit everybody's political needs into what they do. It's not just pick the ridge with the best chance of suc-cess, bang a line down it, and fire it anymore. There are a lot of political needs, whether it be limited and unclean burns, or it's got to be this ridge and not that one, and I see guys making more and more accommodation for politics when I really don't think it's appropriate.

A non-fire manager will bring together a rancher, a recreationist—a group of folks with different agendas—and they all leave with a little bit of what they wanted. Nobody's fully happy, but they can live with the decision. I guess that's known as good management nowadays. Problem is, they bring that to fire. On fires now, the bug guy doesn't want you down over here, and the bald eagle guy doesn't want you over there, and the sacred ferns are over there, and you can't go over there because of the holy rocks. You've got all this stuff keeping you from using the best practices of fire suppression or adding to your crews' exposure time trying to complete questionable assignments.

On fires now, you're looked on as a bit of an arrogant prick when you don't deal with the special interest non-fire groups like they're used to being dealt with in non-fire situations. As they see it, everybody's going to get something; everybody's going to give something up. You can only go so far in fire before you have to draw a line and say, no: beyond here, it has to be a certain way. Well, now you're the arrogant prick superintendent who nobody can deal with—what an asshole. Which is what you hear. And so often the case is you're dealing with people who have fire experience but they're still on the upside of the curve.

I was on a fire in New Mexico a few years ago, and a guy was just dead serious explaining to me that it was okay that we had that smoke down below us because "these conifer stands never burn." I'm standing there looking at him, and we're on this ridge, and I can see six of these ridges, and every one of them is black from top to bottom. The fire's, like, 50,000 acres. It's the Pigeon fire some years ago on the Gila. I can see all these knobs, which have burned off behind him, and he's dead serious that, no, it never burns all the conifer off. Well, buck, you're in X year of a drought, and it's burning them all off this year, and what a prick I am because, no, I'm not going to accommodate him on this ridge.

Brit Rosso (Arrowhead, 1996–2006)

Not trusting in their subordinate leaders and in their people. . . . Trying to do the whole job by themselves. Not delegating at all: trying to do everything themselves without using their subordinate leaders to assist them in the task, in the mission.

One mistake that's easy to make for young supervisors is disciplining employees in public. There are very few exceptions when you should discipline in public. It should almost always be that you discipline in private and praise in public. . . . If it's a safety issue and they almost cut someone's head off, then yeah, make an example, make sure that everyone understands that. Don't make it real personal. Just say, "Hey, when you swing that Pulaski over your head, you call out and make sure everyone's clear." Disciplining employees in public is a huge mistake because you destroy that person's confidence, and you show lack of respect to the others. You can do a lot of damage if you do that, and I've seen it done.

Another mistake would be a supervisor getting in an argument or a fairly heated discussion with a subordinate leader, having a disagreement in front of the crew. That needs to be done one-on-one, and that's fine. That's a good thing: it can be healthy to work things out. But you do not do that in front of the crew. You cannot show the crew that there is dissension in the leadership ranks. The crew goes, "What the hell is going on here? Who's in charge? Who's running this ship?" That's a mistake that young leaders can make.

Richard Aguilar (El Cariso, 1974; Wolf Creek, 1975–1997)

Hotshot superintendents, a lot of them, the mistake is that they become the eyes across the canyon, the lookout. I think a superintendent should be with the crew, making the decisions, making sure the job is getting done right. As soon as he leaves, things will slow down on the crew, a lot of them, and they're not doing the job.

J. W. Allendorf (Wallowa–Whitman, 1980; Arrowhead 3, 1981)

One of the things I see—and I think it's even more prevalent now—is trying to be someone they're not on the fireline, biting off more than they can chew with their experience level. Like I said, the current supes don't seem to get the fire exposure we used to have.

This is only opinion, but I believe this based on what I'm seeing: too many of the modern-day superintendents, they never believed like I did when I went into the job that that's what they wanted to do for their career. . . . [Now] it's a stepping stone, and it's just a job. They go there, and they come home. They don't live it. If the phone rings and it's a crewmember who's got a problem or something like that, it's a pain in the ass to them, more so than helping part of the family.

The way I was treated by Linane and all the guys, I was part of that family, and if I had a problem and I needed to call Mark, he was there to help me deal with it, as was Stanley [Stewart] or anybody else. They could help me out. But none of them treated it—and I didn't—as just a job. It was my life, and that was my commitment.

In fact, at times my wife said I was more committed to the hotshot program than our marriage. Summer vacations were out because I was not gonna miss a frickin' fire, and I was not going to let the guys down. It was that simple. I had a job on the hotshot crew; that came first, and it caused some grief. Fortunately for me, she was pretty understanding. Also, as much as she disliked some of the things that went with the job, she was also very thankful that I had a job that I loved.

Fred Schoeffler (Payson, 1981–2007)

Complacency can be a common and dangerous mistake: "This is just a typical day," or, "just a typical hazard tree," or, "I've seen this kind of fire a dozen times before." Not willing to change when things need to change, especially in an operational sense. How about when the weather is bad all day, the winds are not favorable, but later things change in your favor? Be cautious, but then go for it: fight fire aggressively while providing for safety first. While being discerning, be willing to try out new, innovative ideas or concepts that the younger crowd brings to the forefront.

Succumbing to "political correctness" and the many manifestations of Orwellian "thought police" and the human resource crowd. The "hostile environment" is the fireline, not some conjured-up, alleged scenario. Nothing discriminates more equally than a steep hill on a hot day, with little sleep, in smoke, with a heavy pack.

"Maintain control of your forces at all times" by ensuring that everyone keeps up on hikes, especially on the fireline, so that a squad boss or senior firefighter does not have to stay back with a laggard and end up in a fire shelter or worse. Training realistically, before fires, will virtually ensure safe assignments will follow. The military speaks to this: something to the effect of sweating in training ensures that one will bleed less in battle.

Not dealing with problems or issues as soon as possible, especially disciplinary actions involving unethical or illegal conduct, and poor or unsafe performance. Deal with them now!

Charlie Caldwell (Redding, 1967–1986)

I think I can make it real short and sweet: making line assignments without the expertise to see the full scope of the situation. That's the big one. They've got a map, they've got this, they've flown it; they think they see it all. You don't see it until you get out there on the ground. I had a note here: "Superintendents have a way of changing assignments for safety and effectiveness." (Laughs.)

Ron Bollier (Silver City, 1993–1995; Carson, 1996–1997; Fulton, 1998–2013)
Don't supervise them with threat of firing. That's the worst thing you could do, and I'm seeing it with the new crews we have, and it's only from working around them. They're talking to them like you wouldn't want to be talked to. Talk to them where they can learn from it. They're not just machines.

They're gonna learn the hard way. They're going to learn by a hard, rocky road. You want that crew to perform for you. That's what you want: not because they have to, because they want to.

Shawna Legarza (San Juan, 2002–2007)
I think sometimes there's too much communication, and sometimes there's lack of communication, and people can't seem to find that right balance. By too much communication I mean: when somebody has a medical or something, and the safety guy has to get involved, then the safety trainee, then the ops guy. Then the deputy IC calls, and the ambulance is trying to get in; then the medical unit is calling. There are only a couple people who need to get involved, right? Those people need to talk. Everyone else just listen in.

We had an accident last year where the dozer rolled over and the guy cracked his head open. We had to medevac him out of there. It was me and the air attack talking back and forth, and the division and the ops people were trying to butt in, and I said right then, "I'm going to talk to the air attack and nobody else. You guys talk on this other channel, or you listen in on this channel, because we have a life-and-death situation, and no one else is going to talk to me. It's me and air attack if we're going to get this guy out of here," because the fire was coming at us. It was a bad situation: in a chute, fire, guy with a split head.

Craig Workman (Black Mountain, 1988–2005)

I think the most serious mistake all of us can make is to make this job too complex. It's a very simple job, and we have to keep it simple. We keep adding more stuff: layers on top of layers on top of layers, and we start losing what is important. I think we need to keep it simple.

One of my examples I use with the guys is, you have an engine, and you go out and you say to the guy, "Can you pump it to the top of the hill?" and he gets really into the thing, grabbing the charts and figuring out his hydraulics, and he'll figure in all his hose and all his fittings, and he'll say, "Oh, yeah, I can't pump to the top of the hill." Somebody else that's run that engine for years, he'll look up the hill, and he'll say, "Crank 'er up, and we'll see if it'll go there." We'll keep it simple, and we'll find out if it'll work or not.

Lance Honda (Redmond, 1992–1997; Prineville, 1997–2009)

If I'm a strong person and if I don't have strong leadership, I walk all over somebody. I'll walk all over them and then I'll back up and do it again until I'm bored. On crews that are like that, morale is low, discipline is bad, production is not good, and safety's not good. . . . I've seen that mistake made a lot.

Mark Linane (Los Prietos/Los Padres, 1973–2001)

Number one: division supervisors not listening to, not using, their expert power. Thinking their authority, their badge makes them more experienced for their position. Not using the talent and skill that does it on a daily basis, when they do it occasionally.

Probably the other big mistake I watch people make: because it's written in the plan, that's what we're going to do. A plan is only as good as the first bullet; after that, plans don't mean shit because you've got to be able to be flexible, make changes, initiate changes. I watch folks unwilling or unable to do that. Task-itis, or mission focus: some people get locked on this mission, this focus, not the big picture. When you see this big head, a column on this fire runnin' and gunnin' over here, and this guy's worried about whether you're mopping up down here, the issue isn't whether this piece of line holds, because this means absolutely squat, shit, nothing, sport. We need to move out and get to the big picture. Taking the things that are easy to manage and avoiding the hard things, such as the decision to change tactics, give up some big country to get it done easier—those kinds of things.

What do you teach your people about fatality fires?

Every time is supposed to be the last, and instead we've ended up with the worst ever. In 2013 we mourned the 19 Granite Mountain Hotshots from Prescott, Arizona, killed on the Yarnell Hill fire. The quotes in this section are from interviews done before that, but their lessons are evergreen.

Stan Stewart (Los Padres, 2000–2009)

I guess it would be really good if everybody could hear what Gordon King said today.[18] He wasn't really saying what went on with the fire—just to see the effect it can have, what can happen if you screw up, if you're not paying attention for whatever reason, the aftereffects it's going to have on you.

I think that's the key thing, actually putting some names with some faces there, so it's real. . . . That just ruined Gordon King's life. I can't imagine how anybody went 40 years without talking to anybody about it. That's pretty gnarly. That's a pretty heavy message that he has to deal with forever.

---

[18] Gordon King spoke at the R5 Hotshot Workshop in March 2005 about being the superintendent of El Cariso when 12 of his crewmembers died on the Loop fire on November 1, 1966. It was the first time ever he'd spoken about it to anyone besides his wife.

Jim Cook (Arrowhead, 1981–1995; Boise, 1996–1998)

First thing . . . , fire doesn't care if you think you're elite; number two: every one of your followers is somebody else's son or daughter; number three: don't compromise escape and safety; number four: trust your instincts. If you look at every one of those fires, somewhere before that happened in every one of those fires, every one of those key decision-makers knew something was wrong.

Absolutely, staff ride is the most effective. Example: I always wondered about the [1949] Mann Gulch fire. I saw all the reports, read *The Race That Couldn't Be Won*, read *Young Men and Fire*. . . . I finally had the opportunity to go on a staff ride. . . . Until I physically went to the site, I always wondered, "Why didn't they just go straight up over the top instead of way back up the canyon?" It's never explained anywhere, really, but you physically can't get up. You literally can't get up anywhere until you get near where the survivors did cross over. You don't realize that; you don't understand that until you go there and you look up and you say, "Oh, I see why they didn't go back up-canyon." That's just one small example of why a staff ride is such an effective tool— because there are some things that don't come out in a nice little bound book or somebody's written interpretation.

You can't believe until you try the Four Horsemen's dash— you can't believe what those guys did in that time that they did it, how far they traveled. Those guys had pure adrenaline going through their blood system. It's unbelievable how far they went in that couple minutes. You don't get a scope of that until you go there and see their graves, where their body markers are, and you see where [foreman] Wag Dodge's escape fire is. It's just incredible how far they travelled in that few minutes over that kind of terrain.

Those are the kinds of things that a staff ride will do for you. It'll put you in their shoes and start you thinking about the decisions they made and why they made those decisions. It's experiential learning. Do that once, and you don't forget those lessons because you were there.

Mark Linane (Los Prietos/Los Padres, 1973–2001)

Probably the one thing I think they should understand: that it's a chain of errors. It's probably never just one thing. There were several pieces of the system that probably failed—like the Columbia [tragedy] we just had[19]. . . . There were probably some system failures, some human failures—both—in recognition of fire behavior changes that were about to happen, breakdowns in leadership, too much mission focus, inability to give up a piece of dirt, staying in too long.

Romero fire is probably a classic one, where the line boss told them to get out: flew in, told them they weren't doing any good, so come on out of there. He [the dozer operator] kept staying there just a little bit longer to polish up the line that wasn't going to do any good anyway. Then, when they got out to the point of no return, made a bad decision because they wouldn't trust the local operator to take the other road out instead of the path that they knew. Two operators got burnt, one operator got killed, and three dozer bosses died.

Probably the thing we don't do very well is we don't document successes. We don't have a good contrast. The military has a lot of documentation on screwups, but they also have a lot of good documentation on successes, and we don't have that. I don't think you should focus entirely on fatality fires. That's a piece of the pie of recognition. I think you should study them, but also you need to take into account that there may have been some reasons: it could be a piece of safety equipment that's mandated now that might've made a difference; had radio communications

---

[19] The February 1, 2003, Space Shuttle *Columbia* disaster, in which the spacecraft broke apart during its return to Earth, killing all seven astronauts on board.

that could've made a difference. And again, it's never just one thing. It's rare that it's unusual fire behavior like all the old fire reports talked about, that it was unusual or erratic fire behavior. There's stuff that's telling you a long time before most of those events happened that shit's about to happen, and I think you just have to be smart enough. Look into those things, recognize the fire behavior, and you can get there.

Rusty Witwer (Mendocino, 1978; Hobart/Tahoe, 1979–1995)
My gist is that we're killing people when it isn't extreme fire behavior. We're killing them when it's short runs. I think extreme fire behavior . . . goes right back to fuel between me and the fire, and that can be when something gets outside my line, then roars up and hits me in the face. Anytime when you go out, expect extreme fire behavior. Extreme fire behavior could be a short run. Anything that kills my crew is extreme fire behavior. I don't need to see 300-foot flame lengths to be worried about whether my crew gets hurt or not. To me, it's steep ground; it's downhill line construction; it's foot not in the black; it's watching the diurnal winds, the hot part of the day.

It depends on the fuel type: Southern California, it's a no-brainer that it's liquid gasoline. You need to treat it as that when you're driving into a fire, or if you're cutting a corner off. If fire gets slapped into that and has the right alignment and right time of day and fuel moistures are low enough, and it's under 140 percent [fuel moisture], it'll put up enough fire that if it wants to get going, it'll kill you. In the timber types, it's when you see multiple spots, if you're getting 100 percent probability of ignition. That's part of the green sheets that isn't hard to learn, in the Fireline Handbook. If you're getting lots of spot fires, you have potential, if everything gets into alignment in timber, for extreme fire behavior.

Why are people still getting killed on the fireline?

Kurt LaRue (Diamond Mountain, 1993–2001)

Because fighting fire is dangerous. Adding to this are our management policies, which are increasing crews' exposure. We stay the safest when we stay at the most basic level: if you're not on the edge, then you're burning a clean edge. As long as we continue to use the tricky forms of fire management that are generated on a computer through a program that generates odds as to our success and safety, we're going to have escalating losses.

To be honest, it has always been just a marvel to me that we don't have more fatalities than we have. When I look back over my years on the line at the rocks that have come down in between two people who are walking in line, and the rock's that big, and they've been doing 10, 12, 15 miles an hour, shooting down the hill. It would've killed either one if it had hit them.

There's more than one instance of stuff like that. The green tree falling over and falling right in the middle of three guys, and they get up laughing, get their picture taken next to it. By all rights, at least one of the three should've died. The woods, when there's a fire going, are inherently dangerous, and if you walk around enough and roll the dice often enough in an inherently dangerous situation, you're going to have fatalities.

It's been interesting how some of the most mundane things we've been doing have had some of the most serious injuries I've dealt with. We mopped up one day on a spot fire on a larger fire; I forget now where we were. I was assistant supe then. Light rolling terrain, high trees and grass. Nothing—just a mop-up shift. Walked off of it along a ridge, coming down to the road. No big walk, nothing tough. Walking down a dirt road, and about 100 yards from our trucks, and I hear somebody fall behind me. Just walking along.

Everybody's laughing, and the guy's laughing. He gets up; his wrist has been slit open by his chain, and you can see the blood coming off the inside of his wrist. I mean, it's going that far [about three feet]. He almost bled to death before we could get him out. He was unconscious. He was bleeding out, and it's the only time I've ever seen one of our EMTs use an actual, no-shit tourniquet. He almost died. All he was doing is walking down the road in a line, fell over; chainsaw just happened to get the wrist just right.

I've seen guys get hit by logs rolling down. One guy had a log about that big [circles wide-open arms] and about 20 feet long. He cut a round off it about that big [about four feet], and they were trying to push it out to make it go. You couldn't have filmed it better for a comedy, for a cartoon. He goes to step over the big fat end, and he's straddling it, stepping over it, and the little end that they're beating on stays there and the big end rolled over on him. It goes all the way over him, and he pops up and falls off on the uphill side, and the log shoots off down the hill. I'm looking over there thinking, "God, he's dead," and he pops up laughing, "Did you see that? That whole log just rolled!" Yeah, I saw that. Fuck, I'm having a heart attack! Didn't have a bruise or anything. We were in heavy forest; I think it just smashed him into two feet of duff as it rolled over top of him.

It has amazed me that we don't have more fatalities. Human nature being what it is, political pressure being what it is, it will never be at a point where we don't have fatalities: people getting into positions where either they don't recognize [the danger] or they're just trying to outperform other people. It's going to happen.

Paul Musser (Flagstaff, 1990–2004)

As long as we are going to fight fire, people are going to make mistakes and people will die. That's not the politically correct thing to say or anything else, but no matter how much training you put into people—we train people to drive a vehicle, and that's considered a pretty safe thing—and we have one drive off the edge of the road and kill someone.

It's a dangerous profession. That's the bottom line: it's dangerous out there. Fire is not one of the things that I worry about as much as I worry about the trees, the rocks, the driving: all the other high-risk things that we do, fire just being one of those.

If a person is not good at their job, we don't go get somebody else; we just sort of work with that person. When most of the selections to teams and higher fire management positions are politically motivated instead of performance motivated, you will always have those people in there who are going to make decisions that are not good.

Tell me about a time when a change you made on a fire prevented something bad from happening.

Richard Aguilar (El Cariso, 1974; Wolf Creek, 1975–1997)

When I had El Cariso, it was the Pacoima fire in 1975. I had people who were survivors from the Decker and the Loop fires, and I got one of them by himself, and I said, "What's happened? What's going on? You guys don't feel comfortable here?" and he said, "No, we don't feel comfortable." I backed off to the top of the ridge, and I started looking down. [Drawing.] The ridgetop is over here, and we're working down. There were some spot fires, and we had a helicopter coming in—not the bucket, but he had the belly [tank], dropping water. He was fanning [the fire], and every time he would come by, I would see some of the smoke come up. I called the crew, and I said, "Let's get out of here. Let's bump out."

The division supe was not an FMO or anything: he was a district ranger. This guy probably didn't have that much fire experience. I told him we were leaving, we weren't gonna be in there—it was too dangerous. He got so upset he called the base camp. He said, "Send me another hotshot crew. El Cariso just chickened out."

I said, "I'm already in trouble. I'm not going to ask him. I'll make my own thing and go back around and go to the bottom of the canyon." There was another hotshot crew at the bottom of the canyon—Texas Canyon—and we were to leapfrog with those guys and dig line uphill. By the time we got down to the bottom, the whole thing went WHOOSH! Blew up.

The next morning, we're digging in daylight, and as soon as we reached the top we were going to go back to base camp. And I saw him [the division supe] standing [there], and he turned his back, but I poked him in the back and I said, "This is why El Cariso chickened out. Can you imagine if we had stayed there what would have happened?" He didn't answer. That was one of the times I know that if we had stayed there, it would have been the third time for El Cariso.

Paul Musser (Flagstaff, 1990–2004)

We were on a little fire there on the Eldorado, and it was in an old burn—a lot of big oak trees. They'd all been dead for ten years. It was burning into the roots and they were falling over. We came up out of the bottom—we'd been cutting some line down in there—and I came up and there's this CDF firefighter mopping up underneath this oak tree and his captain sitting on top of his engine back there, watching. I'm walking by, thinking, "Man, that's stupid." Then I go, "I can't do it," and I walk back down there and tell him, "Pull your hose out. I'll help you pull it out. You can't be underneath this tree." We're pulling it back out, and the tree falls. It's one of those where you just go, "Wow."

I'll always remember Paul Gleason and a couple others after the Dude fire. They'd walked past, thinking it was a bad place to be: "It's none of my business; it's not my crew," and walked on, and then those people died. That's stuck with me over the years. Sometimes you're not very popular when you tell another crew, "Hey, get your guys out."

Dennis Baldridge (Laguna, 1990–2009)

I didn't take on the assignment because we had a training crew and not enough folks to assess the assignment. I think intuitively

I knew the problems but I didn't say anything because the other guy was a superintendent and knew what he was doing. They were cutting midslope line underneath a slopover, and I never asked if they had a lookout who could see below them or anything. When the warning came that there was fire below them, that's when the two guys didn't make it back out through the line and ended up going through the burn. Had I been more aggressive at the time, [I would have] said, "Hey, where's your lookout? You need somebody to look for you? What's going on?" But I just stood back, because we were the Type 2 crew, and they were the Type 1 crew.

I think I could've helped at that time, and maybe they would've had the injuries, maybe not. I don't know. But I knew the risks of that assignment, and I couldn't do it with the crew I had. I still feel bad about that one. I'm not sure, but if I didn't see it, I should've. That's the way that was. That's a tough one there.

There are other times that I may think I see stuff and nothing ever happens. I think in early times in the career, you make decisions based on where you think you fit, and you can look back on them now and say—especially if I knew what I know now—I wouldn't be as silent around other people. At that time, the difference between Type 2s and Type 1s—you just didn't make suggestions to hotshot crews. Even though I probably had as much experience as that superintendent, I just wasn't running a hotshot crew. I wasn't part of the gang. Now I don't think I'd be afraid to say anything, pretty much, to anybody anymore. (Laughs.) The advantage of age.

Charlie Caldwell (Redding, 1967–1986)
The next night after I watched the cats burn up [on the 1971 Romero fire], I had four hotshot crews. [The team] said, "We want to cold-trail this area." . . . We get out there; I've got all these people, and I take one of the superintendents with me. . . . We walked it out, and the whole thing had been underburned. All the brush,

all the leaves were turned up, and you could see the oil on them. I was saying, "Oh, man, this is ready to go." We skirted around that thing, trying to find an edge where we might be able to cold-trail. There was no edge: the whole damn thing was just littered like that. Came out of there, called the line boss and told him, "Good chance this thing's gonna reburn tonight. I don't want to expose those people in there." We're talking 80 people out in that big brush patch.

I told the line boss, "You can come out and look at this situation, and I'm going to hold the crews up here on the line." Before he got out there, the whole thing exploded. Looked just like it did the night before: went up in big fire whirls, and the whole thing just exploded at once. There wouldn't have been a chance for those people.

J. W. Allendorf (Wallowa–Whitman, 1980; Arrowhead 3, 1981)
The Stanislaus Complex in '87: We had a division supe who supposedly had a lot of experience, but he's one of those guys who might have had 12 years, one fire each year. I had a strike team of hand crews. He wanted us to go downhill building handline. We had a strike team of CDF engine crews, and they were going to lay hose behind my strike team of hand crews, down through this canyon, and tie into this road, which was a mile below us.

I went down there before, and it was only, like, nine in the morning when I got down in the bottom. There were spot fires everywhere. They weren't doing much, but they were everywhere. Little smudges, just little wispy smokes and stuff. I hiked back up out of there, and I told him, "We're getting the hell out of here. This thing's gonna go in the next hour or two."

He and I got in damn near a pushing match; it was that serious. I just told him, "I'm taking the crews, we're getting out of here, and you better get out of here, too." I went and talked to the strike team leader from CDF, and I told him what I saw down there. I knew the guy, and he said, "I'm getting the hell outta here, too," so they started rolling up their hose.

This division was really upset. He was going to have my job. I said, "Good. You can have my job. See you later." We took off, and he barely made it out of there. He hung around in there, and he was squawking on the radio about Strike Team Leader Allendorf being insubordinate and all this bullshit. He came outta there like his ass was on fire.

There were a lot of people there. There were two hand crews and five engine crews, and he had never even scouted it.

Ron Bollier (Silver City, 1993–1995; Carson, 1996–1997; Fulton, 1998–2013)

This year [2003], during the Santa Ana wind fires and all of that. When the environment gets so crazy, the human behavior is quite awesome to watch. We were doing structure protection, and we had some OES [Office of Emergency Services] county firemen, municipal firemen, with us. We had one engine with us, and we had half the crew on structure. If you saw any of the footage on TV, some of that stuff was just incredible. We were in a position that was defendable, non-accessible. Once you're there, you're there. You were camping out there.

We were on this structure, and we had one OES engine there and a battalion chief. They couldn't read the fire behavior. What you couldn't read out of a 200-foot wall of flames coming, I'm not sure. They thought they were going to do a frontal assault and protect this structure. . . . We did a little bit of firing around the structure. The main fire had come across to us, and, again, there they were on their frontal assault. . . . You don't need to be a rocket scientist to tell that you're in a bad situation. I'm watching this, and I told our guys, "Get behind the house, and we'll let it take the heat, and then we'll come back out. Then we'll grab the hose and put the house out."

We all dive back behind the house. There they are, ready for a frontal assault, their shields are down. I go grab them, and I say,

"What are you guys doing?" I told them to drop their hose, and I pulled them behind the house. . . . I said, "Just wait here. Wait for the front to hit, and I'll tell you when to go back." . . . The flame front hit, dropped down, mellowed out a little bit, and I said, "Now go to the front of the house and pick up your hoses," so they did.

About that time, the fire repositioned and came up again. The house was sitting on a high knob; everything would come over the top, and it would hit, impinge the house, and lay over everything. . . . About that time, here they went again for another frontal assault, and by the time I get there, they've got blisters on their neck, shields were melting off. . . . They immediately had first- and second-degree burns on the neck and the arms. Their face shields were running off. Just not good. We would've had a couple more fatalities. I mean, when you spray your water and it's going backwards, what are you not getting in this picture?

Ken Jordan (Sierra, 1998–2014)
This fire had been burning for, like, a week. We're sitting in briefing and they say, "Okay, here's a map of this thing. Here're your safety zones, and here's a helispot we'll fly you into. You've got 800 yards of line to put in. The CDC [California Department of Corrections] crew, they're not here, and a couple hotshot crews were working on it for a while," and I'm going, "Well, where are they?" "Well, they're not here anymore," and I say, "Uh, okay."

We started looking at it, and I'm going, "This line's not right, here, Mike [his assistant]." We go ahead and take the assignment and talk to division and operations off to the side of briefing, and I say, "No, really, looking at it on the map, it looks like the fire's right here below, and everything's going to come into alignment with this weather system. It looks like there's unburned fuel between us and the fire. The fire burned 4,000 acres three days before, and it might make a run," "Well, there's a safety zone right here." "Well, I'd really like to check out the safety zone before we commit the crews up in there." "Hey, listen. We gotta get you guys up in there to cut that line and put the line in. We don't have time for all THAT." I said, "I know, but you don't have time to just let me fly up and look at it first?" "Hey, you can fly out and look at it when you're bringing the crews in, on your first load."

They walk away, and I tell Mike, "Don't let the crew get on the stinking helicopter until I tell you to." I go over to the helibase, and I find somebody I know, and I said, "Hey, do we have a ship that's flying up there on a recon or anything?" He said, "No, but we've got one going to the other fire on the complex." We talked to the pilot, and I bootlegged this flight without telling anybody.

I go look, and here's the fire below us in the hole, with 120 percent slope, continuous fuels running up drainages to the helispot they want us to land on. Flashy fuels mixed with heavier fuels, and I couldn't see the safety zone. It was all indirect line on the top of this ridgetop with no safety zones. You'd basically have to beat your way down through a chute to get to the fire to have a safety zone—below you. I looked on the map, and what they're showing as a safety zone is in really heavy fuels on the lee side of the slope about as big as this room, for a whole division.

I call Mike and I say, "Mike, don't bring the crew up. Just leave them there." Then operations got all pissed off, and he gets on the [radio to the] helicopter: "Hey, it hasn't done anything for a day and a half. We'll keep it pinned down with heavies in the hole while you guys work it." I was being really political, and I go, "No, we really need to have a safety zone if we're going to do this. I'm not going to put my crew in." They argued for a while, and we finally got the crew to come up near the bottom, near the ocean, and put in some work. . . . Of course, they sent us home the next day, the whole division that refused the assignment. That's one of the many times that they're trying to get us to do something which could've proven to be fatal, but it was still my responsibility; it wasn't the IC's.

If Paul Musser and Bob Wright tell you it's not a good idea, maybe you should listen.

Paul Musser (Flagstaff, 1990–2004)

We were on the Mendocino, us and the Sacramento hotshots. We got in there, and it was burning in there right above Clear Lake. We're looking up there, there's a fuelbreak, and we're going, "Yeah, we need to get up there and fire off that fuelbreak." Then they call us in to do the briefing, and they tell us they won't let us go up on the hill with all that fire. Briefing took over two hours. By the time we came back out, it was getting really close to the fuelbreak.

For some reason, we had our truck with us, but Sac didn't have their truck. Bobby and I jump in the truck, and we say, "We'll go up there as fast as we can and try and fire that. You guys can come up, and you can call us when you get there. We'll let you know when you can come over." We got in the truck and we hauled ass.

We're starting down in there, and we're looking: "Shit. Too late." Just a few minutes, but we're too late. "Okay, well, we'll just hold the top of the ridge." About this time, the branch director pulls up. Branch or division, I don't remember. He pulls up and he goes, "We've gotta fire this road." "It's too late." "Well, you guys might not be as familiar with this fuel type as I am, and it's not too late." "It's too late. Well, I have a drip torch. There's one in the back of the truck if you want it. Not the right thing to do." "You guys just aren't familiar enough with this." He grabs it, throws it in the back of his little Ford Ranger.

About the time he's going out of sight, we can see it finally cross the draw and start running for the ridge. [We tell him on the radio,] "Okay, it's crossed the draw, and it's running for the ridge. You best turn around and come up here as fast as you can." The next thing you can see is this wall of flame and this Ranger.

This guy was up there with two superintendents who were going, no, you don't have enough time, and granted, we probably shouldn't have let him go down in there, but we did. We were sitting there, and we knew where our trigger points were going to be, and we called him and he got out. But he was very close to not making it.

Bob Wright (Sacramento, 1990–2002)
[Paul Musser mentioned you in one of his stories. You warned the division supe not to go down in there. . . .]
Fire was licking over him like he was a surfer in a curl. It was funny, because he talked to Paul, and Paul and I went down there, and we went, "Aw, this is useless." It was on Pitney Ridge, and we went down there and came out because this thing was starting to cook and crank.

We left the crew; it was just Paul and me. We left the crew down there because it was unsafe. . . . We came out of there, and we told this division supe, "It's useless. Don't go down there." Then he popped off and said, "Well, you guys aren't from this area." I said, "Did he just say that we're not from this area? We were here before he was probably born." I used to work at Boggs Mountain, which is just down the road, and we had fires there all the time. Paul used to work there, and his dad was a ranger for CDF on the east side of the mountain over there. We hunted there, both of us, and we knew that country there like the back of our hand.

He went down there, and that fire just came a'roaring up there. He's lucky that truck didn't stall or vapor lock, because he would've been dead. He was just like a surfer shootin' a curl, the fire coming right over top of him, and his eyeballs were as big as silver dollars. We just shook our heads and started—in fact, we didn't even wait until he got back—we started firing the road.

How do you avoid burnout?

Bob Bennett (Horseshoe Meadow, 1989–2006)

(Laughs.) I think you go through burnout in stages. With me, toward the end of the season, you're just ready to get rid of everybody. I don't take any vacation time from January to November. Once I lay off the crew, I take three or four weeks off and try to drop it and get away from it. By the time I've had those three or four weeks off, January hits; gotta start getting focused on the season and focusing through.

You do get burned out at times, but if it goes on too long, maybe you should think about it and then leave. There've been times that I've thought about that, going, "If things don't change, I'll leave," but something happens to get me charged again, get me going again.

You get tired, and you get fatigued from all the hours you put in, but I think it's knowing there's a new challenge every year. You get frustrated, but as far as getting where you're burned out, I've never been that way. It seems like it's always in time for that time off in December; and by the time January comes, it's, "Let's go, let's get the crew back on."

By January, I start missing them. I miss having them around. It's just being able to go through, take that four weeks off during December. . . . I've seen other people get burned out—co-workers—and their attitudes just go to hell. I've probably never really experienced total burnout. Moments, but not to where I just lost any interest in the job at all.

Greg Keller (Eldorado, 1985–1996; Modoc, 2000–2007)

For myself, I know it's my job, and I can't wait to come back to work. In fact, I was telling my wife the other day that I can't wait for the weather to warm up and the crew to be back. I want to be in front of those folks; I want to be out doing PTs, and I want to be out on the fireline. It's a job that I have literally loved doing my entire life. I think if a person didn't love this work, they would find it hard to get motivated, and those people are probably ones who do it for a while and move on to do something else. My motivation is love of my job and knowing that I have to be on top of my game because I'm responsible for 19 other people as well as myself.

Paul Musser (Flagstaff, 1990–2004)

I like to hunt. I spend as much time as I can hunting. I am a licensed guide, but I don't guide very much because I don't have time. During the winter I spend almost every weekend—at least part of it—out in the woods, just doing something by myself, away from everything else.

I don't have somebody drive for me. Most of the time I don't have anybody riding with me because I can relax more when I'm just by myself, with the stereo turned up to the volume I want it on. The only thing I have to do is watch the road in front of me and the mirror and the buggies behind me. I like long trips because for me that is a good rest period. I know getting demobed is going to be stressful, and then when I get home, dealing with the district is going to be, but that in-between time, that's my time. In the winter it's hunting or just going out hiking.

Ken Jordan (Sierra, 1998–2014)

I love it. Oh my gosh, what a job we have. We get to travel and eat for free. (Laughs.) What used to be so exciting to me is the fire thing, but I guess it kind of progresses through the years. You start out really fired up about fire: watching stuff burn and putting it out. Then you progress into the hotshots: you've got the camaraderie, friendship, bros, you know, and it's like a gang. You've got all these traditions, all these cool colors and stuff, and that keeps you going. For the last ten years or so, I get so much out of watching the new guys get the same feeling. I see these guys, and they're just so fired up, and then I get to see them come from being just spoiled little brats, punks, or whatever, and then turn into decent, hard-working members of the community. After a stint on the hotshots, everything is easy for them, and they've got the tools to survive. That gets me fired up now. When one thing starts getting old, something else comes up that makes it all worthwhile.

Dave Matier (Midnight Sun, 1992–1997, 1999–2007, 2009–2010)

That's a big part of it [not working year-round]. For six, eight months out of the year, it's not just me but 19 other people, and just being able to get away from that, and for the two or three months I'm off all I have to worry about is me. Don't have to be anywhere at any particular time; don't have to show up for work every day. If I don't want to do something, I don't do it. Just that whole thing is what keeps it fresh for me because after I'm off, I always look forward to coming back. I guess when I don't, I'll quit doing this—when it becomes drudgery, eight to five, go to work, get paid. That's why I'm not in management.

Ron Bollier (Silver City, 1993–1995; Carson, 1996–1997; Fulton, 1998–2013)

I've just finally come to the realization that maybe sometimes you need to take a break. . . . How do I avoid burnout nowadays? . . . I am starting to take a few days off now during the summer and not finding it so important to go to that fire every time. (Laughs.) Might've taken 21 years to figure it out, but I'm starting to figure out . . . that fire will always be there. I probably should've been doing it quite some time before this, but it gets in your blood. That bell goes off, and it's just not gonna be the same if you don't go to that fire! (Laughs.)

So, I'm finally figuring out that maybe it is okay to take a little time away, little time to yourself during the summer. You can always catch up. You can always tie back in with the crew. You can always go where you want. You don't have to go. Maybe that's why I have two fully-qualified, competent captains. Maybe I do want to take my nine-year-old to Sea World—during the summer. Two years ago, I couldn't say that. [It was,] let's go in the wintertime when it's raining! (Laughs.)

Mark Linane (Los Prietos/Los Padres, 1973–2001)
I tried to develop my ICS stuff so I wasn't just a crew boss. Good division supe; became a good operations chief, at least in my mind. Could be an effective IC, too, when I needed to be. Probably always liked to have good equipment so, keeping the equipment up and fire-ready. Being a fire guy all the time, being ready to roll, keeps you young. I took extra assignments and projects, like Look Up/Look Down/Look Around, developing that for the greater good of the community.

There were a couple years I was getting kind of burnt, but after you come back through it you think, "Hey, this really isn't such a bad job." Where else do you get paid to travel all over the continental United States and Alaska and other places? They pay you to see beautiful places and go camping.

What do you do for continuing education?

Ben Charley (Horseshoe Meadow, 1974–1989)
There're people out there who have a lot of information, a lot of knowledge, but they ain't gonna tell you unless you ask them. Billy Sandborg is that way. If you don't ask, he'll say, "Well, you know. Why ask me?" But if you ask him, he'll tell you. He's pretty blunt, too. He's probably one of the more aggressive superintendents I've seen in our time. He's really aggressive. Teach. Invite questions.

Dennis Baldridge (Laguna, 1990–2009)
The biggest group that helps me keep learning now is these hot-shot workshops: essentially, seeing what my peers are doing.

There are so many different ways. They're trying different things, and by coming to this and listening to a few of the folks saying, "Hey, we tried this." "That sounds pretty good, let me try that." We do that all the time, and each year it seems like we learn a different way of trying something out, so that gives us a fresh outlook instead of the same thing every time.

Some of the folks who have moved on out of the hotshot organization, superintendents who have moved to different places, are pushing other things for us. I don't want to say we're ingrown, but we're a pretty tight organization in the hotshots, as opposed to some of the other functions. The folks who have been here always want to come back and talk to us. They're bringing things to us that they've learned that we wouldn't normally hear about.

Bob Wright (Sacramento, 1990–2002)

When I worked for CDF, I wouldn't go talk to the kids; I'd talk to the old captains. They would tell me because I showed an interest. Then I would ask questions on the fire. That's what I did at every place I went to: I'd find the old ranchers. I'd go find old FMOs who were there, and I'd ask them questions, because that's how you learn. Not all the Forest Service people knew all the answers. A lot of those old ranchers fought just as much fire as some of those guys in the Forest Service, so I talked to them, and I learned a lot from those guys about particular weather patterns for that area—for where I worked—and other places.

Having a good memory helps. If you don't, write notes down like Fred [Schoeffler] does. Do that kind of stuff so you can remember certain things about the weather, because every place has its own certain weather patterns. I learned from the old guys. Especially here [New Mexico], and Oregon and Washington, California. Talk to the old guys. You may have to pry it out of them, because most guys are not arrogant. You don't want to talk to anybody who's arrogant, because they don't know what they're talking about.

Craig Workman (Black Mountain, 1988–2005)

I think to keep sharp and fresh, spend time with your peers: other superintendents, also with other overhead. . . . Also, really pay attention to the people you work with, the younger people. It's amazing how much they can teach you, even if they think they're not teaching you a thing. Some of that keeps you young and healthy, also.

Mark Linane (Los Prietos/Los Padres, 1973–2001)

When I started out, there were some books, and you got four hours or eight hours of training, and that was what you got. It wasn't until later that you maybe went to an eight-hour or maybe a two-day school, like a big deal.

You learned right off the top that reading was really important. All I did in the wintertime was work a ten-and-four schedule in the backcountry. Fire season would end; you'd go out in the backcountry: ten days on, four days off, until fire season started again. You had a lot of time in the backcountry, and in the backcountry you'd learn to read because there wasn't much else to do. So reading was real important.

The poor man educates himself by reading, and reading anything is better than reading nothing. . . . Voraciously read, on a lot of stuff. Even stuff you don't understand: read through it, get the highlights, get the gist of it. You don't need to be an expert in it; you get the concepts.

I guess when I was raised, back in the day, there was a lot of oral history that I heard. Used to hear a lot of what we called "war stories." We still have war stories. Back in the backcountry, a lot of war stories were told about the old-timers. Some true, some bullshit. Wintertime and on project burns and stuff, we had some of the old dogs who would talk about old fires, what they did and how they fought them. Always been a student of history. . . . The only thing that changes is the times and the rules, and the same mistakes are going to get made again.

Disasters, tragedy fires: that was really important—to try and understand why it all happened. My career was through a whole bunch of those: the Loop fire, the Romero fire. . . . Try and learn from somebody else's mistakes.

The Most Brutal Lessons: Brit Rosso on a Crewmember's Line-of-duty Death

I own this; I try not to look at it as a burden. I have a unique perspective that fortunately very few other people have, and I try not to look at it as a burden that I'm dragging around. I look at it more as a blessing, an enlightenment that I have of what risk really is, what exposure really is, and what taking care of our own really means.

—Brit Rosso, April 2015

I knew I was hearing something very rare and special when I attended Arrowhead supe Brit Rosso's presentation at the 2005 R5 Hotshot Workshop about Arrowhead crewmember Dan Holmes's line-of-duty death in October 2004. Death on the fireline is not openly discussed often (but more so after the 2013 loss of the Granite Mountain Hotshots at the Yarnell Hill fire), yet here was a supe standing up in front of other hotshots and giving very specific details about getting through what is probably the worst thing to happen to a crew, something someone could know about only by experiencing it. It's not easy, but he was and still is willing to share what it took to serve and care for Dan, his crew, and Dan's family while experiencing the same grief and heartbreak.

Soon after the accident, Brit called and asked advice of another fireman he knew who had lost a crewmember on the line years before. Brit's friend couldn't bring himself to talk about it, leaving Brit and his crew to find their own way through the next weeks as they escorted Dan back to his New Hampshire hometown for the funeral. They met his family, honored him in two memorial services on opposite sides of the country, and then faced their grief in the off-season after they all parted ways.

I asked Brit in 2005 if he was willing to give advice for others who might have to go through something similar, but we didn't do his interview until the spring of 2015. I think he and his advice are better for the long wait. He admits to being in a much better place about the accident now, and he provided some long-term prospective gained from reuniting the 2004 Arrowhead crew to celebrate Dan Holmes's life on the accident's tenth anniversary. As director of the Wildland Fire Lessons Learned Center and as a member of the Peer Support Program, he helped others learn from and cope with mishaps and tragedies on a larger scale.

At first I wanted to make this chapter short and concise, with bullet points on what seemed like the crucial elements and clear how-to's. I soon realized it's not for me to decide what those are; nothing speaks more clearly than Brit's story, told in his own words, with "lessons learned" pointed out along the way. Some of Brit's thoughts on how Arrowhead's crew culture helped them make it through and how risk is regarded in the wildland fire service are included here, as are his reflections on the Peer Support training he's had.

The Accident

October 2, 2004, the accident happens. Dan is struck by the tree, lives for 72 minutes after that with the greatest of care from my crew and the park EMT. Did everything we could to save his life and, unfortunately, he didn't make it. He passed at 1358 hours. Life Flight crew, best of care, all the drugs, AED [automatic external defibrillator], everything you could have.

A couple things I had to do as superintendent after Dan passed was call the burn boss and my boss on the radio, not giving the news, but just to have them report to the LZ [landing zone], where I was at the ambulance with Dan. Brought them out and gave them the news that Dan didn't make it, which was a very emotional time for all three of us. We all talked about quitting the job once we got through this. Then I called my captain, who was back with the crew, waiting on the burn, to gather them up and take them back down to our hotshot camp, which was, like, a mile away. He wasn't to say anything; just have them go back to the station and hang out and wait, and I would be there.

I went over and talked to the Life Flight crew and thanked them for all their energy and efforts to try and save Dan, thanked them with tears and gave them a big hug. Again, I was pretty shaken, and one flight nurse grabbed me and said, "Look, you did everything you could for your firefighter. The nature of this injury was so severe that if this accident would've happened on the doorstep of our hospital, of our Type 1 trauma center, the outcome would've been the same. We may have been able to keep him alive a little longer, but we still would have lost him. It was a fatal injury; he was just so tough he was able to live for those 72 minutes after the accident"—which helped me, and I passed that on to the crew later, and I think that helped us.

Got back to the fire station with Dan in the ambulance, parked in the engine bay securely, with the rangers making sure no one went in there. Talked to my boss about how we were going to notify the family. I said, "I need to get down to my crew and let them know."

I would say that the hardest thing I've ever had to do—probably in my life, definitely in my fire career—was to gather up the crew and look them in the face and tell them that Dan didn't make it. Extremely difficult, because they were already looking in the phone book for hospital addresses, and they were getting ready to jump in the trucks and get down there so we could support Dan, and I had to tell them that he didn't make it. That was really, really difficult for me as superintendent and as a leader.

Taking Care of the Crew, Notifying the Family

I told them, "Here's what I want you all to do: one at a time, go down to the pay phone, call your loved one. Tell them, 'Something bad happened on the crew today, can't tell you what it is, but I'm okay, and I'll call you later.' No more than that. Just tell them they may hear something happened on the crew, something bad happened today. I'm okay. I love you; I'll call you later." I had everybody do that just because that felt like the right thing to do. We were also trying to manage some word getting to the family before we could do the official notification, but because there was no cell coverage in the area of the accident we had an advantage there.

Everyone made their calls, and then I gathered them back up. I'm still not sure why I did this, but . . . now, over ten years later, I think I did it because they didn't get that chance to say good-bye to Dan. The last time they all saw him on the accident site he was alive, unconscious, but he was alive. He went into cardiac arrest once we were in the ambulance and headed to the LZ. Something in me said I needed to give my hotshots, his fire family, an opportunity to say good-bye. I didn't make it mandatory. I just said, "Hey, Dan's up at the fire station, in the ambulance, secured. I'm going to give you guys the opportunity, if you'd like—it's your personal choice—we'll load up the trucks, and those who want to go will get an opportunity to say good-bye to Dan, one-on-one."

Checked with the rangers because of the investigation—a firefighter was killed in the line of duty, so law enforcement had to allow us to do this—and they graciously allowed us to do it. Patrick, my captain, guarded the door to the engine bay and, one at a time, would let each hotshot go in. I told them, "Take as much time as you want, but just one at a time. We'll send one in there, and when one comes out, we'll send the next one in." So we did that, gave everyone an opportunity to say good-bye to Dan. I went into the FMO office next door, and with the park FMO and the district FMO started figuring out family notification: How are we going to do this?

Back then, in 2004, I had a list, an emergency contact list, but I had my hotshot's name, the next-of-kin they'd like us to notify, and then phone numbers. Back then, I didn't even think about it, but we didn't have the address. I started thinking, we can't just call Dan's mom and say, "Hey, we just lost your son today. I'm sorry." That was a big lesson learned. I shared that with many hotshots, still to this day, that you've got to have a physical address for each person.

The Park Service was incredible in helping us at that late hour of the day—Dan's mom was on the East Coast—getting hold of a regional FMO for the Park Service, getting hold of a regional fire information officer. They took the lead and got the local fire department chief, chaplain, and the local grief counselor from the city she was in, all that assembled prior to the notification. We wanted to ensure the notification was done in person, at the door, and that people were going to be willing and able to stay with her as long as she needed someone there by her side. I can't remember exactly, but it was like a grief counselor, the fire department chaplain, someone from the police department, and a friend of hers who was actually on the structural fire department. They had our phone number where we were, and we asked them, "When you make the notification, take as much time as you need and then please provide her this phone number where we're at if she has questions or would like to talk to us, once she's ready."

They did all that, and I waited and waited and waited. Eventually, I said, "I have to get down to my crew," because the crew had finished saying good-bye to Dan. They headed back down to the hotshot camp. I went and said good-bye to Dan myself, spent quite a bit of time with him, and then loaded up and went down to the hotshot camp, down to the crew.

These were all things that aren't in any books or manuals. The majority of what we were doing, except the notification, there's nothing in a binder on a shelf you can pull out and figure out how to do this or get guidance. So, the majority of the decisions I was making that night and for the next couple weeks were based on if it felt right in my heart and in my gut. [I asked,] "Does this feel like the right thing to do?" and I kept circling back to that and always reinforcing, "Does this decision feel right in my heart and in my gut to do this for my hotshots, for Dan's family?"

Had the crew kind of mustered up in the mess hall, and now it's, like, nine, ten o'clock, and we haven't eaten. What do you do now? There're 19 of you sitting in the mess hall instead of 20, an empty chair. There's just no getting around how difficult that is to even comprehend without going through it. I decided [and told the crew], "For right now, here's what's going to happen. An investigation team is probably going to be coming very soon. There is probably a CISM [Critical Incident Stress Management] opportunity for us that will be coming. I'll be working on that tomorrow. Once the county coroner finishes his investigation, Dan will get transported down to the valley floor and get secured in a mortuary. But we've done everything we can tonight." I told them his family had been notified and that we hoped to talk to his mom in the morning.

From what I remember through all the fog and haze, before we broke that night we had something to eat, and then I let them go down to our ready room and have some beers and just hang out and be with each other. I said, "Right now is probably not a good time to go be by yourself. Don't anyone drive. We need to all stay here on compound." We were very concerned about the press coming in, so we had rangers secure the entrance to our hotshot camp so we could be by ourselves that night. I said, "We just need to stick together." So, that night we had beers—and I usually don't, but I hung out, and they appreciated that. We just sat there and we cried and we talked, told some Dan stories and laughed a little bit, but mostly tears and beers, trying to take some of the sting out of it.

I spent some time with a couple hotshots individually who wanted to quit that night. A couple of my guys pulled me aside and said, "I can't do this. I'm done. I need to get the "F" outta here." They wanted to load their stuff up and jump in their car and drive away and never look back. So we had beers together and cried a little bit together and talked. I kept telling them, "I need you here to support me, and I need you to support the rest of your brothers and sisters on the crew here. We need to stick together on this, as shitty as it is, as difficult as this is going to be out in front of us, we need to stick together and continue to be a crew. This is our toughest assignment we'll ever get. We didn't ask for this."

Something else that stuck with me throughout this event, pretty early on, and I kept sharing it with my crew: "This is such a traumatic hit for us all emotionally. If we don't stick together, this could destroy us individually. We need to stick together to support each other. We'll get through this together collectively, but individually this is something that is so bad it could do really bad things for us. We need to stick together and support each other and continue to be a hotshot family together."

The next day was surreal, waking up and not having purpose, not doing our normal PT, those things. Getting phone calls and investigation teams, CISM, all that stuff starting to arrive.

The Next Day: Investigations, Help from Friends

A firefighter is killed in the line of duty—there's going to be a serious accident investigation team showing up. I get that: that's policy, absolutely. We welcomed them. What I didn't know was that if a Park Service employee is killed in the line of duty in the park, then that Park Service unit, our park, had to bring in law enforcement officers, which makes sense, and do an investigation on that death, on that Park Service employee death. Pretty quickly I found out that there were going to be two independent, parallel investigations going on at the same time. I get that. That's policy. But once I found out that they wanted to independently interview my hotshots—two or three different times this team would interview them, and then they'd have to go to this other team and interview—I said no.

I don't remember if it was the team leaders and/or my boss, but I got them together and I said, "No. You're not going to do that to my kids. We're all suffering. I don't need to add more traumatic stress to what we're already going through. You get them one time. I don't care if you all have to sit at the same picnic table. I'll bring the kid in and you ask them for as long as you want one time. You're not going to do that two and three times to my hotshots." I wasn't animated, but I stood my ground, and they finally talked and agreed to do that. That's my job as a superintendent: to protect, to take care of my crew.

I think we spent that day doing investigations. They go through all your records, and everything goes into that investigation that you could imagine. Sometime that morning I got word down at the camp that Dan's mom had called and wanted to talk. She had talked to our FMO and was ready to talk to me, so I talked to her briefly. She asked a couple questions from what I remember. I think she asked if Dan suffered, asked if he got burned or not—did he get burned by fire? I think she asked if he was alone. She pictured that the tree fell on him by himself, out in the woods alone, and he's burning and suffering. I told her none of those were true. It happened right in front of the whole crew; they saw it happen. He didn't get burned. He was immediately unconscious, and he was surrounded by his friends the entire time. I told her from 1246 to 1358 I was by his side. I never left his side. He was not alone; he didn't suffer; and he didn't get burned. That really helped to comfort her. She told me later that was really weighing heavy on her soul.

The next day—day after next, it might have been—the CISM team came in. One thing we learned there that I think would be valuable for others: the request I put in was to make sure that at least one member of the CISM team has had a Red Card (Incident Qualification Card) or has great knowledge of what wildland firefighters do, who we are. I can't have the CISM team show up and start talking about fire hydrants and structural ladders and going inside buildings. I've heard those war stories, and it made things worse, so I requested that someone on the team at a minimum know what the hell we do and hopefully have a Red Card. That played out real well: it took longer to get the CISM team, but Ben Jacobs, who was the park fuels officer at the time and used to work on the crew—a hotshot a long time, one of my best buds—got to in-brief the CISM team and tell them exactly what hotshots are, the language we use and all that.

A good in-briefing to the CISM team before they come meet with the affected personnel is, I think, a best practice. If they can do that, it's worth the delay and time to do that. [The CISM session] had some value. It basically got the guys to talk about some stuff, not too touchy-feely. I talked to the guys later, and it didn't make things worse; if anything, neutral to a little bit better. It didn't hurt, and it probably helped a little bit.

I didn't request it, but if anyone else went through this, I would hope they have the same thing happen: it was just luck, but three of my good friends who are hotshot supes on crews in California, once the word got out, on their own drove up to the park as peer support for me but also for my crew. Because of the investigations and all that, they didn't let them into the camp right away, but they hung out. They said, "What can we do? We're here to take a load off of you so you can take care of your crew." They did everything from office work to trying to help us figure out a flight to get Dan home. It provided tremendous value to me personally and, I think, to the crew collectively.

They finally pulled me aside. One of them said, "Hey, how much sleep have you had since October 2?" I hadn't been home, so one of them said, "Hey. Come down to Horseshoe Bob's house tonight. We're going to go cook some burgers and drink some beers, and you can just hang out with us, just the four of us. Give the crew some space, let them do their thing. You need to clear your head." I guess I'd call that peer support now. I didn't have a name for it then, but it was tremendous peer support for me personally. And then I had to tell my story to them because they wanted to know what happened. That was extremely difficult but also powerful, I think, in the healing process for me. It also helped me clear my head and think a little bit straighter, taking a little break from everything I'd been dealing with.

Bringing Dan Home

We're taking care of the crew, we're doing the investigation, and everything that's happening at the same time as, "How do we get Dan home safely? How do we get the crew back to New Hampshire for Dan's memorial service, to support Dan and at the same time, his family—his blood family?" We were able to negotiate that. Some policy made it difficult, and the Wildland Firefighter Foundation filled some of those gaps and the holes in the policy, as far as the ability to pay for airline tickets on a short notice. They arranged some hotels and did some things for us that we just couldn't do by policy. A lesson learned or best practice for someone who might have to go through this in the future would be to work with the foundation: that's what they're there for. That's why we all contribute: these unfortunate times of need. They were outstanding. They did everything they could and then some to help us out.

A sidebar note in all this is that the National Park Service, at the time, their line-of-duty death manual or policy was still in draft format. Doesn't mean you can't use it, but it was in draft format. Throughout this entire process, I don't think I ever saw it. At the regional office, someone must have been looking at it, but I never cracked a policy book. A couple things I checked with my boss: "Hey, I'd like to do this," or, "I'd like to do that," but for me personally at the superintendent level, I did not have time to go rummaging through a bookshelf looking for some binder. And it was in draft format.

Now we can focus on, "How do we get Dan home safely, and how do we get back east to support Dan and his family?" I talked about the foundation: they were able to get Dan's girlfriend, who lived in Washington at the time, to California to meet up with us before we flew back east. It was the first time we'd ever met Jules, and she came down with us and rode in the back of the buggy down to LAX. We jumped on a couple different airplanes to fly back east, red-eye.

Back then my agency, the National Park Service, did not have a wildland firefighter honor guard. We do now, but we didn't have one then. We had a National Park Service honor guard with law enforcement officers, which did a wonderful job, and they helped us out, but only at the memorial service. There's "honor watch," and we didn't do it then, but I think they're doing it more now: you can get someone assigned to watch over your fallen comrade, fallen firefighter, as soon as possible, and not just leave him or her in strangers' hands. You can request that from the honor guard from your agency, if you have one. Whether at the mortuary, the airport, or wherever it is, they'll assign someone to escort your firefighter wherever they're going.

We didn't know there was such a thing, but I knew I didn't want to send Dan home by himself in the hull of an airplane. It was either going to be me or someone else, and I really wanted to be with the crew. I knew I needed to make sure Dan got home safely, so Ben Jacobs, one of our old hotshots who worked in the park, was the burn boss for the unit, volunteered to do that. He was honored to do that, and it was a difficult assignment. He met Dan down there at the mortuary in the county and then stuck with him all the way to the airport, through security, on the airplanes to the East Coast, and then to the funeral home.

We met Dan and Ben there when we flew in. We got wheels, got checked in, and went directly to the funeral home for the open casket viewing. If you want to talk about a hard thing: the first time you meet the family of one of your hotshots is in a funeral home. That was horrible, but there was also some sort of emotional connection that was made there with the family that night. We filed in and met the family, and lots of tears and so forth, spent time with them as long as we could to support them.

Dan's Memorial Service

The next day was the memorial service. This could be a best practice: if your firefighter is from a town or a place that doesn't have a federal agency or wildland fire department in that area, don't be afraid to contact the local structural or volunteer fire department. The Rochester Fire Department went way above the call of duty to put a firefighter memorial service together for Dan. Everything you could picture: the closed streets, the bag-pipes, the ladder trucks, the American flag, everything, they did it for Dan and for us.

My agency was nothing but supportive throughout the entire event. I never had one complaint whatsoever about the National Park Service. I think they went above and beyond the call of duty to support my crew, myself, and Dan's family. The Park Service fire director, and the assistant director and the FMO came out to Rochester, New Hampshire, for the memorial service and stayed with us afterwards, supporting us. I can't say enough about my agency at that time and the support that they provided us.

The memorial service went through town, with Dan in the flag-draped casket on the fire truck. Went to the church and did the service. We carried him the entire time, myself and six or seven other hotshots, so we were always with him. Had a memorial service afterwards, just for the family. One of my captains put together a really cool videotape of footage from the summer and photos and music of Dan and the crew—mostly Dan—and we showed that at the post-funeral wake with the family there. We gave Dan's mom and a couple other family members copies of it.

That was the last time they got to see Dan and hear his voice, so that was much appreciated. They really felt grateful for that.

Afterwards, the fire department was supercool on shuttling us around. They rented out a sports bar for us and the folks in Dan's family—rented it out just for the firefighters—and we all went there and celebrated Dan's life. Again, that best practice is wherever that service might be, just because there's not an agency unit nearby, don't be afraid to go contact the local fire department because they'll do everything they can. They'll go out of their way to help you out, and the family.

Spent another day or so with the family there afterwards—just went out to the woods or went to the beach and had some quiet time with Dan's girlfriend and his mom, cousins, and nephews. Again, emotional time, but time spent with some laughter in there. Then we loaded up on a plane.

Time Off, Regrouping, and the California Memorial Services
Before we loaded up, I told the crew, "We're flying through Chicago, or wherever it is, and then we're flying back to California. I'm giving you guys and gals five or six days off to go be with your loved ones, your family, to have quiet time. Whatever you need to do, go do it. . . . If you want to get off the plane in Chicago and get on another plane to somewhere else, do it. I don't need all my people to show back up at LAX." I ended it with, "But on this date, at 0800 hours, I would really like to see all of you come back and report to the hotshot camp. I don't know what we're going to do, but I know we need to be together. I understand if you don't want to come back, if you're done doing this, but I'd really love to see you all back there on that date and time."

We split our separate ways, and everyone went and did their thing. . . . I guess to my maybe a little bit of a surprise, everyone showed back up, including myself. I wasn't quite sure if I could show back up, but I did because of the duty I felt as superintendent to keep my crew together and take care of them.

We didn't go on any more fires that year, but just to keep some semblance of organization, I made the crew available for local initial attack on our home unit. Started planning a memorial service, a celebration of life, for Dan with his California hotshot family. We put a memorial service together down in the valley, and if I'm not mistaken, every hotshot crew in the region, in the state, was represented. For the majority of the crews, the entire crew came, buggies and all, on the clock, in uniform. The fire director for the Forest Service at that time said, "Not only can you go, I want you guys to go. You will be there." Again, nothing but support from our fellow agencies and our fellow hotshot crews. Very well-attended. Six, eight hundred people—I don't remember. They arranged a flyover with an airtanker and a lead plane.

We contacted all the ex-Arrowhead Hotshots, all the way back to 1981, to invite them. Number one, to let them know what happened, in case they hadn't heard. Number two, to invite them to the memorial service. I think we got 20 or 30 of the old folks to come. Some had babies; some didn't have any hair anymore, but it was really good to have them there to help support us. Had a big camp so crews could camp that night, and we did all the tough stuff: speeches, park superintendent, and all that. Got through all that, which was really good, and then had a celebration of life afterwards where there was food and drinks. Tough stuff, but also really, really good on the slow path to healing and sense-making of this tragic event.

This was difficult for me as a superintendent. At times I wanted to quit, but not on the clock when I was taking care of the crew. It would be more when I was by myself, after hours. I don't know if it was selfishness on my part and I just wanted to separate myself from it because it was so painful, or if it was just too much—but the sense of duty, the call of duty, was much stronger. That comes with the job as a crew superintendent: to take care of and be there for them and be strong for them rather than be selfish and think about my own feelings or my own personal status. There were a couple times when I thought about it, but I hung in there.

I think if there's a lesson learned in there or a best practice, it would be: do not be afraid to call or to ask for help from your peers, from your agency, from other fire departments, because everybody will trip over themselves or bend over backwards coming to the rescue or coming to help. But when you're in that situation, especially as a hotshot, so many times we've got it. We take care of our own. But this is one instance where, no, actually you don't "got it." You're going to need help. Don't be afraid to call others, because you need it. You don't recognize it at the time, but you do.

Looking back on it, those three superintendents who showed up, the Rochester Fire Department that stood up for us without our asking for that help, the entire hotshot community—especially in California—attending the memorial service, being there for us: those things are more important than we recognize. Three of the Rochester firefighters came out for the California memorial service and were in the procession. We were honored and added them to the procession with our crew when we walked in between all of the 'shot crews. It was really good to have them; it was a really cool gift to us. Their presence was really good.

After the second official memorial service, we went back up to our hotshot camp. We had a very personal memorial service, just the crew and Dan's mom and Dan's brother, at the hotshot camp. That was, I think, very meaningful for the family to be able to do that, and for the crew, to this day.

The Season Winds Down
Then we had our year-end party, and Dan's family was there for that too. Then we took them down to the airport and got them on a plane, on to the next memorial service, where Dan had worked at another park. And then there wasn't much time left. There

must have been a couple weeks left for the crew, if that. That's all kind of a haze. I just remember it was a challenge keeping everyone together, keeping everyone focused. Never ended up on a fire again. The rains came and kind of squashed the season. The crew said their good-byes and gave their hugs and said, "Hope everyone comes back next year."

I think a best practice after that is to do welfare checks on your folks. You've just split up. You just went through this thing, and you've been together for three weeks, plus or minus, and then they're gone for six months. I had my squadies, my captains, and myself doing our welfare checks. We'd call it our "pings," asking, "How's it going? Where you at? What's shakin'? Can we do anything for you?" We're reaching out to those folks . . . and keeping that dialogue going. I think that's an important thing.

Unfortunately . . . I couldn't reach out to any other superintendents I knew of who had lost a firefighter in the line of duty, one of their hotshots. A couple weeks later, we had our superintendents' AAR [action after review] within the region, and I shared the story. There were just superintendents, 25 of us or whatever it was back then, I don't remember.

When the accident happened, as soon as I saw how severe the nature of the injury was, as soon as I got on scene, I asked my captain to start documenting and time-tagging and taking photos of everything. I didn't know this was going to be a fatal injury, but I knew this was a serious injury, and we needed to start documenting everything. I was unaware at the time, but one of my captains had one of my hotshots take photos and had one of my hotshots take video footage so we'd have that. I've only shared that video footage once in ten and a half years, and I shared it that one time to the hotshot supes.

It wasn't for shock value: it was to help them understand what we went through . . . because they want to know. You picture this huge tree tipping over and all this stuff. That's not what it was. So I showed it to them, and I told them, "I'm going to show it one time, and I'm never going to look at it again." And I haven't. But I showed that to them, and what helped me afterwards was they were like, "Man, dude, I don't know if I could've been steady as a rock as you were through that, going through all that. You did way better than I would've done." Someone shared that with me individually: "I'm not sure I could've held it together, going through something like that." That peer support, again, is powerful and, I think, can help a leader get through an emotionally difficult event like this.

Facing It Alone
The crew's gone; we have eight of us, then six of us. We're laying squadies off; we're laying the senior firefighters off; and then it's pretty much down to my captains and me, and then it's down to me, just myself. I'm going to be up at the hotshot camp for three months, probably, by myself, and people didn't think that was a good idea. They started, with the best of intentions, trying to think of things that Brit could do rather than just sit up there and dwell on it, whether that was details or different things. I would've done the same thing.

Didn't recognize it from the inside, but some of my friends were recognizing that I was starting to live off caffeine in the a.m. and alcohol in the p.m. because I wasn't sleeping, really. So that was starting to spiral a little bit. And I had some very good friends who were very good about just saying, "Hey," not, like, "Knock that off," but just, like, "You know, a couple beers is a good deal, but keep it under a case," or whatever it was, just kind of joking with me.

What finally helped me, I guess, get out of that spiral was an old hotshot friend of mine who'd been inviting me for years to go travel with him down to Mexico. I finally took him up on the offer. He'd been offering it for years, and I thought my job was so important I felt I didn't have time to take vacation or travel. In January, I finally thought, "You know what? That sounds pretty damn good." I went down to Mexico for a couple weeks and lived on the beach with my buddy and some other friends, and it was probably the best thing I could've done, looking back on it—just to get out of that environment, not think about it.

Advice to Leaders
I don't know if there's a best practice there, but what it might be is that, God forbid, if someone goes through this, my recommendation to another superintendent or crew leader would be, priority one: take care of your crew; take care of your fallen firefighter's family. Make sure they are getting the best of care, but don't forget about yourself, because if you're shot, if you tip over, you're no good. You can't do your job; you can't take care of the rest of them.

It never goes away. I'm still taking care of the crew to this day. I still talk to them, I still talk to Dan's mom, because that's my job. I guess the other part of that is, once you do a big part of that, and they're gone and they've moved on, then don't be afraid to take a break from everything you've just gone through. Whether it's annual leave to be with your family, whether it's going for a vacation with friends, whether it's just going backpacking for a couple weeks, whatever it is. One part of me felt like I was disrespecting Dan's memory by doing that, by not thinking about him 24-7 and just focusing on, "What else can I do? What else can I do?" There was a part of me that felt guilty about that, but then some bigger part of me that needed to take care of myself overrode that feeling and said, "Look, dude, if you tip over you can't take care of anyone, including yourself." Take that mental break; take that physical break from all of the things you've just done to help your folks get through it.

Revisiting the Event on Its Tenth Anniversary
It was the tenth anniversary last year [2014] of the Dan Holmes fatality. Six to eight months before that, I started thinking about

it. It's those watermarks: the 5-year, the 10-year. The 20-year will probably be another watermark on any fatality, any bad thing that happens. I started thinking about it: "Man, we should do something, but what are we going to do, and how are we going to do it? Should we get the crew back together?" All that. It was very interesting because, probably not long after thinking about it, my captain Patrick Morgan contacted me, saying, "Hey, you know, I've been thinking how this is going to be the tenth anniversary," so right away it felt right, that if we're both thinking this, then we gotta get on this.

Got my other captain, Mike Ressler, involved, and Ben Jacobs, who was the burn boss, a good friend of mine. The four of us built a little tiny committee/group/gang, had a few conference calls trying to map out, "Okay, why are we doing this? Who is this for? Who do we invite? What are we going to do when we get there?" We put that together over a timespan of a few months and decided to invite the crew from 2004, Dan's mom and Dan's brother, anyone from the park fire management program who was close to the incident—they were a division supe or a trainee, the park FMO, the park district FMO, so those who were really close on that day—either they were on the unit or took care of the unit. We also wanted to keep sideboards on it: we didn't want it to turn into just a party, a gathering. We wanted it to have some focus on remembering Dan's life and celebrating his life.

This is part of the lessons learned: one person who kinda got lost and fell through the cracks ten years before was the park ranger, Nate Inouye, who was the first responder to the medical incident, to the accident. He's the one who brought the ambulance out. He went out to the helispot with myself and the crew EMT, with Dan and the Life Flight, and after all that he kind of got lost in the shuffle. I think we invited him to a couple memorials and he didn't make it. But we decided to invite Nate because he, as much as my EMTs, was right there providing the first responder medical response, trying to save Dan. He took medical control of Dan once we put him in the ambulance. Then he moved on. He went to Rocky Mountain [National Park] and had since retired. We invited him and he came out; it was really cool. I'll tell you more about that in a little bit.

So, invitees, objectives and intent: get the group back together, celebrate Dan's life, go out to the tree at the ten-year anniversary time tag—at 1246, when the accident happened—and not let it drift too heavy. It's not a fun thing, but we didn't want it to be all tears again. That was a challenge: we weren't quite sure how to manage that.

We got together and we met at Swale, at the old hotshot camp. Part of the intent was to integrate the 2014 crew with us, with our brothers and sisters from ten years later, and the current superintendent, Joe, was totally into it, very open arms and welcoming us all back to the station. We did that and camped there. I think that we had about 15 or 16 of the crew returning. We were at 20, and we lost Dan, and there was one who left before the accident, so we were at 18. We had more than 75 or 80 percent, something like that, come back. Those who couldn't come back just weren't able to swing it. I was very proud and honored to have them, all those folks, come back: married, kids, other jobs, still in fire, take your pick. They came from all over the country: from Alaska, Minnesota, from all over.

We went up to the tree on October 2 last year. Everyone said something: just kind of went around the circle and said a few things, fairly informal. A little bit sad, of course, to be expected. But I felt a sense of healing, and others said that later over beers— that it was not complete closure but another step in that healing process and sense-making process, especially for Nate, the park medic who wasn't able to attend the memorial. For him it was very good and therapeutic to see the crew again, to hang with Dan's mom, all those things. Dan's brother couldn't make it out— he had a conflict—but Dan's mom was able to come out.

We walked through the burn that we completed the next year, in '05, after the accident, and the burn boss, Ben, showed us some giant sequoia regeneration: "This is why we burn," the reduction in fuels, all these things, the ecological positive effects. That was also therapeutic, I think, for folks. It wasn't just a tragic loss, and we didn't just stop doing what we did. To honor Dan, we did continue. It's what he would've wanted us to do.

Barbecue and all that stuff that night. We hung out and spent a lot of good quality time with each other. I found that it was important to do that to remember Dan, to celebrate his life, support his mom, and for us to support each other and to see that some were still struggling more than others. Everyone processes these types of tragic events differently, but it was really cool to see hotshots from ten years ago—single, married with a couple kids, with a great job, all these different things. You don't forget about these things—you never will—but life does go on, and you cannot let tragic events like this derail you off of your track in life. You make it part of you. You just internalize it—not hide it, not suppress it—but you just make it part of who you are and remember the good things. You try to absorb the lessons and share them with others.

It was really good; there was no regret. I think, talking to others, it helped a lot of people just to process it and help us to move along in our progression in life and living with this loss that we've all experienced together.

On Arrowhead's Crew Culture

As superintendent of the crew, it was very important to me to establish a climate on the crew of the "Duty, Respect, Integrity." We called it "Pride, Safety, and Teamwork." I hammered the crew that you treat others the same way that you'd want to be treated—some of those core values of respect. . . . We're a team; we're a family; we watch out for each other. We stick together through the thick and thin, on the clock, off the clock. If you see one of your brothers or sisters straying across that line—wherever that line may be, on or off the clock—pull 'em back in. Don't let 'em tip over.

Some of those things, just to be a professional hotshot crew and a tight unit, you do that. Those are just best practices. I think by doing that, not just in '04 but prior to that—by trying to have a tight, cohesive unit so you can operate efficiently, effectively, and as safely as possible on the fireline—when you do that dangerous job we signed up for, you reduce the chance of something bad happening. You increase efficiency and production and all those things that we focus on. Most crews do that.

We focus on that, but I think by having a tight, cohesive unit go through something very traumatic like this, you're in a much better place to deal with it than if you were a hand crew assembled: 15 or 20 people who don't even know each other or just got to know each other once something happened. That's horrible. That's my worst nightmare, something like that. How do you then take care of that type of crew? This happened to us at the end of the season—that was just fortuitous—rather than at the beginning. We were a much tighter group and family because we've been growing since early May and building and nurturing that family up until the accident, versus something that might happen early on in the season. I think we still would have done most of the same things but it would have been more difficult because we wouldn't have been as cohesive, as tight. We wouldn't have been as intimate and familiar with each other in May as we were in October.

I would say it's not something unique to my crew or my program at the time. I think the majority of Type 1 crews do that, because by nature of being a Type 1 crew, you're going to do that to do the job that we're asked to do. But where the challenge would come would be for something traumatic like this—an accident like this—that would happen to a module that didn't have the luxury of being a tight, cohesive unit. I think it would really be a challenge to keep that module together and supporting each other because they haven't done the mating dance: defenses are still up, they don't know each other.

I don't know if there's a best practice in there or not. I think it's just be professional and efficient and effective, and get to know each other because you're family. You are a family for six months, and you have internal squabbles just like any real family. I know that being a tight, cohesive unit absolutely helped us get through this horrible event, just by design.

On Peer Support Training

The bottom line for me, personally, is I took the [Peer Support] training, and I want to make myself available to assist others to pay back into the organization what was provided to me and my crew 11 years ago. That's part of my interest in doing this or becoming part of this: to help others who are potentially going through something that's similar to what we went through, and I can show up there with some empathy—empathy and understanding with some of the things they may be experiencing.

I think a lesson to share with others is that help is out there, assistance is out there if you experience a traumatic event; there are systems in place now where we can request peers to come support us. It doesn't usually happen that [when] something happens to you or me we ask for peer support: it's more that our supervisors or line officers request that support. It's incumbent upon the leadership to request that—not the person who's hurting to figure out that they need it, to figure out how to get it.

With that training, I hope to be able to help others who have experienced a loss, some sort of traumatic event. Most of what peers can do is just provide a sympathetic ear, do lots of listening, make them aware of some things they may or may not experience. We all process this stuff differently, but it's mostly being there for them if they need something, someone to talk to, a peer to talk to—not law enforcement, not an investigator, not a line officer or management, but a peer. I can look across that chair, that table, whatever, that picnic bench, and there's one of my own here to help me.

I think the reality—the brutal reality—of it is we have to take care of our own, and we have to provide this support for our own. We can't just rely on other organizations or agencies because they have people to take care of too. They've done pretty good in the past, but I'm really proud of our organization when I say that—I mean the wildland fire community—increasing our capacity and being able to take care of our own.

The other thing that I'll share [about] that training is that the peer supporters, the people who have had that training, they have to be mindful of, "Is the incident or the location maybe too close for me?" An example would be if there was a felling accident or someone got hit by a tree back at Sequoia-Kings Canyon National Park, on a prescribed burn, and it's with the hotshot crew I used to run, am I the best person to go there? Some people would say absolutely, but for Brit personally, am I the right one to be there? Could I be objective? Could I maintain composure? I don't know. Those are hard questions that they proposed to us. You have to think about; okay, you're a peer, but how close is too close?

I would say you do not have to have experienced a traumatic event to be a great peer supporter. Like they say in the class, most people might have had some sort of traumatic event: it could have been a loss of a grandparent, a vehicle accident, a serious injury with a family member, or something in the line of duty. Most humans, if you've been around for a while, have experienced something that's not fun, but it's not a prerequisite to have experienced some kind of line-of-duty tragedy or traumatic event to either take the training or be a good peer supporter.

I'll say this: if you're really close, if you've had a traumatic event and you're really close to it still—there hasn't been much time [for] healing or processing—it's probably not a good time to go take the training. I found, even for me after ten-plus years even, some of the training was a little tough. It kind of opened some wounds, took me back to some places that I hadn't been in a while, but I was okay with that. I would say, if you've experienced something fairly traumatic, we'll call it very recently or recently, I would wait a while to take the training, because it might distract you from your natural process of healing and sense-making from the incident that you've just experienced. You probably need to give it some time and space. Help yourself before you try and go help others.

The last thing I will say about [the peer supporters] is they are very good about making it clear to the folks they go to help that they're not part of the investigation or review team. . . . Because if something traumatic happens—line-of-duty death or serious accident/injury—there's going to be some kind of incident review, investigation, something. The Peer Support folks are very good, and they make it very clear right off the bat, "We are completely separate from the investigation team. We don't talk to them. This is all done in strict confidence. We don't share with the investigation team anything that we discuss or share with you. They have a job, and we have a job, and those lines do not cross." They keep a bright line between the two, and that's the only way you can really gain trust and confidence with folks to be able to help them. Not that the investigation team's bad—it's just different. They have a different mission. They're there with different objectives.

I would say, depending on the nature of the incident, the Peer Support teams are very fluid and flexible. They take pride in being able to get there [fast]. Whether it's a team of three or five or two, if they can get just one person there first, whoever's closest, quickest, they're going to launch them. They'll get them some marching orders and get them there and start spooling up whatever they need: a meeting room, meet with a line officer, do those things. I would say, depending on the size and scope of the incident, and the logistics of getting there, the Peer Support team is probably going to get there first. I think that's appropriate because the people are there waiting. They know something's gonna happen and they're looking for some support. There's not a black-and-white answer, but I would say they're different, and the peer supporters take pride in being able to get there as soon as they can and start standing that up to help those folks in starting on the healing process. . . .

On The Perception of Risk

It's the brutal reality of this job. If you look at our history and you go back to 1910, X number of fatalities per year, it's not going to stop tomorrow. It's not going to stop today because we make a new training book or put out a new video or new report, or get a new radio or piece of equipment. It's an extremely hazardous occupation with inherent hazards that we just can't make go away. We've talked about gravity and overhead hazards and the starkness that there are certain things we have no control over. If we engage wildland fire out in that environment, even under the best circumstances and to the best of our abilities, following all the rules, there are still opportunities for a bad outcome.

For the most tragic events, time doesn't heal all wounds, but it'll help you process and learn to live with some of these things. What I don't have is the answer. I think it's healthy to actually experience that because it makes it more real, and it makes it easier to acknowledge how much risk we accept and how dangerous the wildland fire environment is versus, "Follow the 10 & 18, and no one's gonna get hurt."

When we were FNGs [fucking new guys], that was the response: follow these rules, follow me, no one's gonna get hurt. It's all good. Unfortunately, that's not true. They weren't lying to us: that's how they were brought up. That's how we teach young firefighters. We don't say, "Hey, you know, it's a really dangerous job. There's a chance that you might get hurt or killed out there." You want to tell your folks there's a chance: "You probably want to fill out a will. Here's your emergency contact list; let's fill it out now. In case you get killed, we'll know who to call." That might be what we need to be doing. I think we're getting there. We're slowly getting there, but that's a whole different way of doing business than we're doing it now.

How different does it look when that same young human being, male or female, goes to the military at the same age: 18, 19, 20 years old, right out of school, and signs up for boot camp? What do they tell them—not the recruiting desk, but when they actually show up for work? They actually fill out a will. [I was] talking to some veterans, and they actually have them fill out a will. Again and again, they talk about how dangerous the job is. Yes, some of us may not come home.

Some people say [fire] is the moral equivalent of war. I wouldn't say so much that; I would say it's just another really dangerous environment. The only difference is the tree or rock or fire is not actively trying to take us out like an enemy combatant. But I think that we need to get there. We're slowly, slowly, getting there, but we're not there. We have a long way to go to that full acknowledgement of the risks, the hazards, the inherent risks that we're willing to accept when we step out onto the fireline.

I think it was in a recent FLA [facilitated learning analysis] or incident review, a quote from a hotshot supe, where they were asking, "Why did you accept this risk of putting your people in here?" and the superintendent said, "That's not where I started to accept risk. I started to accept the risk for this assignment when I accepted the assignment back at my station and said, 'Yeah, let's go,' and told the kids to jump in the trucks. That's where the acceptance of risk started: when we put young firefighters in the back of big trucks and start turning wheels. It doesn't go away from there. It only increases from there." It was pretty good. It kind of put it in perspective. It's not like, "Oh, let's get to the fire, and then we can figure out if we're gonna do this risky business or not." No, actually, you gotta back that way up to when you accept the assignment at the module level, at the firefighter level.

This is very high-level perspective—looking back 10, 11 years—that these are best practices or lessons learned for others who might experience something like tragic loss, especially a line-of-duty death. Number one: don't be afraid to ask for help, but be mindful that you probably won't because you have your blinders on and you're not going to see the help around you. You're only going to really see the thing that happened and the people who were right there. It's kind of a two-part recommendation: don't be afraid to ask for help, but on the same side, be willing to accept help when someone offers.

People are going to want to help you, but be willing to accept that, when someone reaches out to help you, and you're thinking, "We've got it. I got this." Actually, you probably don't. Be willing to accept support when people reach out to you. I would say that's a recommendation of best practice for others who may experience something down the road.

I guess the other [lesson learned] would be that risk is very personal. There are lots of really smart people right now and lots of workshops and meetings trying to figure out even the definition of risk in accord with the wildland fire environment. The conclusion I'm coming to—and I'm not there yet, as I'm on my sense-making journey of what the hell risk management means— the message that I would want to share with others is that risk is personal. Risk is based on the chair you sit in or the label you have on your hard hat. It's based on the position you hold. If you're a first-year firefighter digging line, you're probably not even thinking about or told to manage risk. You're thinking about danger and hazard: "Is that thing going to fall on me? Is this thing going to cut me? Should I stand here or over there?" It's very personal, close-up. It's not even risk, almost. I think we used to refer to it as danger or hazards: "That thing is dangerous; that thing wants to kill me; that's a hazard right there; that's a hazard tree."

So, risk is personal based on the position you hold. If you're the line officer, you're the FMO, the division chief, the regional FMO, it's all different. It's all based on the position that you hold. I want people to think about that and share that. If you think of it through that lens, then when you're the FMO, you're going to think about, "Okay, through my chair, this is based on my putting people out there and providing this type of equipment," whatever it may be, versus someone very high up who might be [saying], "Risk is programmatic. If we lose this burn, we may lose the prescribed fire program for a year." The politicians, the air district, there are all these different levels of risk, and we can't manage all that risk. We have to think about the risk that's right there in front of us, the risk that's personal to us and what we're doing. If you're running a crew, you make sure those 19 kids get home every day. That's your job. That's the risk; that's the exposure.

Ken Jordan's Advice

Ken Jordan and his Sierra Hotshots lost two crewmembers in separate incidents and different years during off-duty hours.

For one thing, just acknowledge that if they die after work—and it's part of the culture as firefighters that kind of puts that in motion—don't discount that it's maybe a shared responsibility. If you did everything you could to encourage the guys not to drink and drive, or drink whiskey all night, or drive somebody else drunk; if you did everything to discourage partying at a bar after work together and then driving home, then you're cool. But if you didn't, and somebody dies, guess what? It's your stinkin' fault. Or it's my fault. I'm not going to say yours because people don't like me preaching like that. It hits you hard. Especially if you think there was something else you could've done to discourage it.

When I didn't with Tony—the first fatality—discourage him from going down to a bar and doing chug-a-lugs after work, I was just right in the middle of that, and I lost him. That was painful. After that . . . it saved a lot of other firefighters' lives after that because I was adamant about not doing that anymore. Making it all right—at least giving them the permission—not to do it.

My buddy, my captain, he doesn't drink. He was told when he first came to this crew, "Hey, you can cut line and work hard, but can you drink?" That was the roughest one: with Matt, I felt that I did everything I could as a supervisor to try to prevent that fatality, although there are still some things that I felt I could've been harder or harsher or more on top of; it always goes through your mind.

As a superintendent, just like Brit did, you have to take control. As much as I just wanted to curl up and forget about everything and just lay down and stinkin' cry, I knew I had to hold it together for the family and the rest of the crew. So, you take a big sacrifice there: you want to just kind of retreat but you have to organize. You have to call in critical incident stress debriefers. You have to show sensitivity to the families. You have to organize the funeral arrangements as far as it pertains to the crew. You have to lead there because everybody else is pretty much a mess at that point.

You have to maintain your cool, calm, collected self until all that stuff is taken care of, all the way to the end where you put him in the ground. Then, after that, what I'd recommend is taking a break, and I'd suggest once you get that done, then you get yourself to church. You look at an eternal perspective, and you hope that he went to a good place and that you're going to see him again someday. With that perspective, it doesn't hurt as bad.

PART FIVE

MOVING ON

Moving up, moving out, leaving and coming back, staying put: whatever you decide to do, they've gone ahead to let you know what it's like and help you choose.

Greg Vergari Realizes It's Time

The reason I left Union was I'd had it with the fire teams at that time. A lot of the fire teams were learning about how to be managers and forgot how to be firefighters or, more importantly, leaders. You build a team up, a hotshot crew that's giving 150 percent on a fire, and everything you've done could be subverted by a couple bad calls by division supes or by operations or by ICs.

After the Silver fire in southwestern Oregon in '87, I couldn't take it. I set up a burn that was just spectacular: worked on this for days . . . had it all set to go and started to burn it. We had an east wind to burn it, and the team's fire behavior officer said we had to quit because he'd heard that east winds on the west side were a bad thing to have. It was the most ridiculous call you ever saw, and that was it.

I got on the radio, and I called the operations. I said, "Hey, this isn't Outward Bound. I've got a hotshot crew down here. We've been prepping this for four days." I said, "We're ready to go here, what the hell are you doing?"

Everybody was cheering on the radio, and I got back and I got my butt reamed. I was pointing fingers in the IC's chest, and he was pointing fingers in mine. I went back home and I told my boss, "Hey, you've been trying to get me off the crew. This is it." That's how I left Union, and I'm glad I did, because I was so angry at some of the management of large fires. I wasn't doing the crew any good because I was getting bitter.

If you like suppression, how do you know if you should stay or go into management?

Greg Vergari (Union, 1980–1987)

This is really a fine line. Let me give you a different perspective. You don't see the military keeping officers in their Special Forces ranks for more than so many years. They can go, they can do something else, and they can come back. It makes for a whole organization. We don't do that. We have hotshot superintendents who have been there 15, 20, 25 years. We have jumpers who are 55 years old. Now, is that good? To me, it's not that great. A lot of people, I think, have gotten into a lifestyle. They can't quit because they're making $100,000 a year as a GS-9, and I'm probably a bastard child for saying this, but are they doing it because they're such good leaders? Do we need them to do that, or can we have somebody young come up and put the new energy into it and do just as good a job? My preference, being where I am in management, I would rather see people come and go off of hotshot crews so that we can take that leadership and have good division supervisors, have good operations section chiefs, and fill up the ranks that we're so direly missing on the overhead teams.

Now that I said this about staying too long, I have to insert a very important caveat: There are a few—a very few—who have stayed many years as a jumper or hotshot and not only did the job justice but set the bar for what the job is and should be. I have no heartburn with these folks because they are living the life they were meant to. An analogy is that there are a lot of paintings out there but only a few Rembrandts or Picassos. It makes me proud to call some of these pieces of "art" my friends.

What has hotshotting done for you?

Jim Cook (Arrowhead, 1981–1995; Boise, 1996–1998)
In my job right now as a training development person, it's probably been the best laboratory a person could ask for as far as guinea pigs and trial and error. [To his former crews:] Sorry, guys. (Laughs.) I think what a lot of our training developers don't get the opportunity to do is develop a training program—something where you're trying to develop an end product—and, using a crew, apply it, watch it at the end of the year, and then come back next year and make it better. I did that for 18 years: finetuned it. It was a great lab for learning how to train firefighters to achieve different tasks.

Got a great circle of peers out of the deal. The other thing that I really miss in my current job is that it [doesn't keep] you in touch with the youth. You knew the music; you knew the slang; crew carrier music wars, the whole thing. It was cool.

Stan Stewart (Los Padres, 2000–2009)
Well, it's taught you how to work. It's got you a hell of a peer group to help out on your new job. It's taught you a lot of skills. It's taught you some leadership stuff, some people skills. The only

problem is, every job after that will be kind of an afterthought. It'll be hard to find something that keeps you going like that.

I think it's the guys; again, it's the peer group that you work with [and] that you'll still be in touch with. . . . That group is always going to be there. They're like your best buddies. My wife used to call Brit my girlfriend when we were on the committee together, from being on the phone constantly. The key thing is just the friends more than anything—the friends and the contacts you have and the people you've met along the way.

Greg Keller (Eldorado, 1985–1996; Modoc, 2000–2007)
It gave me an appreciation for the guys on the bottom of the totem pole, if you will: the people out on the line. I always felt that I was fighting for the guy who worked for me or was below me in the pecking order. I got on an overhead incident management team, and I think I became the conscience of that team. I'd say, "Remember what we're doing this for. Remember the plan is not for us. The plan is for the people who are going to go out and go to work for us." I remember just insisting that food or accommodations or the shift length—all the things were thought of with the people [in mind] who had to go to work.

I think that was a revelation of sorts for people who were on the overhead team; and I think sometimes teams forget some of the reasons why they're there: to put the fire out. The finance and cost people are there to document costs and to save costs, and the supply person is there to make sure they know where every set of gloves and earplugs went to. . . . People lose sight of the fact that we're there to put the fire out and to take care of the people doing it.

Leaving hotshots, that was the thing I took [with me] the most: to try to not forget my roots, where I came from. Although, having been on the other side and having been part of management and part of the management teams, I now can go back to the hotshot world and have a greater understanding. When the guys want to complain about something or they don't understand what's going on, I say, "Folks, I've been there, and let me tell you how that process works." . . . At least you understand the process and that people aren't necessarily out to make your life miserable or something like that. It's just how the cookies crumble sometimes.

Seeing both sides has made me a better person. I think it's made me a better fire manager and a better leader now. I think it was a unique step, and so for that I'm grateful, but I was very grateful to get back into the hotshot business, too.

Steve Karkanen (Lolo, 1990–2011)
It was easy for me to jump into an FMO position during a busy fire season [after] having had the experience I had as a supe. What was really fun in 2000 was that I got to go out to all the districts as they were having their problems and kind of help sort out what needed to happen. It was easy for me because I had the experience, where some of the FMOs were struggling and having a hard time placing priorities, working the system, trying to get the stuff they needed to deal with that situation. The difficult part of it is dealing with the administrative hassles: trying to respond to the regional office for information that they were needing to get back to Congress, dealing with the [National] Fire Plan at the time, and having short turnaround for fuel-related issues, that kind of thing.

That part of going into management—from [being] a superintendent going into management—that's probably where we're lacking a lot of skills. We don't have a lot of that kind of background, and that was difficult for me. That was a big transition, and it was really hard for me to understand that part of the way the agency operated, because I hadn't done it much. But that's why I get back to saying the superintendent job is the best job in fire and probably the best job in the Forest Service, because we don't have to deal with that crap. We don't.

In '94 I wanted to be an FMO. I really did, and I'm glad that I didn't [become one], to be honest with you, because I see the FMOs tied up in the planning process and not getting out on fires and not being able to deal with their firefighters. It's an office gig anymore, depending on the situation, depending on the person.

Barry Callenberger (Palomar, 1979–1982; Eldorado, 1982–1988)

I think the hotshots [program] teaches people a lot about big fire organizations and fighting large fires, and to stay in the role as a superintendent really takes away from getting that experience and passing it on to other people who don't [normally grow in] the same kind of regimented way that hotshot superintendents grow. You go in either as crewman and then foreman and then superintendent, and you learn a lot about managing large fires that you don't learn in any other position in the Forest Service. I don't care if you're an engine captain who goes out and becomes a division supervisor and goes to every fire. You still don't get the kind of experience you get as a hotshot.

You understand what it's like on the line at the bottom level and how everything that goes on up above affects that bottom level. They're the ones who are getting the work done. It's not the division supervisors. The division supervisor, I think, is one of the key positions, but you have to keep the people, the lower ranks, happy, and getting them as much as you can is what we have to do.

People who don't stay in that little group don't get that feeling. If you move through really quickly, and suddenly you're an operations section chief or an IC— if you haven't spent a lot of time on the ground—you don't know what's going on down there, or you forget. Of course, I was accused of that, too, when I became an operations section chief.

On the Ortega fire on the Cleveland—I'll remember it till the day I die—I know because I was the operations section chief, and

I made the crews walk in to their assignment. They got me cornered the next night when they came off of shift. Of course, they appointed Overacker, my buddy, as the one to deliver the message, and I got accused of forgetting what it was like. You have to make some decisions sometimes that people don't like, but at least you understand that the decision you're making will have an impact, and you know what it's going to be.

The other thing is, I always thought that in order for the hotshots to be able to relate to an operations section chief—on any team, whether it's a Type 2 or a Type 1—that person's had to have been a hotshot: either a foreman, a crewman, or a superintendent. Then they can relate to that operations person. If not, it really becomes difficult.

J. W. Allendorf (Wallowa–Whitman, 1980; Arrowhead 3, 1981)

[It] did a lot for me. I went to Vietnam in '68–'69, and just by some screwup in the army, they made me a buck sergeant in the infantry. It wasn't my fault—it was theirs. I think they must have had the wrong name written down or something. (Laughs.) Anyway, I ended up getting into the long-range recon patrols and ended up as a team leader. The team concept was something very near and dear to me because we worked in six-man teams, but usually we didn't have six—we had four, and we depended very strongly on each other.

I did that for 13 months, and then when I came home, all of that was gone. I went from this high-intensity, high-stress, team-dependent atmosphere to coming home and trying to go to school and get my shit together and missing that whole team thing. That's part of why, like I told you, when I first saw the LP 'shots on Highway 33 . . . I mean, it was instant. I knew, "I gotta get with these guys."

Hotshots provided me with something that I'd already had a dose of but that I needed, and that's the teamwork, brotherhood, camaraderie. That's something I've always had a strong need for, ever since the military. The hotshots did nothing but strengthen that. It re-instilled that, and it also gave me some insight. I watched Mark [Linane] very carefully, and although I was probably only a couple of years older than the guys on the crew when I got hired on, I had been in some different places and seen some different things than they had, so I was aware of some things, maybe, that weren't apparent to them. . . . Watching Mark operate and how he pulled people together in little, subtle ways without people even realizing it, I was amazed at his genius at it.

The hotshots gave me purpose. Really, the best times in my life have been on a hotshot crew. They were the high points in my life. The absolute best fun I ever had was being a hotshot, bar none.

Greg Vergari (Union, 1980–1987)
[It] put me next to the best firefighting opportunity that anyone can ever have, put me into the best supervisory role anyone could ever have.

Dennis Baldridge (Laguna, 1990–2009)
[It's] given me more fire experience than any other person putting in for the job. On the ground, right at the fire's edge, we get more experience in a season than most people get in several seasons. I think that's a real advantage to anywhere I would want to go. I mean, we even do better than the jumpers. The jumpers go to lots of fires, but they don't see the fire behavior that we see. They don't see the kind of fire that we see. They don't have to do the endurance type stuff.

Even if you stay on the same crew for most of your career, because we travel to all the different regions and do stuff, the breadth of experience we get just in the feel of different fuel types is going to help, no matter where. . . . Engine crews aren't asked to go out and sleep on the line for four or five days in a row. Neither is helitack. We can go out and take care of ourselves in a lot of different situations where most people don't have to do that.

Adaptability, the ability to handle change. Here's your assignment, and you go out there and it's something different—you adapt, you change what you're doing, you fix it. I think that is a real advantage.

Ron Bollier (Silver City, 1993–1995; Carson, 1996–1997; Fulton, 1998–2013)

Can I just not answer the question and say I'm not leaving the job? (Laughs.)

That's a tough one. Depends on what my next job is. Depends on what I target next as a job, if I ever even target another job. What would it do for me in that job? It would give me a lot of skills, give me a lot of skills and traits that people don't like you for. You become very self-sufficient. You become very self-opinionized. You become very strong-headed. You become very strong-willed. You become really adaptable to adversities.

I think, being what I am and where I'm at, adversities are not a real problem. You encounter them, and it just gives you a really good foundation on how to deal with life in general and how to deal with the next job you want to take. It just gives you a solid background in any job you want to pursue, even if you leave the agency altogether.

Bob Wright (Sacramento, 1990–2002)

You look back at the people you met and trained and worked with, and that makes it worthwhile. They're like brothers to you. You could go into a room 50 years from now, and it'd be like you were with 'em when you were 20. That's been the best part about it.

Seeing these kids become better. When you'd first seen them, they were just a bunch of kids who didn't know anything, and then when they leave, they're telling you, "Hey, this is how it's gonna be," and they're doing a good job. . . . That leaves you some pride.

Craig Workman (Black Mountain, 1988–2005)

It did give me a drive and a passion for what I do, and I carried that on as an AFMO.

I've talked to my wife about this before: when you're running a hotshot crew, you don't have a lot of tact a lot of times. You tell people what you want done, and they do it. There's not a whole bunch of quibble between that. You get within other avenues of the Forest Service, and you tell somebody you want something done, they don't necessarily think they're going to do that. . . . It doesn't work real well in the other world. Every fall I'll have to adjust myself a little bit with my wife, because I'll come home and expect something to be done a certain way, and she doesn't think that way.

Where are some of your former employees?

Kurt LaRue (Diamond Mountain, 1993–2001)

I actually sat down and wrote that one down. [My foreman] Kay looked at it and filled in where I missed some of them. I have three superintendents, three assistant superintendents, six engine captains or FOSs [Fire Operations Specialists]. You'll love this: it was three FMOs, and now it's two. One of the guys who was an FMO just took a job as a squad leader: GS-11 FMO just took a Silver State squad leader job. It's a GS-7. He didn't like working year-round. I've got some in dispatch. I have one that's a doctor, one that's a physical therapist, one helicopter pilot, and I've got a couple guys in the Marine Corps.

I do like to keep track of the kids. I get emails from them peri-
odically. That's one of the fun parts: keeping track of them and
watching where they go, whether they stay in fire or not—just
watching where they end up.

You figure you do 25 years at 20 each, so you get a lot of
people who have floated by over the years. There are a handful
out there that I have no idea what they went on to do, that I really
would like to know how things turned out for them. (Laughs.)

Mark Linane (Los Prietos/Los Padres, 1973–2001)

He wasn't exactly an employee, but the chief of fire management in the Washington office right now, Jerry Williams, he
was my division boss trainee for two or three fires, back when
he was a smokejumper. That starts at the top. Deanne Shulman is a GS-13 or 14: she works out of the Sequoia [National
Forest].[20] She does all the international stuff with Russia and
does all that Eastern bloc stuff because she speaks Russian.
She's got that position. Diane Price is the air platform manager
for the Reno area, here in Nevada, for the BLM.[21] Stan [Stew-
art] is a supe. [Anthony] Escobar was a supe at Kern Valley.
Several FMOs or battalion chiefs and AFMOs, a whole bunch of
fire chiefs from Southern California. We've got the president of
the Montana Bar Association. We've got a heart surgeon. We've
got an orthopedic surgeon, world-famous. Maritime lawyers.
We've got newspaper editors—one's the editor for the editorial
section of the L.A. Times. Another one's the editor for three
newspapers out of Vail, Colorado. Captains, battalions—got a
lot of them, too many to list.

---

[20] Deanne Shulman was the first female smokejumper. She rookied at Mc-
Call, Idaho. Michael Thoele, *Fire Line: Summer Battles of the West* (Golden, Colorado: Fulcrum Publishing, 1995), 138.

[21] From another part of Linane's interview. Diane Price was the first female
California smokejumper and later the first female Alaska smokejumper.

Brit Rosso (Arrowhead, 1996–2006)

There's this GS-11. . . . We're going to go do work for him at the Grand Canyon. He came to work for me in '94 as a GS-4 seasonal grunt, and now he's the GS-11 prescribed fire manager at the canyon. The sticks that I told him to stack in '94, now we're going to go stack those sticks for him. (Laughs.)

I see it as spreading the wealth, spreading what I teach within our little world, our program, and the things I've gained from it. One of the last things I tell previous employees when I talk to them on the phone is, "Don't forget what you learned here." I tell them not to forget what they learned here, and to share the wealth of what you learned here with others. What warms my heart is to see that, and also to see people who have left fire and done well.

A gal who was on our crew years ago, she's working on her doctorate in microbiology at UCLA. I saw her at our 20-year crew reunion a couple years back, and she told me over some beers, "You know, I use what I learned from you as a hotshot almost every day." I said, "Come on, in school, in biology?" "It's a work ethic, there's teamwork, there's being on time, there's holding people accountable, there's having high standards." She said, "It's invaluable. The things I learned, I can use in my life."

It's not where have they gone in fire; it's where have they gone, and what are they doing, and what have they learned here? I don't think we just create better firefighters—we create better citizens. I think we instill in our people those things that maybe they didn't receive or didn't gain in their upbringing with their family: some responsibilities, accountability—some of those values, those basic human values, that people aren't coming to us with like they used to. When they leave, I hope if they only spent one year in fire that they can carry forward what they learned here and become a better human being.

Why did you leave management to return to the hotshot crews?

Dan Fiorito (Union, 1996–2006)

Because being an ADFMO was really boring to me. (Laughs.) I mean, it was a good job and everything; it was great when our kids were small and I got to spend time with the family.

Around that time, the Forest Service was implementing the NFMAS [National Fire Management Analysis System] program, and my district lost a lot of funding because of the way NFMAS allotted firefighting resources based on average fire size and use of individual resources on a unit. We joked that "Christmas was when you get stuff and NFMAS is when they take it away." When I first started as the ADFMO, I had a prevention technician, a lookout, and three engine crews to manage. After NFMAS, I had only one engine crew and I figured, "What do you need an ADFMO for when you only have one engine to manage?"

The South Canyon [fire] incident in 1994 had a big impact on me as far as wanting to get back into the IHC program. I thought that I could have a greater impact on wildland firefighter safety as a hotshot crew superintendent. I have always wanted to do this job. Being a hotshot is the best job in the Forest Service, as far I am concerned. It's a job that is hard on individuals and families, but if you have the right mix, a supportive spouse and family, you can make it through it all. I have had a great career as a firefighter.

Shawna Legarza (San Juan, 2002–2007)

I hurt my shoulder in '98, and so I had to go do the AFMO job because of that. When I was in the AFMO job, I wasn't ready for that management level: writing burn plans and finding projects and being higher up in the agency administrator stuff. I knew I wasn't ready for that. I could tell I wasn't comfortable with doing what they asked me to do, and so I knew that I was still young enough that I should come back and continue in the hotshot world while I was young and just had that passion for it. I like the small group of people and to train those guys or gals how you want them to be, and you have control over that unit.

Craig Workman (Black Mountain, 1988–2005)

For myself, as an AFMO, that did not work for me. I enjoyed two years, and then after that, I didn't enjoy it. I really missed what I do for a living, and that's being a hotshot. Coming back in as a hotshot, that rejuvenated me and gave me life, and I've loved it ever since.

PART SIX

HOW IT WAS, IS, AND SHOULD BE

Part of being a good supe is having an opinion and not being afraid to share it.

What changes for good and bad have you seen in fire?

Jim Cook (Arrowhead, 1981–1995; Boise, 1996–1998)

I think the crews have learned to work smarter. They've learned to integrate better. I can remember as a crewmember literally racing another hotshot crew up the hill on a hike into an assignment. We don't do that anymore. I can remember sitting in buses, two crews to a bus, not being allowed to speak to people on the other crew.

We've become a more professional organization. We've got more incentives: we've got more permanent appointments. When I first started, there was only one permanent appointment on the crew I came from. Now we have a minimum of five and maybe seven to ten on a crew. That's got some plusses and minuses, but I think mostly it's a plus.

282 • THE SUPE'S HANDBOOK

Changes for the bad: concern for creature comforts. . . .
We've become overly concerned about hot meals, overly concerned about all the goodies that we need. At least part of what
drew me to this job was a minimalist approach to doing something that was difficult, that a lot of other people couldn't put
up with. I always told my kids: to be a good hotshot, you've got
to enjoy being miserable. I'm not saying it's all bad, but I think
we've gone overboard with video tents and laundry things in fire
camp, bringing bands in and flying hot meals in for breakfast
every day. It's gotten to where it's impacted effectiveness. I think
the superintendents are actually starting to recognize that, and
they're starting to be proactive about trying to get more spiked-
out assignments and trying to be more supportive of doing those
kinds of things where before they just kind of let it roll, figuring
it's easy money one way or the other.

This is more strategic and I think the crews are falling prey
to it too: analysis paralysis—looking for the 100 percent, surefire
solution to get this job done. It's a hazardous business, and it's an
uncertain business. Our job is to balance the uncertainty with the
benefit and the risk. I think a lot of times we ensure short-term
safety, and we buy off on long-term exposure of more people to
hazards. We were safer today, but now the fire is three times as
big, and we're going to be here three times as long. What's better? Why don't we just not show up, come back when it snows,
and clean up the edges? . . . When you avoid risk today, a lot of
times you're just putting the risk off until tomorrow and letting
it multiply.

Ben Charley (Horseshoe Meadow, 1974–1989)
That's the only bitch I've got against the Forest Service right
now— that they're not getting out and doing the job out there in
the field. In the old days, we used to go to briefing, and we'd go up
there and they'd call your name out. Get a shift plan. Take it, see
where you got, go out and find your crew. Say, "Okay, here's what

we gotta do, guys. Let's go." Half-hour later, you're gone. You're out in the field already, working. Now [it takes] four hours sometimes. That's too much. . . . Just too much time.

Then you work an 8-hour shift, 12-hour shift—half that's spent briefing. That's just changed in the last ten years. When I retired in '90 I started driving the buses. I'd go down there, and I've seen the other side of the fire business, plans people and ops people, and it's just changed. The aggressive isn't there anymore—the old idea of, "Let's go do it!" It's not there.

[At the Cleveland fire] I had the buses: I was taking Blue Cards up there. We got up on top, and I talked to Dan [Kleinman]. I said, "What are you guys gonna do?" He said, "We're going to punch line from here down to the road." They had Dalton and Del Rosa coming up. He said they were going to put line over there as secondary. Flame front was about this tall—pine needles, itty-bitty guys, you know? I said, "Go through and kick it back and put your line in. You got two crews coming up. You've only got about three-quarters of a mile to go. Kick it back, put your line in, just go for it. You can do it."

Well, Kleinman went back and told Jack Lee [his former FMO], who was the IC. He says, "You do this all the time: go up and tell these guys what to do, how to do it. You might be right, but leave them alone. You're not in fire anymore." But you could do it. It made common sense, a little-bitty flame height that high—it's not even hot. Ridgetop, kick it back, put your line in, and go for it. Do it. You've got four crews, two up and two down. You can put a lot of line in. And they lost it! (Laughs.)

About three times I got bawled out on fires. I said, "That's enough. I'm not telling 'em what to do."

J. W. Allendorf (Wallowa–Whitman, 1980; Arrowhead 3, 1981)

It used to be, the good professionals—and I worked for a few of them—they were not office rats. They were out in the field. I worked for one ranger—you could never find his ass in the office. He was usually gone before anybody even got there, out in the woods. That's where he was born to be, and that's where he was. He knew every inch of that district. He was always one of those guys who, if you had a fire and you looked at who the last tool was, he had joined in with a shovel or a Pulaski at the end of the line. He was out there doing it. He didn't tell you what to do or what you needed to do. He just went out there and followed instructions and fought fire with the rest of you. But now, half these sons o' bitches, they've got square eyeballs from staring at a computer, and they think that's the Forest Service. That ain't the Forest Service.

Greg Vergari (Union, 1980–1987)

Back in the old days, you'd pride yourself on how much line you dug. We were in the bush a lot more. Now the fires are so big, so outrageous. It's like Overacker says, "Give me a road map of the state, and I'll show you where my firelines are." There's some truth to that. Some of these things are moving so fast, so we don't do as much as then. I'm not saying that's good or bad, but I am saying it is different and that is scary. The climate change is eerie.

You see a lot of driving, and that is different, and that worries me also—lots of exposure.

Dave Matier (Midnight Sun, 1992–1997, 1999–2007, 2009–2010)

Not that pay's an important thing, but I think that it's better for kids now. Federal employees are still getting the stick on pay and everything, but it's better than it used to be when I started. I still think it has a long way to go.

The fact that we're not recognized as professional—we don't have our own series as far as hiring and everything—and what we do is totally comparable to any other firefighting profession, structural or whatever. The fact that it's a little better now is better for the kids. There are more opportunities to move up in the organization. There are opportunities for training, compared to when I started, which was part of the reason I got out of the Forest Service.

It was like we were sheep, and you express your opinion and you're doing something different—it's the same thing, but easier—and they don't want to hear it. If they jumped off the cliff, they wanted you to just keep falling over; and if you expressed an opinion to the opposite, then you were branded a troublemaker.

Ron Bollier (Silver City, 1993–1995; Carson, 1996–1997; Fulton, 1998–2013)
We've developed some good things in the hotshot organization and put them into use. We have really become a tight-knit group in the hotshot organization. We didn't used to have that. We finally have become a group and a whole. It's really brought a lot of things together. The trust level and the working relationships are outstanding now. Twenty-five years ago, they didn't used to be.

We've developed some good programs, leadership programs, out of the hotshot organization, which is good stuff. All our leadership stuff is good. We've developed some good human factors programs, fatality packages. That's all driven out of hotshot superintendents and ex-hotshot superintendents, which is Mr. Cook. Staff rides are starting to come about. The hotshots are the drivers of the programs, and that's hopefully because superintendents such as myself will leave the position and move up. Jim Cook's a fine example of that. Mark Linane is a good example of that. Mark Linane's out of the agency, still doing good things for the agency. It's all a hotshot background. Lot of good things come out of the hotshot background.

What are good things that I've seen change? (Chuckles.) Are there any? (Laughs.) Some of our regulations have gotten better. The agency as a whole is always going to try and strive for the best agency it can have. The fire shop in general has come a long way from where it used to be—sharing information, training programs, and trying to make things better for the fire suppression people.

Charlie Caldwell (Redding, 1967–1986)

For one whole winter, all we did was kill oak trees. It was the saddest thing I ever did in my life. (Laughs.) We were killing 'em with 2,4-D/2,4,5-T, which is basically Agent Orange. We used to spray Agent Orange on the roadsides, with no protective equipment. Stand up on the back of a stakeside and run a sprayer out of a 55-gallon drum. It just fogged over you. I knew it wasn't good back in those days.

I got married in 1959. I told my wife, "Don't touch any of my clothes." I wouldn't let her. I wouldn't let her do the washing or nothing. (Laughs.) It was bad stuff. We didn't know that until the Vietnam War.

I remember I went to the San Bernardino and showed 'em how to kill the stobs. I was putting a burlap bundle on a drip torch with 2,4-D/2,4,5-T in it and diesel, and putting red dye in it so you could see which ones you killed when you chopped the brush off. You'd just daub 'em, and they didn't come back. The fuelbreaks were working better, but we were using bad stuff.

In the early days in the Forest Service, when you talk about supervisory skills, we're talking really hardcore stuff. There's no writing a letter and putting it in the file; if he screws up, you fire him. In my early days, I saw the hotshot foreman walk right over to a guy, and he says, "You're outta here." Nine miles from the nearest road. He had to walk out. You're done, just like that. I had the same foreman walk over to me in my sleeping bag one night and point his finger at me, and he said, "You're walkin' on thin ice, bud!" He said, "You think you can cap me, you got another think comin'!" Because I was always kinda smart-mouthed. (Laughs.)

Dennis Baldridge (Laguna, 1990–2009)

I think for the good is [that] we provide all the personal protective equipment. We used to go out and buy some of our own stuff. We take care of our people: the kids may not agree with it, but we take care of them better now than we were ever taken care of 20 years ago. They've got better trucks to ride in; they've got better safety equipment. We feed them better when we can. They get paid better. Those are all positives.

The negative is that we've made it so complicated to fight fire. The Incident Command System was meant to grow with the need for the fire. Now it seems there's no growth. It's either small or it's gigantic. The briefings are an hour long; we can't go out and do things because we don't have all the stuff they need to give us. It's just gotten more complicated. The trend is we don't cut as much direct line as we used to. They use us to back off to ridges and burn out, which increases the risks. It looks simple, but it's not.

I think the politics of fighting fire are a lot worse than they used to be. The urban interface is hitting us. We used to be able to go out to a fire, anchor, flank, and keep moving. Now we have to protect the structures over here; we can't cut over here because it's in the wilderness. We can't do this, we can't do that. Then we get yelled at because the fires get big. That's the negative side.

Lance Honda (Redmond, 1992–1997; Prineville, 1997–2009)

The fact that we've promoted people based on their race or their sex or anything else is wrong when we should be choosing merit and competency. That doesn't mean we can't seek and recognize those people, but we need to recognize competency and merit as the choice. I'm not saying affirmative action is bad or promoting any type of group is bad to equal out things—as long as we select quality, good quality. That's what's important and will make the agency better.

We've got folks who are in the professional series who don't know much about firefighting. Maybe that's the natural progression from having emphasis on career and moving up rather than performing work. It seems to be a change that it's more important to increase your GS level than increase your competence. That's what I see about careers—person who has a career isn't necessarily concerned with what they're leaving, what they're doing, as opposed to advancing their career. I think there's been a change in that since the mid '70s and '80s.

Rusty Witwer (Mendocino, 1978; Hobart/Tahoe, 1979–1995)
Fires burned just as hot 30 years ago as they do now. I've seen it. Mark [Linane] and I, some of the old dogs, have talked about it, and if any of you had been on Romero, you've never seen a canyon go up as quick as that. Fires were just as hot back then. They're just getting more of them and bigger, and part of that is because we're not aggressively putting them out, because we're saying "no" too often; and I think all that does is allow more perimeter the next day and more opportunity for somebody to get into a freaky accident. There is an element of when-you-can, when-you-can't; and to be honest with you, I hate night shifts, but that's when we pick up most of our fires and when we should be doing most of our work.

Greg Vergari (Union, 1980–1987)
[Is it a bad thing that supes aren't as in-your-face anymore?]
Yes and no! I think it is imperative that the supes work with the team to let the team know how the operation is going. When I was the R4 operations safety officer, I would get calls from the supes in R4. They would be telling me about some FUBR [fucked up beyond recognition] assignment, and I would chew them out. I'd ask them why they didn't speak their piece on the fire and get it squared on the line.

This needs to happen: that is why we have AAR's. We should be doing an AAR after every assignment, or at least after a few days' time—to assess how it went and learn. Keeping it to ourselves is not the way to go. Being shy is not a good trait for a hotshot supe, by the way.

Bob Bennett (Horseshoe Meadow, 1989–2006)
[What does "old-school" mean to you?]
(Laughing.) Old-school is just working, all the time. No rules, no-holds-barred, basically. That's to me what old-school was. We didn't have 14 days or 21 days; you could work all summer. You didn't have two-to-one work-rest cycles. The big fires we have now, the ones that last 14 and 20 days, even a month—back in the '70s and early '80s, we didn't have those. I can remember a couple fires where we were on them maybe a couple weeks. But those were your very unusual situations, where now that's the norm.

I think old-school is, basically, when you got to a fire you never backed off. You just got on the edge of it and went. You cut line until the line was finished. If you had to spike out on the line, they'd get food to you; and if you were lucky, sometimes you didn't get food or sleeping bags. You just toughed it out, and that was the norm. I can remember a couple of fires where we worked three days straight. You didn't sleep. You were up actually working for those three days straight.

I can remember in the early '70s, I don't think we even had briefings. You were just in the trucks, and—boom—you were out on the line cutting by, like, seven in the morning, and then you were lucky to get back in and get something to eat and get in bed by 10 or 11 o'clock.

If you had a boss or a supervisor who didn't like you, you could be gone the next day without any warning. The harder you worked, the quicker you could move up. That's how you got promotions back then. If you worked your ass off, you were going to move up in the organization. If you were lazy, you probably wouldn't go anywhere. You had to prove yourself by being a hard worker.

[Not anymore?]

No. (Laughs.) Truthfully, no. A lot of things have changed that. We don't hold people accountable for what they do. I think we do not reward the hard workers by promoting them. We usually promote up—I feel—the people who aren't as strong. Sometimes because of sex, religion, other things. It's not the person who deserves the job sometimes. Seemed like in the past, if you worked hard, you were good, you were going up, where now you could be a good worker but you might stay there the rest of your life too.

Ted Mathiesen (Arroyo Grande Flight Crew, 1990–2007)

The politics, probably, is the biggest thing. We seem to knee-jerk react to every little political thing. . . . We just react instead of think about it and make a good decision. I think the politics is way out of hand. We work for the government, the biggest bureaucracy there is, so I understand it's hard.

Some of the younger ones coming up now, they don't understand the frustration level with the government, and I go, "You will. It's the government," or they quit, and they go to work for the county, and they go to work for a smaller bureaucracy that maybe is worse. At least we're a huge bureaucracy, and sometimes things get lost in the shuffle. . . . Now we've got the OSHA [Occupational Safety and Health Administration] in our face all the time, the Office of General Counsel, and on and on and on. Some congressman's house burns down, and it's too much.

It's not as straightforward as it used to be. The job is not as well-defined because we have to react to all the different things. Just like we were talking about this morning, using crosscut saws to fall a tree, as opposed to being safe and using common sense and using a chainsaw to get it down—that kind of stuff. Politics, wilderness, that stuff.

[Any change for the better?]

They finally realized—or are beginning to realize—that we are a fire department, so to speak, within the Forest Service. We're starting to get credit. Some of the managers who have been in the field are starting to get up in pretty high levels to be able to maybe effect some change that way. There's more money for equipment, the MEL funding. . . . Safety has really, really come to the forefront, so to speak. It was always there, but now it's embraced a little bit more.

Richard Aguilar (El Cariso, 1974; Wolf Creek, 1975–1997)

The hotshot superintendents—some of them—would wander away from the crew, let the foreman run the crew. A lot of times, they were doing politics. They were spending too much time in camp, trying to promote themselves to be a division supe or operations trainee, and not working with the crew. I think hotshot superintendents, they're doing a dangerous job; they should always be with the crew. They are the ones who can make the decisions of when they're going to go direct or indirect. If they're not with their crew at all times, I don't think it should be a Type 1. I think that's a bad thing. I used to see a lot of superintendents just wander off on their own. To me that was a no-no.

Barry Callenberger (Palomar, 1979–1982; Eldorado, 1982–1988)

I can remember when superintendents wouldn't talk to foremen. No way. My old superintendent would go up and they would sit around the table with all the other old superintendents, and the foreman would just kind of sit around and take care of the crew. Every now and then there'd be one old dog who would come over and talk to you. He'd talk to you and spend a little bit of time with you, and you'd go, "Hey, this is all right. That's a superintendent who wouldn't talk to me, and now he's saying hi," or he'd come up to you when you were a new superintendent, and he'd go, "Okay, Barry, what are we gonna do?" I'd go, "Uhh." Now here's somebody that's been a superintendent for 15, 20 years, and he's asking me.

That kind of treatment helps you to build on what you've learned about leadership, and that's important stuff. I don't know if that goes on anymore. I'm encouraged by what I've seen in the quality of folks who are still in the agency. I'm really happy that that is still happening, because there was a period of time I questioned whether the quality was going to go down, and it doesn't matter. There are a lot of high-quality people in the agency, and people need to respect that.

One of the biggest things that upsets me the most is the lack of respect for people who have chosen the profession of being a wildland firefighter. Sure, [you don't] need a college education to do that, but I've always been upset with the foresters' attitude toward firefighters. It's pervasive in the organization. I don't think they respect the firefighters. The people who are firefighters are high-quality. They're very intelligent people. They deserve to have any break they want, go anywhere they want in the operation, not because they have a degree in forestry. . . . You can't get a degree in wildland firefighting. I don't think they have a curriculum in school. Sure, you can get a "degree," but you don't have what it takes unless you spend some time. It's the lack of respect. although it's probably getting more respect.

People talk a lot about Kent Clark. He had a lot of respect. His idols were superintendents. Here's a guy who was in Washington, D.C., and he was the director of Fire and Aviation Management, Region 5, and he often said his idols were hotshot superintendents. But there seems to be that pervasion that it's a caste system, and the firefighters are the lowly end of the caste, and they never got the respect—although they're getting a lot more respect. They've got more career people—I'm glad to see that.

People are getting more employment. When I came in to Eldorado, the superintendent was the only full-time position. The foremen then had an 18/8 [career seasonal position], but we worked them all year, and there were no full-time people on the crew.

Everywhere now, everywhere across the nation, people are respecting the position and giving them more career status and keeping them around. They're smart. They're finally putting something right, and it's taken them my 33 years to get it to the point where it is now. They've got an academy, which I think is a great tool. It's good to see. I was down at McClellan, and you could just see the people coming in there—they look enthusiastic, and they're happy to be in the job.

I'm really discouraged at the fact that there've been a lot of fatalities. The fires are getting bigger, and it's not only a change in fuel structure. I understand that. The weather seems to be hotter, and I understand that, but there's something else going on that has to do with how suppression is taking place. I don't like what they're doing with making the responsibility for what happens on the fireline the incident commander's. He doesn't have much say in what goes on at the division level. There's something going on.

Ken Jordan (Sierra, 1998–2014)
The fitness levels are going up—I think they have to—which is good. People are starting to worry more and more about their health, because they have to. Lot of good changes there.

The experience level is, to me, a total organizational failure because we've accepted a norm that we have forestry technicians fighting fire instead of firefighters. We treat them as temporary forestry technicians without any benefits, when every other department [has], portal-to-portal, four or five times as much pay. It's hard for us to retain quality people nowadays. It's hard. That, in turn, affects everybody's safety. . . . It's changed to a point where we spend so much of our time certifying people and signing people off instead of trying to build an experienced and quality workforce by basically just paying people and giving them benefits that keeps up with the rest of the fire community. That's probably the big thing right there with me, is the organizational failure to do that.

This is totally politically incorrect, but we've had back-to-back social engineering projects since the '70s, and it's been beneficial for some—it's been an eye-opener for some—but sometimes it's just overdone. It's not right, because there are other agencies that pay a lot more money that also have affirmative action programs, so just because you're a minority doesn't mean you want to work for nothing. You've got family, and you want to work for more money, so that kind of creates a vacuum there. I've lost a lot of good people to those. Everybody has. We're in a constant state of trying to rebuild something. Unless we take a real hard stance on paying people like the other agencies—same with diversity— we're not going to do it.

Dan Fiorito (Union, 1996–2006)
There have been a lot of rules and regulations placed on firefighters in the last few years that have not really made us any safer on the fireline. The work-rest rules are an example of bureaucratic rules, made in the name of safety, which can actually make firefighting less safe. The work-rest ratio guidelines are so mismanaged by overhead teams that we often wind up fighting fire by the clock.

Many times since 2002, when the Thirtymile work-rest regulations went into effect, we have been sent off of the fireline before our objectives were met because we would have had to work over 16 hours to meet those objectives. There have been times when we should have worked for a few additional hours and finished a burnout or tied in a piece of line, but because of the work-rest rules, or the interpretation of them, we have been ordered to return to camp. When this happens, we are exposing firefighters to greater risk, due to a fire increasing in size or getting around a piece of uncompleted line and moving into areas that are more hazardous to work in.

The work-rest guidelines work fine for shifts when you are mopping up, but until a fire is contained, we need to be allowed to work more than 16 hours. Not every shift needs to be longer than 16 hours, but when it makes sense, we should work until an objective is met for that shift, not be told to stop working because we hit the magic 16-hour limit.

Wildland firefighters are being told that they should have individual liability insurance. In fact, the government will even reimburse us for half the cost of this type of insurance. This is an indicator of how things have changed as far as the agencies backing up their employees when something goes wrong on the fireline. A person cannot assimilate and follow all the hundreds of rules and regulations regarding wildland firefighting. There will always be some rule that will be found to have been violated by the investigators who were not present at the time of the accident but have the advantage of hindsight.

The fact is that from now on, the federal agencies such as the Forest Service will take an adversarial approach when investigating an individual who is involved in a tragedy fire involving serious injury or death. Every firefighter should take a hard look at what the government did to the incident commander on the Cramer fire in Idaho, as well as the lawsuits and criminal charges brought against the people involved in the Thirtymile incident.

Ron Regan (Del Rosa, 1977–1997)

Thirty-three people was a lot to haul around. When they downsized the crews to 20 and made everything standard and put them in crew carriers where they were mobile, I think that was a good move. Taking the crew carriers and driving to the incident if we were going to another region was an excellent move. All the equipment's there. Probably the 21-day [dispatch]—now I guess it's 14—but that was some good stuff to do . . . because you've got another life besides this one.

The food has gotten a lot better, most of the time. The training is probably the best you can get. I still think that the Forest Service is the best wildland fire agency, as firefighting goes—the highest-trained and the most experienced in the world. Tough to beat 'em. Sometimes you're sent to an incident, and they just fly you in and drop you off at a helispot and say, "Okay, get a hold of us in a couple days."

Bob Wright (Sacramento, 1990–2002)

Those old guys . . . they'd get out and dig line with you, lay hose with you, all kinds of stuff. If you messed up . . . they'd call up at two o'clock in the morning—wake you up—and you'd lay hose until you got it right. Joe Brewer, he used to be one of my captains. When you did mobile attack, he'd have a stopwatch setting there, and if you didn't get it in so many seconds, you'd be doing it until you got it right. If you messed up a friggin' flashlight at night, you'd be out doing flashlight training, pulling weeds all night with your flashlight so you'd learn how to use your flashlight. If you messed up, you'd set in the back of the fire truck while everybody's working their butts off. That's just the way. They were really hardcore, but they were all good firemen.

Steve Dickenson (La Grande, 1990; Redmond, 1994)

When I started, there were no tests. These old guys, 70 years old, were out there fighting fire with us. Were they digging like us? No. But they were my mentors, and they would stop, take two steps, wipe the sweat, catch their breath, take two steps. They were directing us: "Go up there and catch this fire and get around the front of it."

People are not just going to go up there and die. Some people will go slower, but to have that old 70-year-old person out there . . . I learned a lot from them, and I was mentored. Now at 30,

32, people are getting out of arduous because they don't want to go out there and keep in shape and carry the pack and do the pack test—except for the supes, these old supes who keep going every year and keep passing the tests.

We all complain about how bad the rest of the fire world is, and it's because we've set these standards up. We've asked for them, because we think everybody should be digging 20 chains an hour, and it's not true. . . . I regret none of those old guys who are 70 years old, old as can be—I learned a lot from them—and nobody's getting that anymore because they have to stay in camp and run ground support now.

We all leave, too: we go to be FMOs, and we don't get out there on arduous fires either. You have to be an athlete now, and to be young and be an athlete doesn't always mean there's a lot of experience out there. So, do away with all those damn tests. When you get your crews and you hire people, tests won't make you fit. We've lost a lot of experience due to tests. Nobody was ever out there dying from heart attacks. Go out there and look at the fatalities from heart attacks and stuff: it's all in camp, people setting up the tents. It's going to happen anyway, at home; we didn't cause it.

If you can change anything in the future, get rid of the damn tests and get the old hands back out there. They'll go slow, and they'll be mopping their brows, but they're not going to die out there. That kind of mentoring is invaluable. I'm very lucky to have had it. Five years I worked before they had a step test. I learned a lot from some old guys out there who didn't look very fit but had been on a zillion fires.

Lanky and Caldwell's History Lesson on the Couth System

Craig Lechleiter (Redding, 1986–2002)

I don't know if you heard about our couth program here. Most crews that have been around for any length of time have something comparable, and they do it because it builds esprit de corps and it emphasizes a strong safety ethic. It's that hammer that's always watching you and an element that keeps you in compliance. The payment for violating procedures is a dollar, a six-pack of beer, or anything else the crew decides on.

The couth system was a big thing with me, keeping that going—the tradition of it all. Against my better judgment, one year I asked the crew, "Before we implement this, you've heard about it. It's why you came here, right? Is there anybody who doesn't want to partake in this? Is anybody uncomfortable with it?" Well, nobody raised their hand. I said, "Well, I'll make it easy for you." I should've shut up right there, but I went ahead and said, "Take a piece of paper. Put 'yes' or 'no': 'yes,' I have a problem with it, or 'no,' I don't have a problem with it. Throw it in the hat."

I opened them up, and there was one "yes." I said, "There's my answer. We're not doing it this year." I didn't tell the crew how many no's I had. I said, "We had one," and that's all that I needed to say, and there was a hush over the crowd. You should have seen their reaction. Well, like anything else in life, you make some good and bad decisions through your life. That was one of my worst ones.

Charlie Caldwell (Redding, 1967–1986)
[How much did a couth offense cost?]
A buck and a half. It was called a six-pack: a buck and a half was the price of a six-pack back in the early days, when I first started, and that's the way it became. We had old hotshot traditions. This is a big safety thing, too, this couth officer thing.

The Shasta-Trinity said, "You have the most man-hours worked and fewer accidents than anybody. How do you do it?" "Well, I'm really not at liberty to talk about it that much." "Well, we'd like to get you and both your foremen to go to each district and put on a safety program on your system and how it works." I said, "I can't do it." "What do you mean, you can't do it?" I said, "What, you think the Forest Service is going to allow my going out there to the district and telling 'em that if they pass gas and don't check the wind and whistle before they fart that it's gonna cost 'em a buck and a half? No, that won't work."

We had things like pool room violations, dress code, fire shirts, fire readiness; you're going to get fined for any of these things. You step on the rope during rope climbing; you use foul language in a public place; you use foul language around a woman unless she's on the fireline; if you're late to class; if you laugh during "prayer meeting"—without permission; leaving anything in the classroom or the mess hall; wearing a ball cap in a restaurant or the classroom; smoking in the classroom or bus; wearing the hat backwards; leaving the lights on in a room; hall door left open; not pushing in a chair in the classroom.

It cost 'em a case if they had a birthday, if they had a divorce, if they had a wedding, if they got married. . . . If it was a fire on their district or on their forest, it cost 'em a case. If they got a promotion, or a QSI, anything like that—wage grade increase. If they had a baby, it cost 'em a case. (Laughs.)

We had a big party at the end of the year. We'd rent the local golf club or something like that. One time we rented a house, and we had guys on the crew who played the music. We had our own musicians, rented a house, and had it catered.

I didn't let them pick the next couth officer, though. No. We usually gave it to somebody who was whining about whatever they got busted for. (Laughs.)

What do you think about all the overhead movement in the hotshot program?

Kurt LaRue (Diamond Mountain, 1993–2001)
I hear a lot of talk about the young supervisors, like somehow we're crippled nowadays due to the fire plan, that we've hired

all these young supervisors. Mark [Linane] and I were laughing about this a little bit last night: how old was he when he got his crew? How old were Rusty Witwer and Bill Sandborg and Kirby Moore? These guys were all picking up crews, my understanding is, in their late 20s, early 30s. I was running a bus at Fulton with four years' experience. Two years after that, I was the third-oldest guy on the crew.

We had ten years in there where we didn't give out many appointments. When I first got Diamond Mountain, the easiest position to find people for was the eight- and ten-year sawyer who wanted to be a squad boss. They were everywhere. And now, by your third or fourth year, you're supervising. I don't think this is new. It was around in the '70s and before then. You look at the crew pictures on a lot of those crews: those guys were really young. I think people just got spoiled over the years, having the luxury of all the supervisors they were going to hire who had ten years in, which you don't have now.

I think there are some drawbacks with too much time in one place with no promotion. A lot of people who were around for long periods of time in one place lost some of the enthusiasm that some of the younger people have. I think that if you have an intelligent, enthusiastic younger person, a lot of times it's more beneficial to put that person in charge over someone who has more time, because a lot of the time is just repetitious years of the same thing. Have they learned something new every year? Or are they just some jaded old bastards who've done a lot of time because they couldn't find another job? I don't think younger supervisors are near as bad as they talk about.

Look at the assistant supes who are all running around down there [at the workshop]. They were squadies until recently. A lot of those guys, with very little training or mentoring, could step up and make fine crew leaders right now. But by the standards of the '80s, they don't have all the time in that they're supposed to have.

I also don't like the attitude that some people have: "It took me eight years to get carded for that, so I won't sign them in four." Well, either you were a dullard or you worked for a dullard; I don't know what the problem was that made you take eight years to get that. But it doesn't mean the next kid up isn't smart enough to master that in three or four solid seasons.

I also don't think they're giving them enough credit for the fact that all these kids on hotshot crews now, they're turning in 100 line shifts a year. You get a kid with five years' experience, he's got 500 line shifts, 5,000 hours of overtime on top of his base pay. You go back to the '70s and '80s, how many years would it take you to build comparable experience on line? Twice that.

Paul Musser (Flagstaff, 1990–2004)
I think the hotshot program is already fundamentally hurt just from all the other things that we need to do. We always needed to treat our people better and stuff like that, but this is still a military organization, and there are times when it has to be that way. When we've lost the ability to hire strictly on qualifications and ability, we're not going out and hiring strictly for the best people for the crew. We have to look at too many other things. We need to find the strongest, the most healthy, the people who have the desire to go out there. When we get the people who don't have that, we can't do anything about it.

I think we're going to go through a period where people are going to move through the position to get other places, and I would probably do it if I was young too, because right now there is a tremendous amount of opportunity. But I truly think that if you don't move through that opportunity, it's going to stop in five or ten years. We didn't hire for so many years or we hired so few people that all of us are getting ready to retire.

But you look at when we hired last year [2000]—a thousand GS-5s—all of a sudden you're going to push that thousand GS-5s into 900 GS-6s, 500 GS-7s, 300 GS-9s. We've changed the bottleneck from the GS-7 position to the GS-9 position because we didn't develop them. But history is, in the Forest Service, you bring in a great big, large group, and then you're going to force them into a small overhead or career. I think for a while people need to move up as fast as they can.

That's what happened in the early '70s, too: old guys left, and everybody moved up real fast, and then it just stopped. There's a good chance that that's going to happen again. I'm telling all the people who work for me: if you want to be here, that's fine, but if you want to move up, I would do it while the opportunity is there. . . . It's a pain to keep refilling behind, but it's going to just be a revolving door in all of the positions, from the GS-5's on up, for a few years. We have to resign ourselves to the fact that we are going to be continuously hiring people.

What direction should the wildland fire service be going in?

J. W. Allendorf (Wallowa–Whitman, 1980; Arrowhead 3, 1981)

The fire department—to me—should be just like law enforcement: it should be a stovepipe organization, with them in charge of their own budget. The fire department suffers from what I call "fiscal virga." You've got lots of raindrops in the form of dollar bills starting out in the WO [Washington office], but very little of it hits the ground to the folks who need it. As a result, their grade levels are kept capped. For every hour of overtime they work on the fireline, it should be contributed to their retirement. They should be in charge of their own destiny with their budgeting. They have capable people in the fire organization to manage those budgets effectively, and if they were managing their own budget, they could provide real training instead of the band-aid approach that we're taking to our employees.

Greg Vergari (Union, 1980–1987)

We're getting closer to a professional fire department, which in my opinion is where we need to be. We couldn't get there fast enough for me on one hand, but I have some strong ties to the land we manage, and I would hate for us to lose that.

To me it's not as much about the money as it is the safety side. With work-rest, I'd pay people 24 and 7. It doesn't matter to me. The money isn't the part that worries me—it's the hours we're working. It's the miles we're driving. That's what scares me. I look at it this way: how would I want my kid trained, my son or daughter? Who would I want driving my son and daughter in that crew crummy? If everybody's tired and the superintendent is pushing because he or she doesn't know enough to call it quits for an extra day, then that's trouble.

I think the system now is conducive to this type of behavior. Like a very top-ranking safety professional told me once about the Forest Service and wildland firefighters in general, "The monkey on their back is the overtime." I think he is correct for a large portion of our profession—if money was not a motivational factor, you would see fewer mistakes.

Rusty Witwer (Mendocino, 1978; Hobart/Tahoe, 1979–1995)

I think publicizing or vocalizing how much overtime we're making doesn't do anybody any good. It doesn't politically do us any good. I don't think it does good for the initial attack crews that are staying home trying to stop the next multimillion-dollar fiasco from happening. I told my engine crews when I was a battalion chief, "You make one save, you paid for the cost of your module." I don't think the hotshots can make that claim—that if they make one save they can pay for their module—because they're usually not IA.

We need strong first-line supervisors on our Type 1 crews because the overhead mix that we have comes from all over the country, with varying experience levels—so you're a leveler out there. The pitch I would make: don't get tunnel vision into leveling just your bunch. . . . You need to broaden that leveling-out to the adjoining forces that are working around you, and keep them in the loop, not just your 20, because you have seen more fire than the majority of the people in the system, even at upper-level management.

What are your "pet issues"?

Pet issues are those things that we just can't stop talking about and always return to. I wanted to know what gets supes up on their soapboxes.

Stan Stewart (Los Padres, 2000–2009)
I've got a couple pet issues with the work-rest. That pisses me off because there's no common sense in that anymore. We pulled it off just fine on the Cedar fire: worked 70 hours straight. We took a couple hours here and a couple hours there: we got some sleep; we were fine. Came into camp at ten o'clock at night, slept through the night, went back to work. If we'd gone back to the old ways, we'd have been off for, like, two days.

J. W. Allendorf (Wallowa–Whitman, 1980; Arrowhead 3, 1981)
I always said we were the extinguisher hanging on the wall: "Break glass in case of fire," or in case the septic system plugs up, then get the hotshots to go dig it up. They didn't think of us as talented individuals. The truth of the matter is there's so much talent buried in these crews—of all kinds—that unfortunately is overlooked and not taken advantage of. We've got people on hotshot crews who could be working in WO-level jobs. Very well-educated, knowledgeable people, and they get treated like dumbass technicians because of management. That's wrong. You don't waste talent.

Bottom line is, and I've heard it a hundred times, that the fuel conditions and fire behavior have changed, and I won't argue that it has. I know that it has. But tactics have changed also. It seems like we're taking two approaches: [1] We're doing absolutely nothing: standing back and watching it go when we could in fact get in there, anchor, and start flanking—do something, for God's sake—but using the crutch of safety, we do nothing. [2] The other is just some stupid-ass decisions made on the fireline under bad conditions, when everything's apparent. It doesn't take a genius to figure this shit out, but [it takes] experience.

Firefighter safety is my biggest pet issue. I think this runs contrary to what I just said, but I'm against these matrix checklists that we've got. That's a bullshit deal. It's a time-waster on the initial attack. For crying out loud, you're now in a reinforced attack by the time you get through the second checklist. Get in there and anchor the son of a bitch. Even if it's slow progress, make progress.

My last, but not least: "Taj Mahal" fire camps. I know I'm an old fucker when I go to fire camps now. The fire camps I remember when I started were a pallet of C-rations. They used to make boxes that used to hold the banjo canteens; there'd be 30 or 40 of them dumped off, and maybe a trailerful of water that said "potable" but didn't taste like it. Showers were a Mark III pump plugged into a creek with an R5 nozzle on it, and it seemed like it worked pretty good.

Granted, that was a rough fire camp on the initial reinforced attack, but one of the things I think is killing the fire department is the suppression costs per acre. Every year you see it on these large fires: how many millions of dollars it took to put out some piddly-ass fire that we used to be able to suppress for under $100,000, and then you look and everybody's trying to say that it's equipment and aviation costs. Bullshit. It used to be that fire camp was set up on about the seventh day of a fire. Now the caterers are beating a lot of the hotshot crews to camp, and they've got a kitchen set up and showers.

Unfortunately . . . the young fire folks have come to expect that that's how it ought to be. The first thing they ask—I've heard it asked—is, "Where're the showers?" There shouldn't even be any here yet. You haven't sweated. That's just part of progress, I guess, in some respects, but I think it's detrimental because it contributes to the huge costs.

Fred Schoeffler (Payson, 1981–2007)

For many years now, I have been studying several ongoing weather modification phenomena occurring as they relate to fire weather, mostly winds and RHs. Weather modification is real and occurs every single day. I'm speaking mainly of the HAARP [High Frequency Active Auroral Research Project]—a joint effort between the US Air Force, Raytheon, and the University of Alaska—as a result of physicist Bernard Eastlund's patents. It basically is a series of antennas that are able to superheat the ionosphere. This ongoing project ("work in progress") can and does manipulate local and global weather, including the jet stream. Mr. Eastlund acknowledges so in his many patents. For several years, I gave talks and presented papers and documents at various hotshot workshops regarding HAARP. Indeed, the reactions were mixed. My intent was to teach fireline supervisors to look for and heed HAARP-cloud indicators that preceded the winds that follow as a result.

There's also unintentional weather modification that has occurred near military bases utilizing chaff in aircraft maneuvers in order to avoid heat-seeking missiles and such. There's a recent documented case adjacent to an Arizona base where a chaff cloud was tracked off-base by nonmilitary meteorologists during thunderstorm activity. The chaff cloud all but neutralized the lightning activity yet intensified the associated thunderstorm winds enough to shear off nearby telephone poles. Surely this was unintentional, but it could have had a drastic effect on nearby firefighters engaged on wildfires in the path of an intensified chaff-induced thunderstorm.

Greg Vergari (Union, 1980–1987)

The world does not end with hotshots: it just begins.

When you find yourself not doing PT with the crew, not walking the line with the crew, not stopping to teach at a teachable moment, find yourself sitting in the pickup—even if you have an excuse—you're being lazy. Then you're not only cheating yourself and your crew, but the hotshot name. Even if you can giggle with someone else doing the same thing, it doesn't make it any better. It only means there are two of you who should quit.

[Another pet issue:] Not being able to go on fire assignments because you are the forest duty officer.

Dennis Baldridge (Laguna, 1990–2009)

It's not specifically hotshot, but I'm part of the Wildland Fire Service Association, which is a political action group trying to get better pay for wildland firefighters. Wherever I'm at and people ask the question, or open the door, I talk about that. We're trying to get portal-to-portal pay, trying to get our hazard pay to count toward retirement, trying to get classified as firefighters instead of forestry technicians, and have been dealing with that since 1991. That started in the hotshot organization, but we're trying to expand that.

I'm the chairman of the National Hotshot Steering Committee now [2003], so I get a lot of issues brought to me. I'm trying to figure out how to forward those to the Washington office level. That's probably what most of the folks know me for. They know I don't have much of a life, so they vote me into stuff. (Laughs.) But if I didn't want to do it, I wouldn't do it. It's a good thing.

Lance Honda (Redmond, 1992–1997; Prineville, 1997–2009)

I learned years ago the importance of having a vision. The crew has a vision, but my own personal vision for how I want to lead and how I want to supervise is that I've been dissatisfied with how our agency passes on its knowledge. We don't do a very good job of mentoring and leading and teaching our folks, and there are not a lot of good supervisors. My personal vision is to hire the best people I can, teach them in the best way I can, and then let them go. Let them go someplace else and repeat the same process.

A lot of superintendents, they want to grab folks and keep them, and they're theirs—it's disloyal to go somewhere else—and that's wrong. How is our agency supposed to get better? How are we supposed to make the firefighting world or community better without getting good folks, the best ones we can, and teaching them? Really and truly, that's the best and most effective way to make change.

Steve Dickenson (La Grande, 1990; Redmond, 1994)

In the jumpers, we have a standard to get into the jump program, and the bar is this high. This is the entrance test, and this is what you have to do through training, so let's say it's four feet. There are people you work with who can always jump eight feet. A lot of leaders and supes will expect those standards. Be proud that you can leap over it at eight feet. Help other people who are doing it at four feet. Recognize that four feet is what it is, that's good enough, and help them get to five feet, to six feet. I'm very intolerant of people in this business that go, "I have a God-given talent, and I can leap at eight feet, and why can't everybody else?" Know where the bar is—realistically—and give people credit for getting over that bar. If we say it's four feet, four feet's what it is. If you're doing it at eight feet, or if you've got people on your crew who expect everybody else to be gifted like them, explain that about the bar. You can give up your foot so you'll only be jumping seven, and they'll be jumping five.

Knowledge is not power. A lot of people like to hoard power and hoard knowledge because, "I know; I'm one up on everybody," and that's so stupid. You can never lose your power. You can just only give it. Yours never diminishes. Communication is everything. Be free with it, and you'll never lose yours. Other people will be empowered.

Fighting fire, you'll never save a dime, so don't ever try to save money on a fire. You can't. What you're trying to do is not waste money, and I hate people who try to save money on fires. Do what's right, spend the money it takes, know what that is, and don't waste money. The minute that fire starts, it's going to cost somebody a penny. Don't ever think in terms of saving money on fire incidents. It's always going to cost, and we get in trouble when we try and cheat or be cheap or cut corners. Use the appropriate tool the amount of times you need. They'll always mutter behind your back, "Man, that was 25 loads of retardant." Too bad. That's what it took, and be serious about it. Put it out. Hold that division. Do what it takes.

The 35-acre fire: very dangerous fire. You know, the Type 3 fire. Hire an airplane. Send one of your foremen: they don't have to be an air attack. Have dispatch get a [Cessna] 182 . . . and have somebody over the top of you that's a firefighter you know looking out, just going around. They're not looking to separate helicopters, lead air tankers. Anytime you can put one of your assistants in an airplane over a fire where you can't account for the perimeter, I highly encourage it.

Dispatchers always go, "We'll get you an air attack," but no, it'll be days before they get you an air attack. Send one of your guys in—go in yourself—make out rental agreements. That's so inexpensive. Like I said, you don't need training. What you're doing there is being a lookout in a different platform. Great way to have an assistant screwing off all day, flying in a plane. They like it a lot.

What aren't firefighters being taught, or what aren't they learning?

Brit Rosso (Arrowhead, 1996–2006)
Some of the things we need to continue to teach are, obviously, supervision and leadership: how to deal with people, how to mentor people, how to be an effective instructor. We mess around with "Facilitative Instructor" and a few other courses, but we really need to focus on developing instructors—good instructors—because anyone can pull a binder off a shelf and regurgitate out of that binder, but you have to have somebody who's engaging and effective up there at the podium teaching the class. Otherwise, the kids, their heads just spin; they just bang their foreheads on the table, and it's all about just trying to stay awake.

I think emphasizing those things to be a more effective leader [is important] and also all the administrative stuff that comes with it. Most of us had to go through the school of hard knocks, whether it's how to run a credit card, filling out CA-1s and CA-16s—all that stuff.

Paul Musser (Flagstaff, 1990–2004)
When I came up, we spent so much time working in the woods that we had a pretty tight tie to the land. In the Forest Service as a whole, not too many people go to the woods anymore. You don't go out there and do stuff hardly at all. There're some projects and stuff like that, but we don't quite have the tie to the land or anything like that.

Because we're on fires so much, I don't think the superintendents will ever become as tight with the crew as they were. For me, when we were doing project work, I got to know people more. When we're on fires, I'm dealing with the team and I don't see the crew. I'm dealing with the team, I'm on the next ridge over, but I'm very seldom with the crew. I try to do things to make sure I am, but I don't think we have that close tie with the crew that we used to.

Also, years ago, you just lined up and started cutting line, and you were going to cut line until you either dropped or you came around and tied in the line or whatever. The superintendent was closer with them. We spiked a lot more then, and that helps to bring people a little bit closer. We spiked several times last year, and most of the time we spiked with the vehicles, so the crew's in watching movies on the VCR. But every once in a while, you build a campfire and everyone stands there and talks. I think, because we're becoming so spread out and there are so many other jobs, we can't become as tight with the crew as we used to. *[I thought it was the other way around: that supes know their crews better now, that back then the supe wouldn't even talk to you.]*

You didn't speak until you were spoken to. And then after a week or two, or maybe a month, or maybe never, but once you earned your position, you got a lot tighter with them. When I started for CDF, my engine captain, I could call him Mr. King. That's the only thing I could call him. After a month or two, I was allowed to call him "Boss," or "Boss King," and then by the end of the season I could call him Boyd. But you definitely had to earn your place. Except that once you did, it seems like it was a lot tighter back then.

Maybe it's the different positions, too. Back then, when I was captain or squad boss with a crew, I was with the crew all the time, and the supe was the one who was out arranging every-thing. When I first got here, each day I was out doing project work with them. [Now] they show up to the Hotshot Ranch, and I show up here [the office] so I can work on the computers and get stuff done. When we go to a fire, everybody goes their sepa-rate ways.

Fred Schoeffler (Payson, 1981–2007)
Leadership skills. Only recently has this become a prime focal point and training segment. The Forest Service for years used to promote employees who were hard workers as supervisors. The two traits were not necessarily compatible, as evidenced by the vast number of poor supervisors.

The field-level folks are receiving and using this training. It's the managers and upper-level supervisors who need this training and then [need] to apply it to their daily tasks. I think it's at these upper levels where we're really lacking in leadership skills.

Supervisors need to be taught ethics—doing the difficult right thing—and then practicing it.

What from your own training and development did you hate and make sure to change when you became a supervisor?

Jim Cook (Arrowhead, 1981–1995; Boise, 1996–1998)
I think the one thing I did—at least in the perspective of running the hotshot crew—is I never wanted someone to have to run a single tool in a single spot all year. I hate that. I'll agree that degraded the effectiveness of the crew maybe 5 or 10 percent, but the fact that people got to move around and see different parts of the line construction responsibilities kept them more engaged, and I think that probably balanced that out.

I know early on, people would go, "You don't have a set tool order." Well, I have a standard of a certain number of tools of a certain kind we use in certain fuel types, but I expect all of my people to know how to use all those tools and to know all the different responsibilities that go with them. Some people might not be the best trench-makers, but that doesn't mean they can't build trenches. Someone might not be the best quality-control or lead P[ulaski], but I want them to do that because someday the guy that's doing that might be TU [tits up]. Then everyone else is, like, "I dunno." Especially early in the '80s, you had a number and a tool, and that was it for the year. I believe people should know all aspects of the job.

Ted Mathiesen (Arroyo Grande Flight Crew, 1990–2007)
Coming up—and I've always said this—you learn as much, if not more, from poor supervisors and poor managers [as] anything else. You can really key in on, "I will never do that."

One is the information exchange: withholding information. I want to make everything available as much as possible: training, what's going on. We have a briefing every morning, talking about our picture and then the bigger picture and then the big picture.

Being approachable: I worked for guys who were just unap-proachable, and this was early in my career. Being approachable is huge. Making time, and making all of these kids feel important, feel like they're part of the big picture and they really are inte-gral to it. They all bring something to the table. I think that's one of the best things that a supervisor can do: make them all feel important. Give everybody the equal opportunity, so to speak; don't play favorites. There will be better performers, and you need to reward that, but still, don't play favorites. Try to develop everybody and give them opportunities for training and so forth.

Kurt LaRue (Diamond Mountain, 1993–2001)
My early superintendents were very, very straightforward when you talked to them. You asked a question; you got an answer. Didn't even have to ask a question, and you got an answer some-times. You knew where you stood at all times. Later in life, I worked with some folks who were less direct and not as straight-forward with the folks around them. It taught me a lot about how to treat people and how to deal with things. I could [compare] the reaction these folks got from people against the reaction that came from the other guys. I really did try hard when I got the crew to be very upfront about, "I don't know," or, "This is what

we're going to do," and you only say "this is what you're going to do" if this is actually what you're going to go do now.

The things that I saw from other supes that I tried to carry with me: one of my earlier supes—although I didn't always recognize it at the time—was really good at letting you fail in a controlled environment. You didn't know you were always being watched. To you it looked like the whole world may be falling in. If all you have is success, if you're successful all the time, you'll just become very arrogant. If you fail, you'll learn things.

I think it's important that you let the crewmen work all the way through to the point of failure. . . . The people who lean toward this type of work have a lot of self-confidence in themselves physically and mentally and emotionally, and they'll overcome just virtually anything. I find that if the young guys are just continually successful, they become arrogant beyond belief: 12-foot-tall, bulletproof. They think they can't screw up. You can screw up in this line of work. As they're learning all these new things, they don't need a lot of success to become arrogant, but they need enough failure along the way to learn some humility too. (Laughs.)

I don't know if my early supe planned to teach me that way, but it worked that way and it worked well, so I decided to carry that over too. I watch the young people out there, and I don't always give them the answers as they are working through problems, but if they're not going to get killed, I'll let them go on, and they'll sort it all out in a little while.

One night I left one of my squad leaders out working with some tractors, and his night just spiraled in on him. He's got the dozers pushing and the crew right behind them burning. Actually, all is well, but he thinks he is lost and all that: I could hear him cussing and stomping about on the ridge in the dark. He finally got to the point where he asked for some help, and it startled him that I was standing about 150 feet away. He called me on the radio and asked me what I was doing, and I was able to just yell back.

Dan Fiorito (Union, 1996–2006)

Be as aggressive as you can within the bounds of LCES and the 10 & 18, give a 100 percent effort, and finish hard. I guess those are the basics that I learned my first season. I have tried to keep those basics in mind for my entire career. When I worked in Southern California, the crew would get run off the hill by the fire, sometimes multiple times during a shift. We would go back to the bottom of the hill, pick up a flank and try again, and keep going. We did not have eight or ten radios on a crew then, so we kept a lot closer to have communications with one another. Our crew leaders kept us safe, and that is what I try to do with my crews.

Greg Keller (Eldorado, 1985–1996; Modoc, 2000–2007)

I think we've kind of kicked out some of the bad stuff. A lot of it was how we treated people, and I don't know that we were very good at that. I think we're much better today at treating people well, but then we also have a harder time in disciplinary issues, possibly getting rid of people who aren't quite successful. It's kind of a hard blend. . . . We spend a great deal of time today teaching people and trying to motivate through a conversation process, a leadership process, a showing process. In the old days, you would get one chance to succeed. You would get a fairly stern ass-chewing, and then you might get some hazing/harassing, and you either succeeded or were kicked out of the organization. That's changed, and probably rightfully so.

Steve Karkanen (Lolo, 1990–2011)

Our FMOs, our AFMOs, don't get involved in what's going on with their fire folks. That's sad. A lot of the kids who are on the district here, on my crew, hardly ever see their FMO. They don't know who he is. Walked in the door and they didn't even know who he was. It's sad, and I think that's the case on a lot of forests.

We have the task book system, which is good in a sense, but what's happening is that there's no accountability there. People are going off and getting task books signed off, and nobody's really mentoring that person and watching to make sure that, "Yeah, Karkanen can go off and be a division supe now. He's ready." I had that. But a lot of these folks don't have that now.

Richard Aguilar (El Cariso, 1974; Wolf Creek, 1975–1997)

When a young person asks a question, you have to answer their question—politely—even if it's a dumb question. Never hurt that person or embarrass that person's feelings. I think that's a big mistake. You really don't know what's going through a person's mind. A lot of times they want to talk about something: they have a little problem, and they don't know how to get your attention, and they'll ask anything. If you don't answer the question and try to dig in: "How come you asked me that?" or something, you don't know what's going on with that person. That is very, very important. I would never embarrass the person on the line or in base camp, or anything. I will always be honest and answer their questions.

Barry Callenberger (Palomar, 1979–1982; Eldorado, 1982–1988)

(Laughs.) When I was a foreman, I was the one who got the job of telling all the sawyers that if they didn't shave their beards they were going back on McLeod. I brought them into the office, and the battle began over their beards and their long hair. My superintendent was adamant that he wanted 'em clean-shaven and short-haired, and I said to myself I was not going to attack individuality that way. I wasn't going to allow that to happen.

I didn't quite approach it that way when I became super-intendent, but I did want the crew to at least attempt to make themselves presentable when they were in camp and just in general. They have a certain amount of individuality that you have to respect, and you have to give in a little bit on the cohesiveness. I was really fortunate in becoming a foreman and superintendent when I did because I think it was the transition from the old days to the new days: the transition from how crews were treated, how they worked, how the crewmen were treated on the crews.

Dave Matier (Midnight Sun, 1992–1997, 1999–2007, 2009–2010)

When I was on Smokey Bear, it was more like we were there to fight fire. Project work was a secondary thing. I think that if you don't maintain the type of attitude that everything's important—the work ethic—everything is harder doing that. You can go out there and work, and if you get a fire call, you're not going to miss the fire. You may get there a little later, but I think it's important to maintain the same type of consistency whether you're doing project work or whatever.

Ron Bollier (Silver City, 1993–1995; Carson, 1996–1997; Fulton, 1998–2013)

Always do what you want to do if you have the power to do that, and don't be like somebody else because, "That's the way we did it when we were there." Always do what you want to do and choose your own destiny and tailor the program to the way you want it to be done. Don't make the people who work for you ever do something you wouldn't want to do and not help them. Hopefully, you bury your foot in it right next to them doing it.

Ron Regan (Del Rosa, 1977–1997)

This is back when we didn't have credit cards to take care of the crew: there were a lot of times that we would leave one incident and go to another one, and the crew wasn't fed or anything. We'd get to fire camp and everything was all locked up and closed, so the crew didn't eat. Now the superintendents have the luxury of credit cards . . . where they can take care of the crew a lot better. That used to bother me more than anything. You expect the guys to put in a 16-to-18-hour shift, and they haven't even been fed.

You can't do that to people. They have to have adequate rest, and there are times when you have to say, "Enough is enough. We've got to put them down for eight to ten hours at least, and then we'll go to work."

When I first started, I went to a three-day fire school where small fires were lit in a designated area. We used to do it here on the San Bernardino at Summit Valley, where the fire wouldn't run up into any housing or take out a large chunk of land. It was all dozed off. It was early in June, and the burns would take place when the weather was favorable. I said, "This is good," and that's what I carried. I would light small fires for individuals to put out by themselves. It gave them exposure to the elements.

Art Torrez (Vista Grande, 1994–2004)
I know the stuff that I said I was going to use, and I'm using it to this day: treat people the way I wanted to be treated. When I first started ... the actual chain of command was very strict, regimented. You very rarely spoke to the superintendent as a first- or second-year crewperson. If you did, there was probably something wrong. It was usually a reprimand of some sort. I changed that policy in my program. I have an open-door policy.

Craig Workman (Black Mountain, 1988–2005)
One of the things I really don't like—and I've seen it throughout my career with different supervisors and people I've worked with or for—is where you just do busywork that has no value. I do honestly believe that guys need to work, to keep busy, or they get in trouble. (Laughs.) I don't like it to be just busywork, and I do like it to be effective work.

I think I had a period in my career, with this crew, early in the career, where we used to get detailed to a forest almost every year for about two or three years. The FMO there, he always had the most god-awful, stupidest projects for us, just to keep us busy. We'd paint rocks and all these stupid things. After about two years of it, finally one day I just told him, "You know, I know there's got to be some real work to do that would accomplish the same thing, and it'd really be better for us and better for you." He thought about it a little bit, and he said, "Yes, we do." Then we started doing some effective work, and it was much better for the crew.

Greg Overacker (Stanislaus, 1979–2006)

I learned a long time ago as a subordinate: What latitude would I like? How would I like to be treated? How would I like to be communicated with? How would I like to be involved? I would like to give my opinion. I would like it considered—not that you'll use what I say, but I'd at least like it considered. I would like to be treated respectfully, because I want to develop an environment that allows people to step forward.

A first-year crewmen must be comfortable enough to step forward and not feel that they're going to be shot in the head. There can't be reprisal because it eliminates information. The thing I learned is, being that stand-on-a-rock, hard-core, just an image—I don't care how good your background is—that doesn't buy you anything. Your interactions on a daily basis with your crew and other personnel are, in fact, what you're about. I've learned a lot of things I won't do.

Dennis Baldridge (Laguna, 1990-2009)

As far as what I tell myself I wouldn't do that I had to put up with—in the old days with the supervisors when I was growing up—it was, "You'll do what I tell you to do, when I tell you to do it. You won't ask me any questions. Put your head down." It was "assholes and elbows"—that was the term. If you don't like it, it's my way or the highway because there are a hundred people out here who want jobs.

That's not the way I want to treat the kids. I want them to know that I encourage questions. I want them to ask. If my answer has to be, "Because I say so," then I'm not doing my job. By their asking questions, it keeps us honest, keeps us thinking: we don't go stagnant. I think part of it's an evolution in the organization.

Young Mark Linane's Old-School Training

In '67 our engine crew had made second or third engine in, and the fire had run out as far as the engines could go. We'd run hose up 7,000, 8,000 feet, and that's as far as the hose could go, and then the fire ran up the hill. They said, "Well, we're going to release you guys back for initial attack."

We were back down in the parking lot, waiting for the plans guy to get there to get walking papers, and Stub Mansfield, the FMO, said, "What are you doing, Mark?" and I said, "Sitting here waiting to go home, Stub. The fire's up on the hill. That's hotshot country. I'm gonna head home, and I'm gonna kick it." He goes, "Well, yeah, your crew and your engine are, but you're not." I said, "What do you mean I'm not going home? We can't lay any more hose."

He said, "Well, I've got four Indian crews: two Hopis and two Navajos," which at the time I didn't know were life-long enemies of each other, "and I want you to be a sector boss." I said, "Stub, I'm no sector boss." He goes, "You are now," and that was my introduction to being a sector boss.

I ended up having to hike the four crews to the top of the mountain. Lynn Biddison was up there, and another guy. Those Indian crews knew I was a young buck, and they made me work. I had to go through their exact chain of command. I couldn't just tell a firefighter to go pick up a spot fire: I had to go find a squad boss, who had to tell his crew leader, who would tell his crew boss. Then I had to go find the crew boss, and then they would pass the message back down through the chain of command. They worked me hard.

Then I found out from Lynn and a couple other guys who said, "Mark, you don't want to work those two crews too close together," and I said, "Why's that?" "Well, they're historical enemies. You get them working too close together, they're liable to kill each other." I went, "Oh."

There's another one: right before the Loop fire in 1965, we had an early fire. Myself and one of the El Cariso hot-shots . . . on a big wilderness fire. We had him and myself and 150 inmates. These weren't the trained inmates: these were when they used to dump them out of the prison and call them emergency firefighters and were like the regular con crews; 150 inmates, amazing drought-driven fire behavior, and we're cutting line just to keep them from falling asleep. There are just the two of us, and there are no other state supervision or guards or what have you. That was an interesting learning event.

I guess part of what I'm saying on that is in days of yore, there was a lot of expectation from your bosses that you stepped up. If you screwed up, you weren't going to get to step up again. If you made a little mistake, they kind of watched a little bit. They had a big expectation that you were supposed to step up: "We gave you the basics, son; you're supposed to be smart enough to know how to handle this." That was kind of their philosophy back at the time. From that concept, I always used to do that. Once I gave you the training, once I gave you the knowledge, knew you had the skills, I expected you to get a job done. Handle it. I don't want to hear why you can't, shouldn't be, what have you. Handle it. I got other shit I gotta do.

PART SEVEN

UNUSUAL INTERVIEWS & PARTING THOUGHTS

Any big project has times where things don't turn out the way you thought they would. Most of my interviews were similar: take a road trip, meet the supe at a conference or their workplace, sit down, turn the recorder on, and have a Q&A session lasting anywhere from one to three hours. This section is about the ones that didn't stick to the template, as well as the supes' answers to the question, "Anything else?""

Bill Sandborg's Complete Written Answers to Interview Questions

I have yet to meet Bill Sandborg, Fulton's supe from 1970 to 1983. I heard, "You have to talk to Bill Sandborg," many times while I traveled around, recording interviews; so I wrote to him after getting his address from Dave Provencio.[22] He politely declined my request for an interview, citing his ranching, dairy farming, and

---

[22] Provencio worked for Sandborg on Fulton and detailed as Fulton's supe himself in 1982. He also served as Geronimo's supe from 2010 to 2012. *Hotshot Crew History in America*, National Interagency Hotshot Crew Steering Committee, updated October 2016, http://www.wildfirelessons.net/viewdocument/ hotshot-crew-history-book.

orange growing duties. Imagine my surprise and gratitude upon opening an envelope he mailed me a few weeks later and discovering he'd taken the time to sit down and hand-write answers to every question I sent him. I'm giving his responses as-is because, like the Spartans' one-word reply to Philip II of Macedon's threats[23], a few carefully-chosen words can say a lot. I doubt he would have said much more had we recorded an interview face-to-face.

Dear Angie,

I hope you had a busy and profitable season. I'm sorry it's taken me so long to reply to your letter, but my farming and ranching operations keep me going 24/7. I have read your questions and given them a lot of thought. I don't know as my answers will give you anything new that others haven't shared with you. The Forest Service has changed a lot since I started work for them in 1959. As the service is still trying to reinvent the wheel, I decided a long time ago, just make my wheel roll round and smooth.

1. What advice do you have for young and/or inexperienced fire supervisors, especially hotshots?
Stop, look, and listen. Study fire history! Study and learn fire behavior!

2. Briefly outline the course of your career: where you worked, for how long, the positions you held:
Two years engine crewman, two years engine operator, eight years engine captain, twelve years superintendent, eleven years battalion chief.

3. Anything you would've done differently so far as career course?
No.

---

[23] When Philip II wrote to the Spartans, "If I bring my army into your land, I will destroy your farms, slay your people, and raze your city," the Spartans sent back, "If."

4. Your career planning advice:
Go to every fire you can at any position. Know as much about other fire functions as your own.

5. Who you hire and why:
Before the service changed hiring systems, I hired local kids right out of high school with work experience (farming, ranching, etc.) and sports.

6. Who you promote and why:
Demonstrates experience, follows orders, does things needing done without being told, can make logical and common-sense decisions.

7. What are the "marks" you leave on people you've trained (ways others know you trained them)?
I hope no. 6 [above].

8. What are the toughest things to teach about fire and supervision?
Look at the total picture, not just the flames. Think before you act, using knowledge, common sense and projected fire behavior.

9. Priorities between crew's first day and first dispatch of the season?
Training and discipline.

10. Favorite field drills, classroom exercises?
Good hard work (constructing fuelbreaks and fireline). Basic 40 hours and relate personnel experience and observations.

11. What parts of your own development have you used on your own crews? What have you made sure to change?
Knowledge gained from experience and stress no. 9 [above].

12. What kind of crew do you intend to have at the end of a season? Do you change expectations with the people you have, or do you try to make every crew the same?
Work as a team, have cohesion, be proficient, make commonsense decisions and think and act safely.

326 • THE SUPE'S HANDBOOK

13. Does your crew have a traditional personality? What is it?

Be tough, have pride, accomplish goals.

14. What tells you your crew isn't doing well as far as health, attitude, etc.? How do you keep them going?

Communication! Eat healthy and get plenty of sleep.

15. How do you compensate for fatigue during decision-making?

Take more time to analyze "if" time permits. Allow more time to accomplish goal. Provide for safety first.

16. How do you avoid burnout?

Try to eat and get rest. Set a strong mind and place one foot in front of other.

17. Are good crew bosses made or born?

Personality plays a large part, but training, experience, and discipline will overcome a lot.

18. What do good supes have in common?

Tough (mental and physical), knowledge, common sense, experience, and correct anticipation.

I've never known a superintendent yet who couldn't go to hell with a thimbleful of water and put out the fire. I plan on it, because that's where all my friends will be.

19. How did you develop your own leadership skills?

Knowledge and experience.

20. Tell me about a close call with your crew that made a lasting impression on you and perhaps changed the way you work.

Having been burned over once, trapped temporarily several times, and run out numerous times makes one stop, look, and listen. It's sometimes a close call between catching and losing it. (Sometimes it's something others have done that you have no control over.)

21. What are the most serious mistakes you see supervisors making on the fireline? Other times?

Not having the ability or guts to make a decision, lack of initiative, lack of knowledge.

22. "Could've-beens": Give a time you saw something others didn't and made a change that prevented people from getting hurt, whether your crew or others. (I realize this happens frequently; I'm looking for the really big "could've-beens.")

Lake Elsinore wind shifts, was lead crew. Fire showing erratic direction change, sudden spotting. Prevented three crews from being in front of a 180-degree wind shift, flames pushed through heavy brush downslope for about one mile.

23. An occasion when acting on gut instinct worked out especially well:

Used it all the time.

24. How should a young or inexperienced supervisor handle pressure from above, whether on the line or at the home unit?

Study, ask questions, make sure you understand instructions, think, act decisive. (I remember a Standard Order that covers this.)

25. How do you teach your crew about fatality fires like the Dude, South Canyon, Thirtymile, etc.?

Discuss events causing fatalities. What should have been seen in order to prevent. On going fires, point out similarities or other hidden or potential problems.

26. Most memorable fire behavior you've seen?

Numerous firestorms, long-range spotting, erratic wind shifts, area ignition.

27. Where are some of your former employees?

Fire management regional offices, ICs on national teams, FEMA, Governor's Council for Disaster Planning, KCFD [Kern County Fire Department] chief—most retired or close to retirement.

328 • THE SUPE'S HANDBOOK

28. Changes for good/bad over the years:
Not fighting fire at night, lack of initiative, political and bureaucratic "BS"! Decision control too tight. Too much importance on education and not on experience and common sense.

29. What has being a hotshot done for your career?
Given me knowledge and experience in the decision-making process. To fight for what I believe in and to roll with the punch.

30. Why you stayed in fire/a superintendent so long:
I enjoyed it. It was fun and challenging.

31. Describe your firefighting and supervisory styles:
Aggressive, proficient; get it done and move on to the next one.

32. How have you changed over the years as a firefighter and a supervisor?
I got old and retired.

33. Sacrifices necessary to be supe of a good crew:
Time, energy, no outside distractions. Helps to be single. Know the line between one-of-the-guys and control.

34. Do you have any favorite topics you teach or write about often?
Wrote ICS lesson plans for Plans and Operations. Taught fire behavior and most ICS position courses.

35. Anything else you want to add?
The outfit will never be the same. Some good and some bad. It's now high tech and scientific-based but not applied in a practical means. Positions too politically influenced. Us old fogies used brute strength, knowledge, perseverance, experience, and common sense—any-and-everything.

I'm retired now and have been turned out to pasture. Now I watch the airtankers overhead and the fire trucks pass in opposite directions and remember the "good old days."

Paul Gleason and Jim Cook: Two Winners Show Me How to Lose

Supes do a lot of great things, both for the wildland fire community and for individuals like me. I saw demonstrations of both over the course of several days in 2003.

January 26, 2003

Dear Mr. Gleason:

Brit Rosso gave me your mailing address and encouraged me (as others have) to write to you regarding a project I'm doing. I'm interviewing experienced hotshot superintendents and recording the advice they have for younger or inexperienced fire supervisors. I intend to publish the collection as a book, a kind of manual or guide for the firefighters I just mentioned. I would like to interview you and will travel to Colorado if necessary.

I'm not a journalist. I got the idea for the book one summer after realizing how few superintendents with 10 to 20 years in are still around and how many relatively inexperienced people are filling the new permanent positions. When long-time supes retire, everything they've learned goes with them, except for what they've taught to a rather small number of people. I want to spread that knowledge to more firefighters and perhaps do a little to keep the next generation from needing to reinvent the wheel.

Your service to the fire community is well-known, and all of the supes I've interviewed so far have urged me to contact you ASAP. This book would be incomplete without some input from you, so I would greatly appreciate your help.

Thank you very much for your time.

Sincerely,

Angela Tom

***

"Hello, Angela, this is Paul Gleason."

Whoa, what a jolt. I'd been hearing about this guy for years, and here he was on the other end of the line. It was a week, maybe ten days, since I had sent the letter, but I hadn't expected him to simply pick up the phone and call me. Why would he? He had terminal cancer, and he didn't know me. I had no idea how advanced his illness was when he called. In hindsight, perhaps I should have scheduled the interview sooner, but Paul seemed fine with the date we agreed on.

Jim Cook called me the day before I started driving to Colorado for the interview. He had taken an interest in my project after I interviewed him, and he subsequently introduced me to people he thought would be helpful. I was going to ask Paul a few extra questions for Jim's "Leaders We Would Like To Meet" series on the FireLeadership.gov website. Jim wanted to interview Paul himself, but he had too much going on at the time. He said he would call Paul and put in a good word for me.

I called Paul when I reached my hotel the night before our appointment. His shortness of breath made talking difficult as he explained that he was on supplemental oxygen to make breathing easier. He told me that Jim would be joining us in the afternoon, which was a big surprise. A little later, Jim himself called, solemnly giving me a heads-up that Paul had taken a turn for the worse. That explained the oxygen. Ominously, Jim had cleared his schedule to fly to Denver for a day or two.

When I arrived at Paul's house the next morning, his wife Karen answered the door. She stepped outside, pulling the door shut behind her as she warned me in a low voice that Paul was very weak; she didn't want me to be shocked when I saw him. I did my best to reassure her that I wasn't there to wear him out—I would leave whenever they wanted. Karen said Paul was waiting for me, adding that he'd talked about the interview in his sleep during the night. He was resting in a recliner near the front door. Karen introduced us, and the three of us chatted for a little while. Paul pointed out a basket full of cards and letters people had sent him in recent months. He said he'd wept when he first read them, overcome by their sentiments and praise.

I set up my recorder and microphone, and we began. Paul had a lot of trouble speaking, needing to stop to catch his breath after a few sentences. Karen pointed out to him that—as usual—he was trying too hard. He decided to take a break; I left and returned at one in the afternoon, when Jim was due to arrive.

Jim and I resumed the interview together that afternoon. When Paul would have trouble answering a question, Jim would throw in a comment and then Paul would turn and reply to him with relative ease. Once I picked up on this, I turned the interview over to Jim. Then, all I had to do was mind the recorder and enjoy the two veteran supes swapping good memories.

After about an hour, Paul needed another break and fell asleep in his chair. Karen said she would call us when he was ready to continue, so we headed out for coffee. Paul was still sleeping soundly a few hours later when we stopped by. We agreed to stay on call until ten that evening and return at eight the next morning if Karen didn't call.

Jim was late for breakfast in the morning. I waited ten minutes before heading for his room to knock on the door. I met him in the hallway just outside his room. I said, "Morning," but he just kept striding along, stone-faced. When we reached the breakfast room and approached the buffet, he stuck out his arm and blocked me from taking a plate. He dialed his cell phone and held it up to my ear so I could hear the message from Karen. She was crying and asking us to come later than eight. I knew then that Paul was dead, and I started crying too.

Jim and I ate a little, drank a bunch of coffee, and discussed what to do next. He started thinking out loud about memorial services. Karen called my cell phone, and I started crying all over again. She apologized for calling Jim first, explaining that he had known Paul much longer, and I told her that was as it should be. She offered to help with more material for my book; I thanked her and asked her not to worry about it. She asked to speak to Jim, and they set a new time for us to arrive at the house.

Some close friends—fire people—and Paul's brother Phil were at the house when we arrived. They immediately started making plans for Paul's Forest Service memorial. Firemen to the core, they used ICS to distribute responsibilities. I did my best to stay out of the way, listening as they shared their favorite stories about Paul. Later that afternoon, I went to a nearby copy center to scan a photo of Paul as a young Dalton hotshot for the memorial program. That evening, Paul's friends and family gathered for dinner. Some out-of-towners were traveling home the next day, so they took the opportunity to share memories and enjoy each other's company before they went their separate ways.

***

I used to tell myself that I never got to meet the "real" Paul Gleason. As sick as he was when I met him, how could he have been anything like the strong, energetic fireman he once was? At one of his memorial services, his wife Karen remarked that she had spent most of their time together just trying to keep up with him. However, as the many cards and letters Paul received from well-wishers attested, his enthusiasm, intellect, and teaching abilities were an inspiration to other firefighters. He shared his love for and dedication to his vocation until the day he died. Tired and hurting, he was still happy to let a stranger into his home to answer her questions about his life fighting fire and give young firefighters his advice. I believe I saw the purest essence of who and what Paul Gleason was because cancer had stripped away everything else.

***

"Jim, I'm really sorry, and I'll understand if you don't want to meet with me tomorrow. I don't know how it happened, but your portion of Paul's interview didn't get recorded."

My nose was stuffed up and my eyes bloodshot from crying after I had double-checked, disbelieving and panicking, that the best part of the recording didn't exist—and I was responsible. Paul was dead—there was no chance to try again. I had dreaded making that phone call. Having to leave a voicemail was even worse because I would have to wait for a response—what could I expect besides disappointment and anger from someone I respected and liked? I knew there would be no more interview referrals, no more chances to hang out, drinking beer and bullshitting about fire. I had failed—epically. How on earth it had happened was beyond me: hadn't I watched the recorder properly close itself down before I powered it off? Hadn't I carefully made track marks while Jim and Paul talked? It didn't matter. "This is the worst day of my life," I wrote in my journal before going to sleep.

"What do you do when you fall off the horse?" Jim asked me a few days later via cellphone as I drove the Arizona 101 Loop toward Scottsdale. He had responded earlier to my weepy voicemail, and to my surprise he hadn't seemed angry. Putting his own disappointment aside, he said we'd figure something out, and he still invited me to his committee meeting's informal gatherings to hang out and meet more possible interview subjects.

"Get back on." My answer was automatic, and I was instantly wary: what did he mean by that?

"You brought your recording equipment, right? 'Cause I scheduled you an interview for 1500 this afternoon. This is someone who'll be good for you."

Luckily, I always lugged my bag of project materials and recording equipment wherever I went. Later that day, I met Steve

334 • THE SUPE'S HANDBOOK

Dickenson and recorded an interview with him. He was indeed a good subject: enthusiastic about sharing his opinions and advice, happy to make himself available on short notice.

When the day's business was done and people were loitering in the resort lobby, making plans with their pals for dinner and beer runs, Jim grinned at me and held his phone up to my ear: "Listen." I cringed at hearing my own snuffly voice on the recorded message, saturated with self-pity as I informed Jim of the lost recording. I was embarrassed about sounding so pathetic, but I guess that was Jim's way of saying things were going to be okay. He was right: our notes and memories provided what the recorder could not, and he published Paul Gleason's interview as part of his "Leaders We Would Like to Meet" series as planned.

It has taken me years to appreciate how much Jim's graceful handling of my failure has meant to this project and to me personally. Jim's breezy get-back-on-the-horse approach was exactly what I needed, especially from someone I looked up to. It was a great first-hand demonstration of the leadership values and concepts he's been talking about his entire career and beyond.

Anthony Escobar: Cutting Big Brush Without Mincing Words

It took a couple of years to prod and cajole Kern Valley supe Anthony Escobar into an interview. He demurred or delayed each time I asked him about it whenever we crossed paths, usually at Region 5's Hotshot Workshop in Reno. He said he wanted to be the last one I talked to. Eventually he relented, and I traveled to his home in Bakersfield, California, to interview him.

When I arrived, Anthony was lounging on his couch, barefoot and wearing jeans. He was writing a speech, papers spread out all over the living room carpet. I grinned to myself at having to squeeze past his Buell motorcycle, resting on a lift in the dining room, as I made my way to the bathroom.

We chatted about his cherished Great Books of the World series on the living room bookshelf while I set up the microphone and recorder. They were his favorite reference materials, and he rarely wrote anything without referring to them for information or a quote. A thunderstorm rolled through during the interview, interrupting the household power at least twice. My recorder switched off and on a couple times, but it seemed to be working fine, so I kept him talking.

I asked Anthony about his favorite team-building exercise for crew training. He smiled, tipped back his head a little, closed his eyes, and slowly replied, "Cutting big bushes." He'd been transported to his happy place. For him, a crew cutting line in chaparral was like an orchestra, all the players coming together in expert precision to accomplish a large, difficult piece of work.

He related the story of getting hired to the Los Prietos Hotshots, and of supe Mark Linane asking if he had any more friends who might want to work. He introduced Linane to Tony Duprey, later known as "Killer," who eventually became a battalion chief on the Los Padres National Forest. I wish I had his exact words because it's a classic, polished with each of its many retellings.

Anthony talked about how he became known as a public speaker and the voice of the California hotshot community after airing some passionate views at a hotshot workshop. He spoke of the challenges he faced putting his thoughts to paper after going back to school so he could take his career further. [He retired as the LP's FMO.] Speaking came naturally, but producing essays for English class required different ways of thinking and writing.

Anthony is also a skilled mentor, and he told me how he fell into it. A dispatcher in Bakersfield asked for his help with her speaking skills, which she knew could boost her career. It was the first time someone had specifically asked him, "Will you be my mentor?" He refined his process and technique as they went along and has repeated it with other aspiring, promising young people who sought him out and/or happened to work on Kern Valley.

When asked who he hires, he said that at first it was a feeling of having something in common with an applicant. He also joked that his early crews "looked more like a lineup than a crew lining out." What were his priorities before first dispatch? "Making sure they know what right looks like, what the right way to do things is," he said. "From that comes knowing what success is, so that when the unexpected comes, the confidence is there to be successful again."

Does KV have a traditional personality? His simple answer was, "No." He explained that since he hadn't been around hotshot culture before being hired to LP, he didn't buy into it; it doesn't matter whether KV keeps up traditions because they can always be counted on to do the job. He doesn't believe his crews have a consistent personality either, since you can't compare any one crew to another. On the other hand, he acknowledged that if there is one thing KV hotshots are known for when they leave the crew, it's this: "They are the ones who lead, who teach, and who are out front."

How does Anthony monitor his crew during the tough parts of a shift and a season? "By using empathy to watch people. If you're secure in your masculinity, then empathy isn't a problem."

When asked if great leaders are made or born, he replied, "I am proof that leaders are made," and he acknowledged that he has made a conscious effort at self-improvement. He's been studying leadership for some 20 years. When asked about personal characteristics that suit him for fire, he described himself as overwhelmingly cerebral and good at distilling high-level information into basic concepts, adding that he is thick-skinned and has mental and emotional stamina. One serious mistake he has seen other supervisors make is expecting respect from a title or position rather than gaining respect by earning it.

I enjoyed the interview immensely and wished I could keep Anthony talking even after all my questions were answered and he had said his piece on a couple of his favorite topics. I excused myself to go out for dinner; he had graciously offered up his guest room for the night. I checked the recorder as soon as I got to my truck—as I did after every session—mostly to congratulate myself on another successful interview. To my horror, the disk was blank, every word zapped into oblivion somehow. Again? Wasn't one irretrievably, irredeemably lost recording enough? Hyperventilation, silent panic: "What do I do now?"

My answer: nothing. I dined at a nearby Italian restaurant and scribbled as many notes as my shame-addled brain would let me recall. I couldn't bring myself to tell Anthony that night or the next morning that, after all the time he spent talking, there was no tape. My guilty conscience pummeled me further as I drank a cup of his rare Jamaican Blue Mountain coffee. I told him as I left that I wanted to come back and talk to him some more. Little did he know exactly how much I meant it or why.

Seven years later, the manuscript was nearly done and most of the loose ends tied up, but I had nothing written about Anthony. I learned of his retirement in late 2012 and his retirement party in early 2013. I wrote to the party contact, asking her to pass along to Anthony that I wanted to get back in touch with him. She replied with his email address, warning that he might not respond right away because he so enjoyed the freedom of retirement. I wrote him a short message, explaining that I had no material recorded and hoped he would do another interview because I hated to go to press without him. I offered to travel to meet him, as before.

He never responded, and I can only assume that his silence was a product of his disappointment. After all, since I hadn't made the most of the first opportunity, why should I be granted another? If that's how he sees it, I understand. Whatever his reason, I have given him the best ink I could.

Postscript

Anthony Escobar didn't care that I'd lost his entire interview, but I didn't get to find that out until 2020. I'd gotten back in touch with his longtime friend and Los Prietos brother J. W. Allendorf, who gave me his number and said, "He really wants to talk to you. It's all good." A long phone conversation or two later, Anthony offered to write the foreword to the book, one of the biggest compliments he could ever have given me. Hashing out his self-appointed writing "assignment" and how it fit with the rest of the manuscript was so much fun, and I look forward to collaborating with him again someday if I get the chance.

Anything else?

After a few interviews, I learned how much good stuff comes out when the interview is almost over and you just ask the wide-open question.

Ted Mathiesen (Arroyo Grande Flight Crew, 1990–2007)
I don't care whose idea it is; I don't care if it came from Texas Canyon, wherever it came from. If we can take that idea, put it on the table here, integrate it into our program, we'll make it that much better. Don't be closed-minded and say, "This is the way we do it here at AG, and we've always done it that way, and by God that's always how we'll do it." I think that's a huge mistake. Surround yourself with smart people. It's gonna rub off.

Don't shirk your responsibility.... This job, it's a huge responsibility, and you have to be willing to accept it. There's no room for those who won't. Don't be afraid to make a decision—right or wrong—because if you make [the wrong decision], it's easy—you know where to go for the right one. If you make the right one, it's just so much the better. A lot of guys are afraid to make a decision because they don't want to make the wrong one, and I think that's silly. I'm not talking about life-or-death stuff, but if you make the wrong decision on a personnel issue or whatever, then you'll learn from it.

Stan Stewart (Los Padres, 2000–2009)

Learn, learn, learn. Pay attention. Soak up as much information as you can get from the people on your crew, your peers, other people you see around you. Just like Paul [Gleason] said, be a student of fire. Just learn as much as you can. You can never learn too much. Take as many classes as you can, and go to fires. Just be like a big sponge, and soak up what everybody's trying to teach you. They didn't do anything in the old days, but it's out there now, and there are a million places to get it, too. There's really no excuse—if you're interested in it—not to find something and hammer away on it.

Greg Keller (Eldorado, 1985–1996; Modoc, 2000–2007)

If you can be successful in hotshots, I think you can be successful in any occupation you choose. You know how to work hard. You know how to go through hard times. There's something that is taught or learned or absorbed by being a successful hotshot that applies not only to firefighting but to the rest of your life as well. It's a step in the building process of life. . . .

Richard Aguilar (El Cariso, 1974; Wolf Creek, 1975–1997)

If they have a goal that they want to become a hotshot superintendent, anybody can do it. I used to tell my kids, "If I was able to do it, you can do it," because I didn't go to school. The kids I would get at Wolf Creek, I would tell them, "If I was able to do it, anybody can."

Kurt LaRue (Diamond Mountain, 1993–2001)

One of the things that I do push in Crew Boss [class] and I do push toward younger supervisors is that even if you don't have a lot of experience, the agency's put you in charge of whatever crew they wanted you to run. . . . The agency's put you in charge of it; you're the one making the decisions. That means you need to make the decisions based on what you're comfortable doing, not because you see other people running around, going off and doing stuff.

If you're a young supervisor and you opt out of doing an assignment, and somebody walks by you and does that assignment, you shouldn't look on your decision as wrong or let their actions lead you to do what you're not comfortable with next time. Once they've made you the crew supervisor, you will have people who will explain all the reasons you should do an assignment. If you're not comfortable, remember they're not going to be there with you when you've got to haul everybody out. You're on your own when things go to hell. A lot of the people who are there telling you how safe it is and all the political reasons to do it are people who aren't leaving the road. If as a young supervisor you're not comfortable with it, you don't have to do it.

They've got that big table on PowerPoint for ICS: there's the IC, the ops, and the planning section at the top of the page, and you work all the way down there, and strike team leader is about as low as it goes on that screen. Crew boss doesn't even show up here on many of them. I ask them, "How many of you have ever seen an operations section chief out on the line?" None of them. How about your branch? Well, he's in the truck over there. Division? Well, he's in the truck next to branch.

Once you are put in charge of a crew, don't look on yourself as the lowest dog on the totem pole in that table of organization. Look on yourself as the last chance to make the right decision for those kids who work for you, because the kids who work for you, their sphere of consciousness is about two feet. Their feet hurt, they're tired, they hope they get through the shift and don't run out of water. That's their life. You're the last chance in this giant pyramid of camp slugs we have anymore . . . to make a decision worthy of your kids' efforts, both from safety . . . and to see they're doing something productive; they're not just out there making dust for no purpose whatsoever.

Barry Callenberger (Palomar, 1979–1982; Eldorado, 1982–1988)

Change is inevitable, and I think you learn to change and adapt quickly as a hotshot. Any fireman does, . . . but don't just do that on fires—do it all the time. If you can adapt and change, you'll be far better off no matter what you do in your career. If you resist change, it will be a problem for you.

Anytime you can contribute to change in the agency—positive changes, not negative changes—contribute and make the positive changes. You may not think that they're positive at the time. I can remember when the Consent Decree came to California: a lot of people looked at it as negative change. They moved away instead of trying to participate, and I know this is something that everybody says about it, but I really think it's true. We all resisted it, and I'm not saying I didn't either, but you have to think about it.

It was a positive change. I have often said that the crews mellowed out when you had women on the crews. We didn't have the stupidity that went on; you still had some. I think the way the Forest Service went about it—pushing that change—we went a little bit too fast. It wasn't good or bad—it was tough, tough times—but if you wanted to survive, you went along and helped create the change in the right way. I think that's what you have to do. You may not agree with the change, but if you don't agree, then move on. Do something else. If you want to stay in the organization, you want to make it better. If it's a good change, go for it. Make it happen.

Fred Schoeffler (Payson, 1981–2007)

The main responsibility is to bring your people home safely, each and every day, on every assignment. All supervisors have a huge responsibility, so live up to it or get out and get another job. You must stand by your crew, no matter the circumstances, in all situations. You may have to chew their butts out later on from time to time, but then let it go. Give them second chances, expect and get improvement, and loyalty will generally follow. Being a supervisor requires a lot of sacrifice and sometimes a lot of extra effort. It's almost always worth it. The reward of watching people grow and knowing you had a hand in it makes it all worth it.

Ken Jordan (Sierra, 1998–2014)

I was told this a long time ago by the other supes: pick your battles. I'd say try to avoid the battles, and be proactive so you don't have to fight the battles; but once you do, pick 'em. You only have so much time and energy. Make sure they'll buy the firefighters something, as far as safety or the betterment of the fire organization. You're there for a reason, and it's not to better yourself, and that's what we can pretty much share. It's a constant trying to do something for somebody else.

Dave Matier (Midnight Sun, 1992–1997, 1999–2007, 2009–2010)

You're always learning. As long as you keep that attitude that you're always going to learn something, I think you'll make a good firefighter. No matter how long you've been in it, if you start getting complacent and taking things for granted, thinking you know it all, then get out. I don't think you should be in this. I don't care how long you've been in it.

You have to project not necessarily that you know it all but you do know what you're doing. . . . You may come across that you do know it all, but to me, to be a leader, your people have to have confidence in you that you do know what you're doing, and that means all the time. No matter how trivial it is . . . whether you're doing project work or you're on the road or whatever, being on top of things and not being lost is real important. . . . Keep your mind open, and you've never seen it all, no matter how many years you've been doing it.

Dennis Baldridge (Laguna, 1990–2009)
I don't know anything for sure other than understand the responsibility of being a supervisor and a leader. It's a big responsibility. You have the ability to harm somebody by your lack of decision or by making a decision. You need to know that up front and be willing to take that on. Number one rule is take care of your crew; get them home every night.

Charlie Caldwell (Redding, 1967–1986)
You've got a window for everything. You've got a time slot. I don't care what you're doing. Don't forget that window. I don't care if it's a burnout situation, a backfiring situation, a line-building situation, or even going for a run in the morning. You've got to be in the classroom at nine, so you better give yourself time. You've got to build yourself a window. You have to have a window for everything you do.

Ron Bollier (Silver City, 1993–1995; Carson, 1996–1997; Fulton, 1998–2013)
Learn all you can. Learn every step of the way. Learn all you can from every position you hold. Learn and take what it has to offer. Pick some folks who you admire, who you want to learn from. Hopefully, you work for them. Learn everything you can from them. Learn every part of the job before you step up to bat in another position, before you promote. Become proficient at everything that's in front of you at the time, and take care of the people you have under you.

Bob Wright (Sacramento, 1990–2002)
You need to be out there learning stuff. Every day you learn something out there if you're burning or working. Every day I learn something. You never want to stop learning because the day you think you learned everything, you're in trouble. My old

FMO, Dave Yarborough, said there are some guys who have been fighting fire for 30 years and they're still fighting the same fire— they never learned anything, they never progressed past that.

You have be able to make decisions, right or wrong. You can't be wishy-washy. You may make a wrong decision on a tactic, but as long as you've got a place to go, and you can get there in a reasonable amount of time, and the crew's not going to get burned over or you're not doing underslung line where rocks and trees are falling down, you'll be okay. Your tactic may not work, but at least you've got a second plan ready in your mind, and you can go from there.

Get involved with your crew. You talk to people in the military, especially in the Marine Corps—they always remember their sergeant. Get with your crew like that: where they respect you, and you get to know that crew, and they look up to you. . . . Take care of people, instead of just me, me, me.

That's one thing I always liked about the crew: it's a crew effort. A lot of these kids nowadays are me, me, me. You have to instill into them: we're one crew. If he's hurting, you need to help him, and that kind of stuff. That goes back to just daily life and helping people who need help in life. You need to do that.

Learn as much about fire as you can; but you could be the best fireman in the world and if that crew won't follow you, it's not going to do any good. . . . A good crew, they're pushing you; you're having to tell them to mellow out.

Just treat people good. It'll all come back to you. All the ones who are really mean and hateful . . . it'll all come back to them worse than they ever gave out. If you're good to people and they know that, it's all going to come back to you tenfold sooner or later. You may not think so—a lot of times I didn't think so—but it's coming back, because you look at all the friends you have. I miss it, but that's the way it is.

Craig Workman (Black Mountain, 1988–2005)
Go for the job that interests you and that you love to do. Don't get too stuck in your career or your next ladder or next step. Do what you really love to do. I think when I went to AFMO, I did what I thought others thought I should do, and it was probably a good thing for me, but I really did miss what I loved. Money isn't everything. It's whether you're happy.

Lance Honda (Redmond, 1992–1997; Prineville, 1997–2009)
Know what your values are, and find out who you want to be. Everybody's got morals, and everybody knows what's right and wrong. Choose what's right. Choose what your conscience tells you is right in everything. Don't be afraid to stand up for what's right.

I think that all our choices come from one of two things: from either fear or love. Know what you love—be able to identify that. Pay attention to the things that make you feel good: being honest, having integrity, having a great work ethic, helping people, helping your crewmembers, being respectful. All those things make you feel better as opposed to the opposite of those: lying, being lazy, being disloyal, betraying somebody.

Don't be afraid to stand up for what's right, whether it's on your crew, whether a team is doing it, whether it's an agency policy. If you don't, then you have no reason to complain.

Mark Linane (Los Prietos/Los Padres, 1973–2001)
They need to be a student of fire, using Paul Gleason's terminology. Need to be a student of human behavior. Need to develop their leadership and decision-making skills. Need to be aware of the things that affect situational awareness. Need to always look for a better way to do things—don't get stuck in that same rut. Need to look outside the box—other agencies, other places—for how folks do things better. Stay away from the not-invented-here concept. There are a lot of people with a lot of ideas in a lot of

places around the world, and you can learn from it if you take the time and energy to learn from it.

They need to read. They need to develop and take the time to read. Take courses, and where they can't take courses, read so they can develop their own general educational level. Education does help you in this little world.

I think when you become a superintendent you have to be your own person—that's number one. You can't emulate somebody else's style. You have to develop your own.

The whole intent of everything isn't to race another crew or blow 'em off the map, to cut more line than anybody else, to be the risk taker. The important thing is that everybody who works for you eats Christmas dinner with their folks and family that winter. That's number one.

Ben Charley (Horseshoe Meadow, 1974–1989)

You've got to enjoy what you're doing. Fire is the dirtiest job in the world, but you meet the best people in the world. I believe that. The best people are fire people, because we've all been through the same thing and it's just a feeling of camaraderie. You never lose it. I've been out of the system almost 13 years and I'm still with it. I drive buses now and I still see the guys. Like my boss says, "If I can't find you around the bus, I'll go find you around the hotshots."

J. W. Allendorf (Wallowa–Whitman, 1980; Arrowhead 3, 1981)

Just take care of yourself, and be thankful you stumbled into a job like you have, because it's the best in the world

ABBREVIATIONS

10 & 18: 10 Standard Firefighting Orders and 18 Watch Out Situations

AAR: After Action Review

AFMO: assistant fire management officer

ADFMO: assistant district fire management officer

BD: brush disposal

BLM: Bureau of Land Management

CDF: California Department of Forestry and Fire Protection

CISM: critical incident stress management

DOI: Department of the Interior

EMT: emergency medical technician

FEMA: Federal Emergency Management Agency

FIRESCOPE: Firefighting Resources of California Organized for Potential Emergencies

FMO: fire management officer, formerly fire control officer

GS: general schedule

IA: initial attack

IC: incident commander

ICS: Incident Command System

IHC: interagency hotshot crew

IMT: incident management team

IR: interregional

LCES: lookouts, communications, escape routes, safety zones

LP: Los Padres National Forest

MEL: Most Efficient Level

NAFRI: National Advanced Fire and Resource Institute

NCO: noncommissioned officer

NFMAS: National Fire Management Analysis System

NIFC: National Interagency Fire Center

NPS: National Park Service

OES: Office of Emergency Services (State of California)

OPM: Office of Personnel Management

PT: physical training

QSI: quality step increase

R1, R2, etc.: US Forest Service Regions 1 through 10—excluding R7, which doesn't exist.

RH: relative humidity

SOP: standard operating procedure

WO: Washington office

ACKNOWLEDGEMENTS

Thanks first and foremost to the supes and their families: they were generous, gracious, and great fun to be around. I have only worked for Dan Fiorito and Fred Schoeffler, but around the rest I still felt like one of "the kids" on their crews. Many things have changed through the years and will continue to change, but I hope that—no matter who they are or where they work—the tradition of members of a good fire crew seeing themselves as extended family does not.

Thank you to Anthony Escobar for the foreword, also for getting back in touch and making me feel better about losing your recording.

Many thanks to Paul Keller, Rowdy Muir, and Steve Jackson. All three said yes to reading a complete stranger's (very long) manuscript and providing feedback. Your advice and support have been invaluable.

Thank you to Samantha Orient for generously providing illustrations that nobody but a professional artist who has fought fire could create.

Thank you to Mike McMillan for allowing me to use his photo of Stan Stewart for the cover.

Thank you to editor Christina Dubois for making me and the supes look good, for your patience and encouragement, and for all your exacting hard work.

A big hug and thank you to the Twin Falls Helitack Crew for making fire such a joy the second time around. Thank you also to everyone else I've worked with over the years. The cliché really is true that the people are what's great about fire.

To my long-suffering parents, whose daughter has yet to grow up and get a real job: thank you—for everything.

BIBLIOGRAPHY

Cavasso, Elizabeth. "Interview with Craig Workman." Leaders We Would Like to Meet (series), Wildland Fire Leadership Development Program, National Wildfire Coordinating Group. Accessed September 14, 2020. https://www.nwcg.gov/sites/default/files/wfldp/docs/craig-workman.pdf.

Davies, Gilbert W. and Florice M. Frank, eds. *Memorable Forest Fires: 200 Stories by US Forest Service Retirees*. Hat Creek, CA: HiStory Ink Books, second printing, 1997.

Delong, David W. *Lost Knowledge: Confronting the Threat of an Aging Workforce*. New York: Oxford University Press, 2004.

Dotson, Travis. "Traumatic Transitions," interview with Brit Rosso. Two More Chains 8, no. 3 (Fall 2018): 1, 3–9. Wildland Fire Lessons Learned Center. Accessed September 14, 2020. https://www.wildfirelessons.net/viewdocument/two-more-chains-fall-2018.

"Fire Terminology." Northwest Area Command. Accessed November 19, 2020. https://www.fs.fed.us/nwacfire/home/terminology.html.

Gilmartin, Kevin M. *Emotional Survival for Law Enforcement: A Guide for Officers and Their Families*. Tucson: E-S Press, 2002. Gilmartin wrote this book for law enforcement officers, but the information and advice also applies to firefighters, both wildland and structure.

Keller, Greg. "Firing Highway 33 with the General." *Wildfire* (June 1997). Magazine article by Greg Keller about Greg Overacker.

Lewis, James. "New Faces, Same Old Values: Revisiting a History of Attitudes Towards Women in the Forest Service." March 9, 2018, Forest History Society. Accessed November 20, 2020. https://foresthistory.org/new-faces-same-old-values/.

"Meet the Trainers and Instructors: Rusty Witwer, Fire Service Training - Instructor." Fire Management Consultant. Accessed September

14, 2020. http://www.firemanagementconsultant.com/Meet-the-Team.asp?i=29#Bio29.

National Interagency Hotshot Crew Steering Committee. *Hotshot Crew History in America*. Accessed September 14, 2020. http://www.wildfirelessons.net/viewdocument/hotshot-crew-history-book.

"NWCG Glossary of Wildland Fire, PMS 205." National Wildfire Coordinating Group. Accessed November 19, 2020. https://www.nwcg.gov/glossary/a-z.

"Oral History Interviews." Forest History Society. Accessed November 19, 2020. https://foresthistory.org/research-explore/oral-history-interview-collection/.

Ott, William. "Leadership Development for Wildland Fire Management." *Fire Management Today* 72, no. 4 (2013).

Stevenson, Liz. "The Making of a Firefighting Legend." Wildfire Magazine (August 1997): 4–5.

US Hotshots Association Facebook post. July 3, 2017. "Ron Bollier retired Friday June 30 [2017] after 36 years with the Forest Service." Accessed September 14, 2020. https://www.facebook.com/ushotshots/photos/ron-bollier-retired-friday-june-30-after-36-years-with-the-forest-service-most-o/1562286620509645/.

"Hotshotting." US Hotshots Association. Accessed September 14, 2020. https://www.ushotshots.com/hotshotting/.

INDEX

About the Author

Angie Tom worked a total of 10 seasons on the Union, Prescott, Midewin, and Payson Hotshot Crews. She has also worked engines, dispatch, helitack, and tanker bases. Some of her non-fire jobs include dogsled tour guide, hunting camp cook, wholesale greenhouse grower, baker, and sapphire checker. She lives and works in Twin Falls, ID.

–

Made in the USA
Las Vegas, NV
10 December 2022

61725806R00225